A GUIDE TO THE
SOLAR CORONA

The Green River Eclipse photograph of June 8, 1918. One of the most famous eclipse photographs ever made. It shows the corona about one year after a sunspot maximum of moderate intensity. Polar plumes are already well formed, but it is difficult to identify an extended dipole for describing them. The remainder of the corona is characterized by a variety and complexity of details. Courtesy, Mt. Wilson and Mt. Palomar Observatories.

A GUIDE TO THE
SOLAR CORONA

Donald E. Billings

DEPARTMENT OF ASTROGEOPHYSICS
UNIVERSITY OF COLORADO
BOULDER, COLORADO

1966

ACADEMIC PRESS • NEW YORK • LONDON

ACADEMIC PRESS INC.
111 Fifth Avenue, New York, New York 10003

United Kingdom Edition published by
ACADEMIC PRESS INC. (LONDON) LTD.
Berkeley Square House, London W.1

LIBRARY OF CONGRESS CATALOG CARD NUMBER: 66-26261

PRINTED IN THE UNITED STATES OF AMERICA

PREFACE

The reader toward whom this book is specifically directed is the space scientist or engineer who is not a specialist in solar physics, but whose work requires a fairly detailed knowledge of the corona. It is my hope, however, that the material will also prove useful to most graduate students in astrophysics, and that my colleagues in solar physics may also find some topics of interest and value to them. The first three chapters are descriptive. From them a casual reader may draw a concept of the corona as it is evident through more or less direct observation. Anyone who wishes to use coronal data should be interested in Chapter IV. Chapters V–VII present theoretical considerations as they are applicable to the corona. The following four chapters combine theory with observation to provide a description of the various aspects of the corona as we see it. Finally, Chapter XII is a combination of established ideas and speculation.

Many people have contributed to the book. The idea of writing it originated with Dr. Harold Zirin. With the encouragement of Dr. W. O. Roberts, then director of the High Altitude Observatory, Dr. Zirin, Dr. Gordon Newkirk, and I worked together to draw up the general plan and outline. Our concept of what is content should be was strongly influenced by the excellent volume on the same subject by I. S. Shklovskii of the Sternberg Astronomical Institute, USSR. When the manuscript was completed, Dr. Charles Hyder of the Sacramento Peak Observatory scrutinized it in detail and offered many helpful suggestions for its improvement.

Through the kindness of Dr. John Firor, present director of the High Altitude Observatory, several members of the Observatory staff have contributed their efforts to make the book possible. Ruby Fulk retyped the manuscript through many revisions. Dallas Tanton provided drawings and illustrations, and John Goff, assisted by Mary Cay Travis, did much of the photographic work. Many of the photographs and illustrations came directly from the files of the High Altitude Observatory.

Others were supplied through the courtesy of the Mount Wilson and Palomar Observatories, the Lick Observatory, the Royal Astronomical Society,
the Sacramento Peak Observatory, the Stanford Radio Astronomy Institute, Washburn Observatory, the Naval Research Laboratory, the University of Chicago Press, Sky and Telescope, the National Aeronautics
and Space Administration, and Lockheed Solar Observatory. I am grateful
for the efforts of A. E. Whitford, Marianne Bretz, A. H. Jarrett, W. C.
Miller, W. E. Shawcross, C. Hyder, E. N. Parker, J. W. Evans, Adelle
Wightman, J. Deuter, J. M. Wilcox, J. J. Lister, Edith Flather, H. Ram-
sey, S. Miller, and S. M. Smith in making these illustrations available to me.

The project was supported throughout by the Geography Branch of the
Office of Naval Research—the initial phases by Contract Nonr 393(04)
with the High Altitude Observatory, and the completion by grants Nonr-G
00059-64 and Nonr-G 00046-65, to the University of Colorado.

I wish to express my thanks to the many who have assisted in the production of this book, to representatives of the Office of Naval Research who
have found the effort worthy of support, and to give special thanks to my
wife, Claire, who has encouraged me throughout the enterprise.

DONALD E. BILLINGS

July, 1966

CONTENTS

Chapter 4

SPECIAL METHODS OF DATA ANALYSIS

Chapter 5

THE NATURE OF THE CORONAL GAS

Chapter 6

RADIATIVE PROCESSES IN THE CORONA

Chapter 7

THE MECHANICS OF THE CORONA

Chapter 8

DENSITY DISTRIBUTION IN THE CORONA

Chapter 9

THE TEMPERATURE OF THE CORONA

Chapter 10

MAGNETIC FIELDS IN THE CORONA

Chapter 11

RELATION TO OTHER ACTIVITY

Chapter 12

THE CORONA IN THE UNIVERSE

CHAPTER 1

HISTORICAL INTRODUCTION

A. Coronal Science of the Nineteenth Century

Two thousand years ago Plutarch, in commenting on solar eclipses, noted that "there always appears around the circumference of the moon some light that does not permit total darkness." Until about a century ago only fragments of information concerning the corona were added to that statement. Muratori, in the thirteenth century, noted a circle around the sun with a flame in the lower part. Three hundred years later Clavius was surprised to see the corona, which indicates that earlier observations were not generally known. Kepler attributed the corona that he saw in 1605 to an atmosphere on the moon—a conclusion that had an adverse influence on the science for over two hundred years. Cassini mentioned the corona in 1706, and Wassenius, in 1733, noted red flames that he regarded as clouds in the lunar atmosphere. Thus, when we consider the many centuries of recorded history before 1842 (the date of the first eclipse to attract widespread scientific interest) during which total eclipses of the sun were being observed, the recorded observations of the corona are strikingly few and unenthusiastic, and do not constitute any growing body of knowledge.

Prior to 1842 there was no agreement as to whether the corona was a phenomenon of the terrestrial, the lunar, or the solar atmosphere. However, the existence of a lunar atmosphere was beginning to be considered unlikely. This consideration no doubt contributed to the widespread interest in the 1842 eclipse, which crossed France, Italy, and Austria, and was attended by astronomers from several countries who viewed a spectacular display of corona and prominences. The rapid development of knowledge of the solar atmosphere following this event attests to the importance to scientific progress of a community of interest, wherein a number of scientists communicate with one another and share experiences.

By 1875 eight eclipses had led scientific expeditions to various parts of North and South America, Europe, and Asia. Many sketches had been made, some from widely separated parts of the eclipse path; photography had been used on three occasions; and Young and Harkness, with the use of a spectroscope, had discovered the green coronal line in 1869. The latter discovery was considered definitive evidence that the corona was solar, although it was recognized that such a solar corona must be very tenuous because several comets had been observed to pass close to the sun without an observable drag on their orbits. The existence of structure in the corona was considered to be real, but the character of that structure was not well determined. Sketches even of the same eclipse differed considerably from one another, and photography was so poor that it could not be used effectively to validate the drawings. Secchi (1875) noted, however, that sketches of the same eclipse had more in common than those of different eclipses, and postulated that the structure may change during the solar cycle. He suggested that features such as streamers may be related not only to spots but to prominences and faculae as well, since some eclipses showed such structures much closer to the poles than the maximum latitude for sunspots. However, he did not have adequate information to delineate the coronal forms that are typical of various stages of the sunspot cycle.

By 1900 quite a number of meaningful eclipse photographs had been obtained. From these Young (1896) was able to point out the sunspot-maximum and -minimum structural types. Attempts at photometry had been generally unsuccessful, but it was recognized that the brightness was more or less comparable to that of the full moon and that it varied considerably with the sunspot cycle. Polarization in the coronal light had been established, but the degree of polarization was not known. However, polarization was recognized as evidence of the reflection of photospheric light in the corona by small particles that were described as "fog-like," and a fairly adequate theory for the expected degree of polarization had been developed by Schuster (1879). The coronal spectrum had been investigated further, but there was no clear discrimination of coronal from prominence and chromospheric lines. Prior to 1896 the only true coronal line that had been distinguished as such was the green line, and its wavelength was in error by 14 Å.

A number of characteristics of the line had been investigated, however, in the hope of determining the nature of the element "coronium" to which it was attributed. As an example, it was noted that the upward extent of the green-line emission was considerably greater than that of $H\alpha$. Hence Young concluded that coronium was a lighter gas than hydrogen. A rather remarkable observation by Young, we might add, was that gross motion in the corona, as indicated by Doppler shifts, was much less pronounced than in prominences. Finally, astronomers were aware that the green-line emission was much stronger at the time of sunspot maximum than at sunspot minimum, and that its distribution varied over the limb, but in a manner different from that of the white light.

From the foregoing summary we see that the latter sixty years of the nineteenth century marked the beginning of a real coronal science. The corona was recognized as an object worthy of study, and the familiar techniques for analysis of light—photography, photometry, spectroscopy, and polarimetry—were all applied to it. The technique that was perfected in this period however, was visual observation, which was carried out with enthusiasm and reported so eloquently that we who depend on photographs to record our observations return to the writings of the nineteenth century for adequate verbal descriptions of the corona. We quote here two such descriptions, the first by the amateur astronomer Bailey of the 1842 eclipse, and the second from the end of the century, by Young.

From Bailey, in 1846:

"The dark body of the moon was suddenly surrounded with a corona or kind of bright glory similar in shape and relative magnitude to that which painters draw round the head of saints and called by the French an aureole . . . . The breadth of the corona measured from the circumference of the moon appeared to me to be nearly half the moon's diameter. The light was most dense close to the border of the moon and became gradually and uniformly more attenuate as its distance therefrom increased, assuming the form of diverging rays, which at the extremity were more divided, and of an unequal length; so that in no part of the corona could I discover the regular and well-defined shape of a ring at its outer margin. It appeared to me to have the sun in its center, but I had no means of taking any accurate measures for determining this point. Its colour was quite white, not pearl-colour nor yellow nor red, and the rays had a vivid and flickering appearance . . . ."

From Young, in 1896:

"A total eclipse of the sun is unquestionably one of the most impressive of all natural phenomena, and the corona, which then surrounds the sun, is its most impressive feature. On such an occasion the moon appears of almost inky darkness. From behind it stream out on all sides radiant filaments, beams, and sheets of pearly light, which reach to a distance sometimes of several degrees from the solar surface, forming an irregular stellate halo, with the black globe of the moon at its apparent center. The portion nearest the sun is of dazzling brightness, but still less brilliant than the prominences, which blaze through like carbuncles. Generally this inner corona has a pretty uniform height, forming a ring three or four minutes of arc in width, separated by a somewhat definite line from the outer corona, which reaches to a much greater distance, and is far more irregular in form. Usually there are several "rifts" as they have been called, like narrow beams of darkness extending from the very edge of the sun to the outer night. Sometimes there are narrow, bright streamers, as long as the rifts or longer. These are often inclined, occasionally are even nearly tangential to the solar surface, and frequently are curved. On the whole, the corona is usually less extensive and brilliant over the solar poles, and there is a recognizable tendency to accumulations over the middle latitudes or spot zones."

B. Developments During the Early Twentieth Century

The period from 1900 to 1930 was characterized by the perfection of the optical techniques for studying the corona that had been introduced during the preceding century. No new techniques of observation were devised, nor did any new concepts concerning the corona arise.

Outstanding progress was made in eclipse photography, and several of the best photographs of the period have become classic examples of eclipse of sunspot-maximum, sunspot-minimum, and intermediate types. Large cameras, with focal lengths of 100 feet or more, small cameras, and intermediate-sized cameras were put into use, and photographers were distributed as widely as possible over each eclipse path in order that motions or changes in form might be detected. From the excellent set of photographs that this effort brought forth, two conclusions were drawn:

(1)   The pattern of variation of the shape of the corona with the sunspot cycle that had been outlined by Young was thoroughly confirmed. Furthermore, Ludendorff gave the phenomenon a quantitative description by plotting ellipticity of isophotes as a function of phase in the sunspot cycle.

(2) Evidence for motion or change in form during the few hours of an eclipse was found to be very slight. There was some indication of rising loops, but the motion, if present at all, was not more than a few kilometers per second. Streamers presented a frustrating problem, for it was recognized that in the absence of density irregularities matter could flow along them without detection.

Many improvements in eclipse spectroscopy were made during this period, particularly in the perfection of slitless spectrophotography. From these improved spectrograms it was possible to make a clear distinction of coronal emission lines from prominence and chromospheric lines. As a result, a total of 18 coronal lines were identified, only one of which—the green line—had been recognized as a coronal line at the beginning of the century. Slitless spectrograms also revealed clearly the distribution of emission in the various coronal lines around the solar limb, and it was apparent that although the emission was related to disk activity, it did not occur in all lines in the same proportion. This conclusion led to the fruitful practice of grouping the lines into classes, such that all members of a given class would generally be found at about the same limb position during a given eclipse. Although the procedure was carried out in anticipation that all lines of a given class came from the same element, it paved the way, when the processes of the line formation should be understood, for interpretation of the physical conditions in the corona.

Ideas concerning the nature of the corona were in a state of complete confusion during the period. The element "coronium" was coming into thorough disrepute, for it obviously had no place in the periodic table, and numerous unsuccessful attempts were made to identify the coronal lines with various low states of ionization of known elements.

By 1930 the continuum corona was distinguished from the Fraunhofer corona, the latter being attributed to scattering by interplanetary dust. The electron, by this time a familiar particle, was recognized as the plausible scattering agent for producing the coronal continuum, which had been demonstrated to have the same spectral distribution as the sun. The presence of the electrons in the corona gave a great deal of trouble, however. The idea of a pure electron atmosphere was a tantalizing one, since at 5000°K it would have about the proper density gradient to fit the observed decrease in coronal brightness with height, but the overpowering difficulties were recognized for maintaining such an atmosphere against the electrostatic field that would necessarily result.

C. The Key Years 1930–1942

During the twelve years following 1930 two outstanding events—or, more strictly, sequences of events—occurred that were to refute completely the prediction made by Mitchell (1935) early in the period that "progress in knowledge concerning the corona promises to be slow." One of these events was the development of a working coronagraph. The idea of observing the corona in the absence of an eclipse was far from new. It had been followed along two separate lines of attack for more than fifty years. The demonstration by Janssen, in 1858, that prominences could be studied without eclipse by imaging the region just beyond the limb of the sun on a spectroscope slit, along with the discovery of the coronal green line in the following year, had suggested a similar procedure for study of the corona; but it was soon recognized that the line was too weak for such observation without an eclipse. About 1880 the well-known English astronomer Huggins tried, by placing an occulting disk at the primary image of a telescope and thereby blotting out the bright image of the sun, to photograph the corona in the light coming around the disk. In carrying out this experiment he did obtain a bright halo of light around the occulting disk that looked very much like a solar corona. As a matter of fact, he could find in the picture resemblances to the eclipse of a few months earlier, and considered the experiment a success. At a subsequent eclipse, however, he tried the same equipment with the same exposure time that he had used with the artificial eclipse and found that the photographic plate retained no image whatsoever, clearly demonstrating that the light coming around the occulting disk had been scattered light much brighter than the corona.

During the next fifty years many outstanding astronomers tried without success to observe the corona in the absence of an eclipse, and by 1930 the task was generally regarded as impossible. In the summer of that year, however, the young French astronomer Lyot succeeded where others had failed—but only after a more careful analysis of the sources of scattered light within the instrument as well as without than had been made by his predecessors, and after developing special techniques for removing this scattered light.

During the next few years Lyot put his instrument to use in several different ways. With extremely good observing conditions he was able to photograph the white-light corona directly and distinguish the features in it from the scattering features in the instrument by rotating the telescope into several different positions for successive photographs. He found that a much easier technique for observing the corona, however, was the spec-troscopic analysis of the light coming around the occulting disk. Later, after perfecting the basic telescope, he demonstrated that it could also be used with very narrow–band monochromatic filters (which he had also developed) to form complete images of the corona in the wavelengths of emission lines. He also used it with polarimetric equipment for a much more effective detection of the white-light corona than by direct observa-tion. By 1942 three coronagraph stations were in regular operation—Pic du Midi, established by Lyot at the summit of the Pyranees in France; Arosa, in Switzerland, by Waldmeier; and at Climax, Colorado, USA, by Roberts. At each of these stations spectroscopic observations of the corona were made daily. Thus observing time was no longer limited to the few minutes each decade during which the sun is totally eclipsed.

Within two years from the date of the first successful coronagraph ob-servation Lyot (1932) made a measurement that led to the revolutionary concept of the corona being much hotter than the photosphere. Using a higher-dispersion spectrograph than could be used during eclipse he meas-ured the profile of the green coronal line and reported that its width was 0.9 Å and very regular. A few years later he suggested that the broadening was thermal. He was unable to compute the temperature from the line profile, however, because he did not know the atomic weight of the ion emitting the line.

One earlier hint had already been given of a high-temperature corona. In 1931, while discussing the spectrograms that he had taken at the eclipse of 1929, Grotrian noted that in the spectrum of the inner corona the H and K absorption lines were replaced by a shallow depression in the con-tinuum extending from below 3900 Å to above 4100 Å (an observation still requiring precise confirmation). He pointed out that the broadening would indicate a velocity in the coronal electrons of 7.5×10^8 cm sec^{-1}, com-pared to the average thermal velocity of electrons at 6000°K, "the maxi-mum feasible temperature," of 5.5×10^7 cm sec^{-1}. (We note with interest that the square of the ratio of these two velocities, multiplied by 6000°, gives 1.1×10^6 °K.) Then, after suggesting a relation between such high electron velocities and the presence of He II lines in the solar atmosphere, he finally raised the question as to whether the velocities had a thermal distribution or whether they represented streaming along lines of force.

Apparently Grotrian did not pursue the idea of a high-temperature corona further for the next several years, for we find the following state-ment by him published in 1939: ". . . the symptoms indicate that in the outer zones of the solar atmosphere conditions for the excitation of spectral lines are present that go far above what we would expect from thermal velocities." The quotation is from a very short note that may well be the most important document in the history of coronal science, for it marks the culmination of a series of events that changed the corona from one of the most mysterious to one of the better understood of all astronomical features. Curiously this sequence of events had its beginning in astronomical observations far removed from the sun, as the following account will show:

The spectrum of Nova Pictoris 1925 remained an object of repeated observations for many years, for it contained a number of distinctive lines that defied identification. Among the several astronomers who were concerned about the identification of these lines was Bowen of the California Institute of Technology. Finally, in 1935, he identified some of the lines as forbidden lines of Fe VI; and in 1939, in collaboration with the Swedish spectroscopist Edlén, who had also been interested in the problem for some time, he identified the remainder as forbidden transitions in Fe VII. In the meantime, Adams and Joy discovered beyond doubt five coronal lines in the spectrum of the recurrent nova R. S. Ophiuchi during its 1933 brightening.

These two discoveries suggested to Grotrian that the coronal lines might perhaps also be emitted in forbidden transitions of highly ionized elements. Edlén had already studied the spectra of ions in the isoelectronic sequence beginning with Cl I, up to Co XI, and in the process had identified some lines and terms in Fe X. Grotrian noted from Edlén's results that the wave number corresponding to a transition between the two levels of the ground state of Fe X, from two independent laboratory determinations, was 15,660 in one case and 15,710 cm^{-1} in the other, whereas the wavelength of the coronal red line corresponded to a wave number of 15,683 cm^{-1}. To check this identification of the coronal red line, he noted that its behavior was different from that of most coronal lines, with the exception of the line λ 7892 that had been recently discovered by Lyot. Thus he postulated that λ 7892 should be emitted by an ion not far removed from Fe X. Fortunately, Edlén had also determined energy levels for Fe XI. The transition between the two ground-state levels in this case corresponded to a wave number of 12,670 cm^{-1}, whereas that for the coronal line λ 7892 was 12,668. Thus, within the limits of laboratory accuracy, two of the coronal lines were identified.

Following the lead of Grotrian, Edlén turned his attention to the coronal lines, and by 1942 nineteen of them had been identified, all as forbidden transitions in highly ionized atoms of familiar elements, principally iron, nickel, and calcium.

D. The High-Temperature Corona

The width of the coronal line profiles measured by Lyot, together with the identification of the emitting ions by Grotrian and Edlén, provided evidence for placing the temperature of the corona at one million degrees or more. The presence of such highly ionized atoms, as a matter of fact, was itself a strong indication of very high temperatures. Nevertheless, the idea of a very hot corona was accepted slowly and reluctantly. (The disruptions of World War II no doubt played a role in delaying this next natural step in the development of the science.) As late as 1945, Saha suggested that the coronal ions were produced by nuclear fission, and Kun Huang in the same year discussed a hypothesis that had been put forth by Menzel in 1941 and restated by Vegard in 1944 of ions produced deep within the sun and ejected through the photosphere. However, Kun Huang favored the hypothesis that the ions were produced in a high-temperature (greater than 20,000°) corona. Woolley and Gascoigne (1946) in the following year discussed Saha's suggestion and rejected it in favor of ionization (in thermodynamic equilibrium) at a temperature of 10^5 °K. These authors took note of evidence of even higher temperatures in line widths and solar radio noise. Data from the new science of radio astronomy played a particularly strong role in bringing about the acceptance of a high coronal temperature, possibly because the equally convincing optical observations had become commonplace.

By 1945 Waldmeier was also suggesting million-degree temperatures. In that year he noted three pieces of evidence for this conclusion: the broad coronal lines, the absence of collisional deexcitation at densities much higher than those in nebulae, and the slow decrease of density with height.

Thus the year 1945 saw the general acceptance of the long-delayed concept of a very hot corona. It is remarkable how many phenomena that had puzzled astronomers during the preceding century were explained by this concept. The density gradients in the corona could be maintained in hydrostatic equilibrium at a temperature of one or two million degrees; the heavy atoms could be ionized to produce the observed emission lines; and the complete ionization of hydrogen and helium would bring about an absence of emission lines of those elements in the corona, at the same time providing an adequate quantity of electrons to scatter the photospheric light. The concept explained the observed brightness of the sun in meter-wavelength radio noise, the absence of Fraunhofer lines in the scattered-light spectrum, and the width of the coronal lines. In short, the assigning of a high temperature to the corona rendered it a reasonable physical object.

E. The State of Coronal Science

Although with the identification of the corona's emission lines and the
approximation of its temperature all of the outstanding major coronal
problems were answered, a number of new questions were raised that have
not yet been resolved, although considerable progress is now being made
in their solution. Two of these are obvious: What is the precise value of
the temperature, and what is the heating mechanism? Within a few years
after the discovery of high coronal temperatures, various values were
given by Biermann (1947), Woolley and Allen (1948), Miyamoto (1949),
Shklovskii (1951), Hill (1951), and Elwert (1952), all based on a determination of the temperature that would lead to the degree of ionization
indicated by coronal line emission. Their temperatures generally lay in the
range 5–11 $\times$ 10^5 °K. On the other hand, the widths of the coronal lines
generally gave temperatures greater than 1.8 $\times$ 10^6 °K, and sometimes as
great as several million degrees. Radial density gradients in the corona
that vary strongly from time to time and place to place indicated temperatures lying between those found by the two methods mentioned above,
sometimes favoring one, sometimes the other. The same is true of temperatures determined by solar radio noise; earlier radio-astronomy determinations favored the lower temperatures, but recent higher-resolution measurements indicate that in the more dense portions of the corona, at least,
the temperatures approximate those found by line-width measurements.

The discrepancies among coronal temperatures computed from the
various types of observations has been an outstanding astrophysical
problem of the past decade. Line-width temperatures remained consistently
high, and ionization temperatures stubbornly low. Each method of measurement was vigorously attacked by advocates of the other—the former
because lines could be broadened by macroscopic as well as thermal motion, and the latter because it depends on atomic parameters that have
never been precisely computed. Examination of emission lines failed to
yield any significant evidence of macroscopic motion, however, and progressively better approximations used in the computation of ion cross
sections for ionization and recombination did not reveal any significant
discrepancies from the values already used. The apparent stalemate appears now to have been broken by Burgess (1964), who pointed out that
one of the major processes by which ions recombine in the corona had
been overlooked. As a consequence, a considerably higher temperature is
necessary to maintain a certain stage of ionization than had been computed
previously. The temperatures indicated by the line profiles are still some-

what higher than those indicated by ionization theory, but the difference is not too great to be explained by a moderate amount of macroscopic motion. Finally, Billings (1964) has made some progress in the separation of thermal from macroscopic effects in the line profiles, radar measurements have yielded quantitative information concerning such macroscopic motion, and increasingly precise theories of coronal heating have suggested additional characteristics of such motion. Thus it now appears that the problem of the temperature of the corona is approaching a solution.

The problem of heating the corona was attacked within a year after its high temperature was generally recognized. During the ensuing two decades a considerable number of plausible theories have been proposed, but none is generally considered to be adequate in detail. Theories by Biermann (1946), Schwarzschild (1948), Schatzman (1949), Alfvén (1950), Piddington (1956), Osterbrock (1961), and Uchida (1963) have all considered the energy that heats the corona to be transferred through the photosphere and chromosphere by nonthermal motions originating in the hydrogen convective layer of the sun. The idea of Hoyle and Lyttleton that the corona is heated by the accretion of particles from outside the sun has never been refuted, but neither has it gained widespread acceptance.

Although neither the question of the precise temperature nor that of the heating mechanism has been answered, considerable information gained during the past eighteen years has a bearing on them. Statistics concerning coronal line intensities and coronal line widths have been accumulated, the relation of coronal line emission to solar activity has been studied in detail, precise data concerning the electron density have been obtained both in and out of eclipses, and better atomic parameters have been computed. From all of these considerations has come an increasing realization that the corona is not a simple atmosphere but a complex structure, probably not to be described by a single temperature or simple density distribution.

One important development of the past few years has been the conception of the corona as much more extensive than the few solar radii visible at the time of an eclipse. Biermann, as early as 1951, suggested that solar particles streaming far out into the solar system deflect comet tails. He did not associate these particles directly with the corona, however. The observations first suggesting specifically that the corona extends as far as fifty solar radii were made by Vitkevich and Hewish on the occultation of the radio noise from the Crab Nebula as it passed each year close to the sun. Chapman greatly enlarged the picture by suggesting that the corona extends to the earth's orbit, and beyond, being supported hydrostatically. This suggestion was followed by Parker's idea that the corona is hydrodynamically unstable and in a state of constant expansion, resulting in a "solar wind." Chamberlain contributed a third picture, in which the out flow of particles was described as an evaporation process. A lively con troversy developed among proponents of the three ideas, but further theoretical work by Parker and others, as well as space-probe observations has given the solar-wind concept a preeminent status for describing the extended corona.

The most significant recent development has been the introduction of a number of new and very promising observing techniques. Two of these— the use of high-resolution radio telescopes, and the photographing of the sun in X rays from rockets and satellites—add a new dimension to coronal observing, in that they permit the corona to be studied on the disk as well as on the limb. In this regard their contribution is comparable to the great extension of the time dimension, for making observations, by the corona-graph. An important consequence of such disk observations is that the relation of coronal to photospheric and chromospheric features is more im mediately apparent. An even more important aspect of the high-resolution radio and the X-ray studies of the corona is that each gives unique infor mation about the physical state of the gas. X-ray photography and X-ray spectroscopy lead directly to a better understanding of the atomic features in the corona, since the emission lines in the X-ray region are generally the strong resonance lines of the coronal ions. Radio noise not only indicates the temperature and density of the region in which the beam is located but also gives information about the magnetic field that may be present. Further in formation about magnetic fields is emerging through the study of the polarization of emission lines.

Two active means of studying the corona that were scarcely visualized a decade ago are now in operation and have fantastic possibilities. These are radar, which was first used in 1961, and space probes, which are currently measuring density and velocity in the outer corona near the earth's orbit but may soon be used to penetrate much closer to the sun. It is too early to predict what these new techniques may reveal, but they give promise of answering such questions as: What is the structure of the extensive corona? What sort of magnetic fields are present? How does the solar rotation rate vary with distance above the photosphere?

We stand at the threshold of a new and exciting period in the history of coronal science. Although we think that we have a fairly good idea of the nature of the structure with which we deal, we admit ignorance con cerning many details; and we recognize the possibility that the next ten years may reveal much that we do not now suspect.

During a little more than a century the concept of the corona has changed from that of a phenomenon in the lunar atmosphere to that of the most extensive entity in the solar system. It has passed through the stage of being one of the most puzzling objects in astronomy to that of being one of the best understood. The solar corona is the only part of any star, other than the radiation field, that has been or is currently available for laboratory analysis. Present outstanding problems are: (*1*) the need of an adequate description of the heating mechanism; (*2*) our ignorance of the dynamic structure of the corona; (*3*) the apparent discrepancy between the chemical composition of the corona and the photosphere; and (*4*) our surprising lack of understanding of the relation between the inner and the extended portions of the corona. The new methods of observation, in giving us insight into these questions, will undoubtedly reveal many new and fascinating problems.

REFERENCES

Alfvén H. (1950). "Cosmical Electrodynamics," p. 151. Oxford Univ. Press (Clarendon), London and New York.

Biermann, L. (1946). The meaning of chromospheric turbulence and the UV excess of the sun. *Naturwisschschaften* **33**, 118.

Biermann, L. (1947). *Naturwissenschaften* **34**, 87.

Biermann, L. (1951). Comet tails and solar corpuscular radiation. *Z. Ap.* **29**, 274.

Billings, D. E. (1964). The shape of coronal line profiles. *Ap. J.* **139**, 710.

Bowen, I. S., and Edlén, B. (1939). FeVII in Nova Pictoris. *Nature* **143**, 374.

Burgess, A. (1964). Dielectronic recombination and the temperature of the solar Corona. *Ap. J.* **139**, 776.

Elwert, G. (1952). Concerning the ionization-recombination process in a plasma and the ionization formula for the solar corona. *Z. Naturforsch.* **7a**, 432.

Grotrian, W. (1931). *Z. Ap.* **3**, 199.

Grotrian, W. (1939). *Naturwissenschaften* **27**, 214.

Hill, E. R. (1951). Collision processes involving highly ionized atoms. *Aust. J. Sci. Res.* **4A**, 437.

Huang, Kun (1945). On the excitation of the coronal lines. *Ap. J.* **101**, 187.

Lyot, B. (1932). Study of the solar corona in the absence of an eclipse. *Z. Ap.* **5**, 73.

Menzel, D. H. (1941). *The Telescope* **8**, 65.

Mitchell, S. A. (1935). "Eclipses of the Sun," 4th ed. Columbia Univ. Press, New York.

Miyamoto, S. (1949). *Publ. Astr. Soc. Japan* **1**, 10.

Osterbrock, D. E. (1961). Heating of the solar chromosphere, plages and corona by magnetohydrodynamic waves. *Ap. J.* **134**, 347–388.

Piddington, J. H. (1956). Solar atmospheric heating by hydromagnetic waves. *M. N. R. A. S.* **116**, 314.

Plutarch, Opera Maralia. The Face of the Moon. Quote from Secchi (1875, p. 330).

Saha, M. N. (1945). *Proc. Phys. Soc.* **57**, 271

Schatzman, E. (1949). The heating of the solar corona and chromosphere. *Ann d'Ap.* **12**, 203.

Schuster, A. (1879). *M. N. R. A. S.* **30**, 35.

Schwarzschild, M. (1948). Noise arising from the solar granulation. *Ap. J.* **107**, 1.

Secchi, Le P. a. (1875). Early history of eclipses, *in* "Le Soleil," 2nd ed. Gauthers-Villars, Paris, pp. 330–369.

Shklovskii, I. S. (1951). "Solar Corona," 1st ed. Moscow.

Uchida, Y. (1963). An effect of the magnetic field in the shock wave heating theory of the corona. *Publ. astr. Soc. Japan* **15**, 376.

Vegard, L. (1944). *Geofys. Publ.* **16**, No. 1.

Waldmeier, M. (1945). *Mitt. der Aarg Natur. Ges.* **22**, 185.

Woolley, R. v. d. R., and Allen, C. W. (1948). The coronal emission spectrum. *M. N. R. A. S.* **108**, 292.

Woolley, R. v. d. R., and Gascoigne, S. C. B. (1946). On the excitation of the coronal spectrum. *M. N. R. A. S.* **106**, 113.

Young, C. A. (1896). "The sun," pp. 237–276, Appleton, New York.

CHAPTER 2

OBSERVATIONAL TECHNIQUES

A. Eclipse Observation Techniques

Visual and Photographic Observation

No technique has yet been devised for observing the structural features of the corona that excels naked-eye observation during a total eclipse, for the greater range of the eye than of any photographic film makes possible the simultaneous viewing of faint streamers and bright inner features, one or the other of which would be lost in any photograph. The difficulties of the technique are threefold: the observer is likely to become engrossed in a single detail and lose the overall pattern; he is likely to be strongly influenced by preconceptions of what he is to see; and not being an artist with a perfect memory he is at loss for a satisfactory means of reporting what he has seen.

Eclipse Photography

By the end of the nineteenth century, photography had become the standard technique for eclipse observation, and it still remains of outstanding importance (see Fig. 2.1). The camera designs have varied enormously (Mitchell, 1935). The largest that has been used to date was a coelostat system with a 135-ft focal length, 12-in. aperture lens. Another very large camera, the Swarthmore camera, with a 63-ft focal length, was mounted in a double tower. Several cameras of approximately 40-ft focal length have also been employed, of which the Lick instrument is perhaps

Fig. 2.1. One of the most recent and striking of eclipse photographs, taken by Sheldon M. Smith of the May 30, 1965, total eclipse. The photograph was made from a NASA aircraft flying at 39,500 ft elevation over the mid-Pacific. A rotating image-occulting device just in front of the focal plane attenuated the inner corona, thereby accentuating the streamer structure.   Courtesy, S. M. Smith and the National Aeronautics and Space Administration.

the most famous. It consists of a 5-in. aperture, 40-ft focal-length lens that is mounted on a pier and pointed directly at the position of the eclipse. The film holder—the only driven part of the system—is mounted on a separate pier, and the entire system is enclosed in a tube that does not make contact with either pier.

Many observers have felt that there is little to gain by the use of such long focal-length cameras, and that smaller images, when enlarged, give just as much information. Some of the most interesting eclipse photographs have been made with very simple equipment. Mrs. Maunder's famous

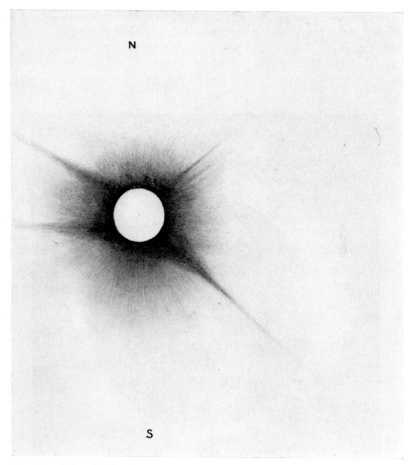

Fig. 2.2. A drawing based on the Maunder's eclipse photograph of January 22, 1898. On this remarkable photograph, made with a Dallmeyer astigmatic lens of $1\frac{1}{2}$ inch aperture and 9 in. focal length, the southwest streamer could be traced out to 15 solar radii. Courtesy, High Altitude Observatory.

photograph (Fig. 2.2) of the eclipse of 1898, showing a long, thin streamer running out nearly six solar diameters from the moon's limb, was made with a lens of only $1\frac{1}{2}$ in. aperture. Firor, in the February 1962 eclipse, obtained good-quality photographs (Fig. 2.3) with a Questar telescope fitted with a 35-mm magazine and shutter, the exposures with this fast system being sufficiently short and that it could be held in the hand during the eclipse.

The difficulty of obtaining exposures of the faint outer features of the corona without overexposing the inner corona has been attacked in various ways. The simplest approach, now possible with modern fast photographic material, is to take a number of exposures of different length during totality—the shortest to show only the brightest features, the longest to

(a)

Fig. 2.3. A Firor photograph of the February 1962 eclipse. This photograph illustrates the possibility of obtaining high-quality eclipse picture with equipment that is extremely simple to transport and operate—a Questar telescope, fitted with a 35-mm camera. The high-speed camera permitted a large number of exposures, covering a wide range of exposure times. The $\frac{1}{5}$-sec exposure shown here (a), the longest used, illustrates quiet-sun characteristics on the east limb and active-sun characteristics on the west. The condensation on the west limb, which shows more clearly on the shorter exposure (b), is one of the brightest ever photographed at an eclipse. Courtesy, High Altitude Observatory.

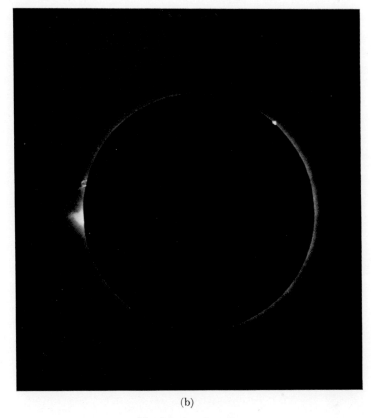

(b)

Fig. 2.3. (continued).

expose as strongly as the sky background will permit. Another technique has been to place circular filters of density decreasing with distance from the center of the solar image at the film plane. A rotating vane with tapered blades (Laffineur *et al.*, 1961) (Fig. 2.4) or an external disk in front of the camera lens have both been used to accomplish the same objective (Allen, 1956a). The disk vignettes the inner corona, whereas light from far out illuminates the entire aperture. Although the disk method is elegant in its simplicity, an optimum occulting-disk size and position has not yet been achieved.

The technique that should be chosen for photographing the corona depends primarily on the scientific use to which the photograph is to be put. A small image, showing little detail, is perfectly adequate for a determina-

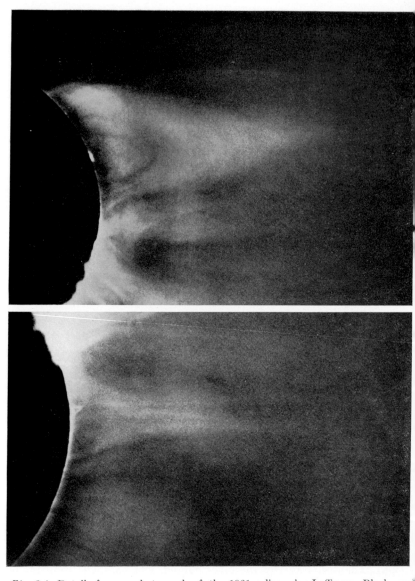

Fig. 2.4. Details from a photograph of the 1961 eclipse, by Laffineur, Block, and Bretz. A rotating vane with tapered blades, near the image plane in the camera, weakened the exposure near the sun so as to bring the various parts of the coronal structures to nearly uniform apparent brightness. The central feature in the upper frame is a very typical helmet overlying a quiescent prominence (see Chapter 3, Section B). The dark arch structure overlaying the prominence is clearly apparent. One gets the impression that the bright portion of the helmet is enclosed in a much larger and more extended envelop of similar shape. The effect may also be the line-of-sight superposition of a large and a small helmet. The shape of the feature in the lower frame is more typical of a streamer overlying an active region.   Courtesy, M. Bretz and colleagues.

tion of the ellipticity of the isophotes. If these isophotes are to be identified, however, the picture must be calibrated. For such a study, a small calibrated picture is of more value than a large-image, fine-detail, uncalibrated picture. If electron densities are to be found, it is furthermore necessary to provide information for separating the Fraunhofer or false (F) corona, which is due to the scattering of lights by interplanetary particles, from the true (K) corona. The separation can be effected either by a series of calibrated photographs taken through a polarizing filter, with the plane of polarization rotated in various directions, (von Klüber, 1958; Saito, 1948; Blackwell, 1955) or by a spectrogram in which the depths of the Fraunhofer lines from the corona can be compared with those from the solar disk (see Chapter 3).

Photoelectric Polarimetry

In contrast to the various photographic techniques used by many different observers, examples of photoelectric polarimetry of the corona at eclipse are few. Consequently, we shall describe here only the apparatus used very successfully by Ney *et al.* (1961) at the 1959 and 1963 eclipses. This device determines the intensity, polarization, and direction of polarization of the coronal light at each of 1000 raster points in the coronal image, all in an interval of time of 30 seconds. The raster scanner consists of a series of holes each $\frac{1}{10}$ solar diameter in aperture, so located on the scanning disk that as the disk rotates the various holes in passing in front of a slit aperture scan the portion of the solar image falling on that slit. Behind the slit another disk rotates much faster. On this second disk are mounted a number of pairs of polaroids, the two members of each pair having their axes orthogonal, while the bisectors of the polarization angles in successive pairs change through a complete cycle for a half-rotation of the fast disk. Finally, the light passing through the total system is received by a photomultiplier. Thus when the coronal light is polarized parallel to one polaroid in a pair there is a maximum change in the signal from the photomultiplier as the fast wheel passes from one polaroid in a pair to the other. As the wheel turns to other polaroid pairs this difference in signal decreases, and when the pair of polaroids with axes both making angles of 45° with the polarization in the coronal image pass in front of the aperture there is no signal difference. Signals from the photomultiplier, displayed on a cathode ray tube, thus are a sequence of pips in which alternate pips may first be far apart, then draw together and seem to cross over before separating again. The mean signal provides a measure of the coronal intensity; the ratio of the maximum displacement of alternate pips to the mean signal, the polarization; and the position of the fast wheel at the crossover, the direction of polarization. The system scans the entire corona, out to 2.5 $R_\odot$. At the 1959 eclipse the observations, when corrected for instrumental scatter—and scatter of coronal light in the earth's atmosphere—were capable of detecting the angle of polarization to about $1°$, and identical instruments showed agreement in intensity to the third significant figure for two stations separated by 30 minutes in the eclipse path.

Use of Interferometer at Eclipse

Jarrett and von Klüber (1961) have developed a technique for observing the emission in any strong coronal emission line over the entire corona with a single photograph taken during a total eclipse, and have used this technique successfully for the 1954 and 1958 eclipses. The instrument consists of an $f/11$ objective lens that produces a 34-mm–diameter solar image. A field lens behind the primary image forms an image of the objective lens on a Fabry–Perot interferometer, and a camera lens behind the interferometer forms an image of the corona in fringes of the coronal line under observation. The coronal line being studied is isolated by placing a combination of interference and glass filters with a half-width of about 30 Å in front of the Fabry–Perot interferometer. The two plates of the interferometer are flat to $\frac{1}{40}$ wavelength and are separated 0.35 mm, which results in fringes 4.04 Å apart. These plates are aluminized to the optimum extent to obtain the maximum spectroscopic resolution during the time available for exposures. The picture obtained with such an instrument shows the monochromatic corona as a system of bright and dark interference fringes (Fig. 2.5). The technique has the merit that from a single photograph one can obtain a raster of line intensities and line widths from points distributed over the entire corona. It also reveals the presence of emission in the line at somewhat greater distances from the sun than is possible with a coronagraph in the absence of eclipse. It has two distinct disadvantages: (1) The space resolution cannot be better than the distance between the fringes; and   (2) Any given line profile is a composite of radiation from all parts of the corona that is imaged within the profile. Thus different parts of the profile are formed by radiation from different regions in the corona. As a consequence, a considerable distortion of the profile results if the brightness change is strong from one fringe to the next. A third but less important difficulty is that with spacings of 4.04 Å, the wings of a very strong line may experience significant overlap.

Liebenberg has recently developed a modification of the Fabry–Perot technique that avoids the second difficulty, but at a sacrifice of the ability

Fig. 2.5. A λ 5303 interferometer photograph of the 1958 eclipse by Jarrett and von Klüber. Courtesy, Royal Astronomical Society.

to view the entire corona at once. His instrument accepts light through an input aperture from only a small portion of the coronal image, collimates it, passes it through the interferometer, and reimages the dispersed light on an output aperture that admits only a small portion of an interference fringe. As the interferometer spacing is then changed slowly, the various portions of the fringe pass across the output aperture. Thus a photoelectric detector behind the aperture records a high-quality profile. The procedure requires that the solar image must not move on the input aperture and that the seeing conditions remain constant during a scan.

Eclipse Spectroscopy

Although spectroscopic observations during eclipses have played a key role in the development of coronal science, their importance has been considerably diminished since the widespread use of coronagraphs. At a coronagraph station it is possible to use larger, more stable equipment than can be carried conveniently to an eclipse site, to follow the day-by-day changes in the stronger emission lines, to study the association of line emission with flares, surges, etc., and to make long photographic exposures of high-dispersion spectra for the study of line profiles. Eclipse spectroscopy is still superior for the detection of faint lines, however, and also for the measurement of coronal emission far from the limb (Athay and Roberts, 1955; Aly et al., 1963; Allen, 1956b). Furthermore, it is the only technique available for the study of the spectrum of the electron-scattered white-light corona. Finally, it has the advantage in line-profile analysis that the profiles are not distorted by the Fraunhofer lines of a superimposed sky spectrum. During recent years much of the spectroscopic observing of the corona during eclipse has been incidental to programs of chromospheric spectroscopy and has not been directed toward specific coronal problems in such a way as to use its potentialities most effectively.

Line Polarimetry

The polarization in coronal emission lines promises to be a useful phe-nomenon for the study of the excitation mechanisms and also of magnetic fields in the corona. Although some information on the state of polarization of these lines can be obtained with a coronagraph (Hyder, 1965), eclipse observations appear to be much easier and more fruitful. Wood (1905) was the first to look for polarization in a coronal line. His efforts, at the 1900 eclipse, showed no polarization in the green line. At the 1954 eclipse, Mogilevskii et al. (1960) measured line polarization by the insertion of a Wolleston prism behind a spectrograph slit, thereby getting two oppositely polarized images of the spectrum. At the 1965 eclipse, Hyder photographed the corona through a sufficiently narrow filter to isolate the green line, the light also passing through a Savart plate. The fringes in the resulting picture (Fig. 2.6) show definite line polarization in some parts of the corona but not in others.

B. Coronagraphy

The Coronagraph Telescope

The essential features of the coronagraph design developed by Lyot (Fig. 2.7) during the years 1930 to 1940 have been followed in coronagraph

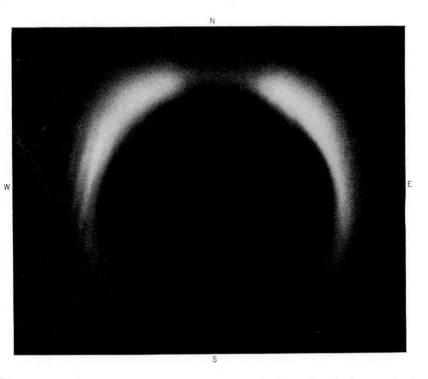

Fig. 2.6. Polarization fringes in the λ 5303 corona. The fringes in this photograph of he 1965 eclipse, made by Hyder by inserting a Savart plate in the optical system, ndicate polarization in the coronal emission line. Their complex interpretation is dis-ussed in Chapter 10. Courtesy, C. Hyder.

tations in France, Switzerland, Germany, Austria, the Soviet Union, apan, the United States, and Peru. The primary part of such a corona-graph is an objective lens that scatters the smallest possible amount of ight. Traditionally, this is a singlet lens, made from a highly selected piece of crown glass in which no bubbles, striations, or other imperfections are apparent. The lens need not be large—4- to 6-in. diameter is used in most oronographs—but it must be exceptional in its freedom from dust and lirt, scratches, and any light-scattering flaws in the glass. Some of the stringency of these requirements has been imposed by inadequate pho-ometry in the observing programs. Since early photometry was by eye-estimate, the accuracy was enhanced by the diminution of scattered background light, and reproducibility depended on maintaining optimum

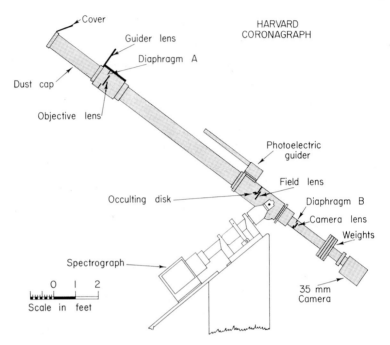

Cover

HARVARD
CORONAGRAPH

Guider lens

Diaphragm A

Dust cap

Objective lens

Photoelectric
guider

Field lens

Occulting disk

Diaphragm B

Camera lens

Weights

Spectrograph

O   1   2

35 mm
Camera

Scale in feet

Fig. 2.7. Schematic diagram of the first Climax coronagraph. This coronagraph which was in operation from 1941 to 1955, illustrates the basic Lyot design in a simple straightforward arrangement. The final image was either directed to the slit of a Littrow spectrograph or photographed cinematographically though an Hα filter. Courtesy High Altitude Observatory.

observing conditions at all times. With photoelectric photometry of the coronal spectrum or of spectrograms it is possible to subtract background from line with considerable accuracy, and the minimization of background becomes a matter of convenience rather than necessity except where very faint lines are concerned. The singlet objective brings the various wave lengths in the solar image to focus over a range of several centimeters resulting in difficulties both in occulting and the simultaneous observation of several spectral lines. We have found at Climax that the need for simultaneous observations of several coronal and prominence lines for interpretation of the physical state of the corona frequently overshadows the need for a low background. Consequently, in our older instrument we sometimes replace the singlet lens with a high-quality doublet. In the new instrument, optics following the occulting disk restore the various wavelengths to the same focus. In any case it is important that the lens be kept at maximum cleanliness, and to this end a long dust-tube, coated on its interior with a sticky substance, is placed in front of the lens.

Next in the optical system, at the prime focus of the objective lens, is the occulting disk. When the objective is a singlet lens the occulting disk is located at the focal point for the wavelength of interest. If several lines are to be studied, each under optimum conditions, the occulting disk must be moved from one focal position to another. The occulting disk intercepts all the photospheric light in the chosen wavelength (except that scattered by the sky and objective) and sends this light out of the optical system in as effective a manner as possible. For this function the disk is generally a metal cone with the apex pointed toward the sun, burnished to minimize the absorption of heat that would create bad seeing conditions in the tube. For optimum occulting, a series of interchangeable occulting disks of different diameters is desirable, to care for both the different sizes of the solar image in different wavelengths and the changing distance of the sun from the earth throughout the year.

A field lens immediately behind the occulting disk forms an image of the objective lens. The light passing the occulting disk from which this image is formed is coronal light, scattered light from the sky and the objective, and—in case the objective is a simple lens—the wavelengths of photospheric light that are not adequately occulted by the occulting disk (called, in coronagraph terminology, the "spill"). The field lens also serves as the support for the occulting disk, which is mounted on a shaft through a hole in the lens.

It is at the image of the objective that Lyot removed the light diffracted by the periphery of the objective aperture, which had frustrated all his predecessors. This light forms a bright ring in the image of the objective and is removed by a diaphram. Also, at the center of the image is a bright spot of light, attributed to internal reflections in the objective, which can be eliminated by placing a small black disk at the location of the spot. This disk is conveniently located on the camera lens, sometimes called O_2 (the second objective), which is placed immediately behind the diaphram.

Finally, O_2 forms an image of the occulting disk, the sky, and the corona. In the bright ring of light surrounding the dark image of the occulting disk the corona itself is generally not apparent, since its light is only a small fraction of the light from the sky, the instrument, and the unocculted photospheric light. In the case of a simple objective lens and a small occulting disk the ring of light close to the occulting-disk image is generally colored, since those wavelengths of photospheric light for which complete occulting has taken place have been removed.

In spite of the fact that the corona is still not apparent, it constitutes a sufficient fraction of the light in the image formed by O_2 that it can be detected by various devices. The most straightforward device is a polarimeter, for taking advantage of the fact that the coronal light is strongly polarized with the magnetic vector radial to the sun. However, the most frequently used device is a spectroscope or spectrograph, for observing and measuring the various emission lines in the corona. Narrow-band filters are also used for observing the entire corona in the light of one emission line. We shall discuss each of these devices in turn, after describing briefly the Mangin mirror system (Rush and Schnable, 1966) by which an achromatic image of the corona is achieved in the new coronagraph at Climax.

The Mangin mirror is a negative meniscus lens of the same glass as the objective with which it is used, and of half the refracting power. It is coated on its convex side with a reflecting material. In a coronagraph arrangement this mirror is used as the second objective, O_2. Thus, when the first field lens forms an image of the objective on the concave side of the mirror, the action of the negative lens—through which the light makes a double pass— is to precisely compensate that of the objective, both in refraction and dispersion, leaving the curved reflecting face of the Mangin mirror to provide the secondary achromatic image of the corona.

The K Coronameter

The coronal component of the O_2 image may be detected by a photomultiplier that receives light from a portion of the image that has passed through a rotating polaroid. Since the coronal light is polarized radially to the sun, its presence is indicated by an alternating-current component in the photomultiplier output, of twice the frequency of the rotating polaroid. This technique was used by Lyot with his first coronagraph.

If the coronagraph is to be used exclusively for polarimetric measurements (Wlerick and Axtell, 1957; Dollfus et al., 1961; Karimov, 1961; Charvin, 1963), it is desirable to reduce instrumental polarization to a minimum. Two techniques for achieving this are to build the instrument so that the optical path of the light being analyzed will always fall along the axis of the instrument, and to eliminate any unnecessary optical components. We shall describe an instrument with these characteristics, called the K coronameter (Fig. 2.8), which was in use at Climax from 1956 to 1963, and is now installed on Mauna Loa, Hawaii. Similar instruments are in use at Meudon, France, Pic du Midi, France, and Kazakh, USSR.

The High Altitude Observatory K coronameter is so mounted on a spar that when the spar is directed toward the center of the sun the axis of the

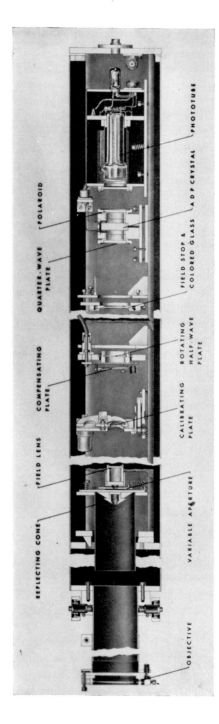

Fig. 2.8. Diagram of the optical system of the High Altitude Observatory *K* coronameter, now located at the top of Mauna Loa, Hawaii. Courtesy, High Altitude Observatory.

instrument is pointed at the corona. A gimbal mounting permits the axis of the instrument to describe a cone around the solar limb. The occulting disk, a burnished cone with a small hole along its axis, permits only 2 seconds of arc of the coronal primary image to pass into the detecting system. (For observing fainter features in the corona a disk with a larger aperture is used.) Subsequent optics contain the usual field lens and field stop for removing the diffracted light from the image of the objective. However, there is no O_2 lens; the light is analyzed immediately after passing through the field stop by an electrooptic detector.

Two optical parts of the analyzing system are inserted for convenience between the field lens and the field stop. One of these is a calibrating plate— a glass plate that may be turned through small, measurable angles to produce varying degrees of polarization of the attenuated direct sunlight that is used for calibration of the instrument. The other is a half-wave plate that rotates the plane of polarization of the incident light by twice the angle between one of the axes in the crystal and the plane of polarization of the incident light. The instrument is adjusted so that when an axis of the half-wave plate is aligned with the polarization plane for best operation of the detector, both are parallel to the radius of the sun on which the center of the scanning aperture is imaged. As the scanning of the limb proceeds, the half-wave plate, rotating at one half the scanning rate, keeps the plane of polarization of the coronal radiation in a fixed orientation with respect to the detector.

The detector itself consists of a quarter-wave plate, an ADP crystal, a polaroid, and a photomultiplier tube. The polaroid is oriented with its magnetic transmission axis parallel to the solar radius in the initial position described above, whereas the axes of the quarter-wave plate and the ADP crystal are set at 45° to that of the polaroid. The ADP crystal has the property of becoming double-refracting when a voltage is applied normal to its optic axis. When the voltage is suitable to make it effectively a quarter-wave plate with the fast and slow axes the same as those of the fixed quarter-wave plate, the two, acting together as a half-wave plate, rotate the plane of polarization through 90°, and a minimum amount of light reaches the photomultiplier tube. When the voltage is reversed, the crystal annuls the quarter-wave plate and maximum light is transmitted through the polaroid. Thus the combination of the quarter-wave plate, ADP crystal, and polaroid is identical in its effect on the incident light to a rotating polaroid interposed in front of the photomultiplier, but has the advantage that it does not have any moving parts.

The alternating-current output of the photomultiplier tube is analyzed by a phase-sensitive detector that reduces noise to a minimum. The direct-current component is also measured, to provide data for elimination of the effect of the polarized component of the scattered light from the sky. The polarization in the sky light introduces the most difficult problem in the operation of the K coronameter, since it varies with the zenith angle as well as with the dust content of the sky.

In addition to the polarization in the corona, which is being measured, and that in the sky, which must be removed by computation, there is a small residual polarization in the optics themselves, of about 10^{-3}, attributed primarily to the half-wave plate. This polarization is compensated by a fixed glass plate that is tilted slightly to the optic axis of the coronameter.

Observing was originally limited to the wavelength range 4300–6700 Å. The lower limit was set by a colored glass that eliminated some of the most intense radiation from the sky. The upper limit is that of the Lallemand photomultiplier tube. In present operation the lower limit is raised by a yellow filter to exclude the green coronal line. The resulting effective band is only a few hundred angstroms wide.

In the course of a scan around the solar limb, which requires about four minutes, both the AC and DC output of the photomultiplier tube are recorded automatically. The reduction of these data to polarization as a function of position angle, involving the elimination of the sky polarization, is quite a tedious process, however, and is conveniently carried out as an electronic-computer operation.

In order for any very definite picture of the corona to be obtained from coronameter observations it is necessary to complete scans at least two and preferably three heights above the limb under quite consistent observing conditions. Furthermore, in order to answer one of the major questions for which the coronameter was devised—the determination of the longitudinal position of the streamers for correlation with geomagnetic activity—it is necessary that good observing conditions persist for several days in succession. Finally, as in all coronagraph work, the sky brightness should be a minimum. Thus the atmospheric requirements for the use of a K coronameter are among the most stringent of those for any astronomical instrument.

Coronagraph Spectroscopy

Coronagraph spectrographs vary from the small but highly convenient direct-vision prism spectroscope at Arosa (Waldmeier, 1951), with a dis-

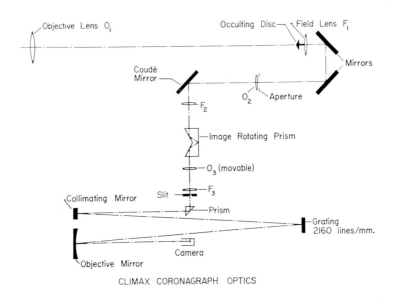

CLIMAX CORONAGRAPH OPTICS

Fig. 2.9. Schematic diagram of the small coronagraph and spectrograph at Climax. Courtesy, High Altitude Observatory.

persion of 29 Å/mm, to the large grating-spectrograph at Sacramento Peak, with dispersions of 2 to 35 mm/Å. The spectrograph in use at Climax since 1956 (Fig. 2.9), which we shall describe in some detail here, is of an intermediate size. It uses mirrors of 150-cm focal length for both collimation and imaging of the spectrum. Spherical aberration is minimized by placing the grating at a distance equal to the radius of curvature from each of these mirrors—i.e., by placing the two mirrors in one end of a box 3 meters in length, and the grating in the opposite end. The spectrograph slit and film-holder are both located on the side of the box, about midway between the ends. Light, entering the slit, is deflected by a prism toward the collimator. As it enters the slit, it passes through a field lens that focuses the corona-graph objective on the grating. The grating is mounted on a turret that can be turned to change the wavelength range of the light that passes through the remainder of the spectrograph, or turned farther to replace the grating by either of two other gratings that are mounted on the turret. The grating currently used on daily surveys in the visible region has 2160 lines per mm, giving a dispersion of approximately 2.5 Å/mm.

Several special provisions are made for fast and convenient study of the spectrum of the corona. The slit of the spectrograph is curved so that the spectrum of almost 90° of solar limb can be observed with a single slit position. Through a stepped motion of the O_2 lens the image of the sun can be moved across the slit in steps of various lengths. (A convenient size step corresponds to 4500 km on the sun, or twice the width of the commonly used 50-μ slit projected by the coronagraph optics upon the sun.) Simultaneously with the stepping of the solar image, the film also moves by an adjustable amount in front of a window of adjustable length. Thus one may either use the entire 10-in. window and photograph several hundred ångstroms of spectrum with the high-dispersion grating (or the entire visible spectrum with a lower-dispersion grating), or he may isolate the wavelength environment of certain lines with small windows and, by correspondingly small film steps, place a large number of spectrograms of small wavelength intervals on a single short strip of film. The latter procedure is particularly useful in recording one emission line at a sequence of heights above the limb (Fig. 2.10).

The 1956-model coronagraph at Climax has a 5-in. aperture, $f/20$ objective. The final 28-mm solar image that falls on the spectrograph slit can be rotated by means of a glass image-rotating prism, which has the dis-

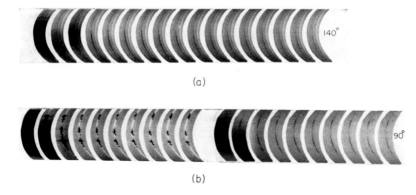

(a)

(b)

Fig. 2.10. Climax graded-height spectrogram sequences in (a) λ 5303, and (b) $H\alpha$ and λ 6374. The steps are 6000 km on the sun, with the position closest to the sun being on the left-hand side of each sequence. The λ 5303 sequence was made with only one window in the film plane. With two windows in the film plane the $H\alpha$ and λ 6374 sequences were photographed simultaneously. Note that the smaller structures that make up the extensive coronal line emission regions are much less in evidence in λ 5303 than in λ 6374. Doppler displacements are more evident in $H\alpha$ than in the coronal lines. The grating ghosts indicate that certain $H\alpha$ features are particularly intense. The narrowness of the ghosts identify these prominence features as quiescent. Spectrograms courtesy High Altitude Observatory.

advantage that the large amount of glass imposed into the optical path attenuates the ultraviolet wavelengths severely.

A larger coronagraph put in operation in Climax in 1962 has a 16-in. $f/20$ objective (Rush and Schnable, 1966). The accompanying spectrograph, with a focal length of 305 cm, is essentially a larger version of the smaller spectrograph. An unusual feature is the presence of several outlets through which portions of the spectral image can be removed for photography, photoelectric photometry, image intensification, or magnetographic analysis.

There are several aspects of coronal spectroscopy that deserve special mention. Since coronal emission lines are almost 1 Å broad, high-resolution spectroscopy plays no useful function. Furthermore, the need of being able to carry out all coronal observations of interest during a day requires that the exposure time should not be any longer than necessary. Thus, with the optical systems generally provided for coronagraphs, the optimum slit width for practical purposes is frequently greater than the theoretical optimum slit width for the spectrograph. Similar time-requirement considerations provide some limitation on the slowness, hence the smallness of grain, in the photographic emulsions to be used. With the 1956 Climax coronagraph–spectrograph using a 50-μ slit, a typical exposure time for moderate to strong green-line emission on a day of good sky, using Tri-X film, is 20 seconds. The theoretically optimum slit for the instrument is 10 to 20 μ. However, the film grain is such that a slit width of less than 30 μ does not lead to any improvement in spectroscopic resolution. By going to the finer-grained Plus-X film, the corresponding exposure time for a 50-μ slit is increased to 50 seconds. A slit of half this width could then be used to advantage, but the additional time spent in making exposures would restrict the scope of the observing program. With a dispersion of 2.5 Å/mm and a 50-μ slit the instrumental profile is 0.15 Å half-width, which is sufficiently small compared to the coronal line half-widths that an increase in the resolution by further narrowing of the slit must be weighed against the increase in time that this would require. As a working criterion, with the kind of slit widths and photographic material imposed by the exigencies of coronagraphic observation, meaningful line-profile analysis cannot be carried out with a dispersion of less than 5 Å/mm. Lower dispersions are useful for line-intensity measurements only. However, because of the great widths of coronal lines, little is gained by increasing this dispersion to more than 1 Å/mm.

A major problem in coronal spectroscopy is that some of the most interesting information concerning the physical state of the corona is manifest in the emission by faint lines in very small short-lived coronal features, such as, for example, appear in the two yellow coronal lines. Consequently, the most tantalizing observational phenomenon is frequently a few extra exposed film grains, and the most refined attempts to analyze these merely reveal the scarcity of the information. Under such circumstances the best observational technique is a compromise among the various factors affecting speed and resolution in the instrument.

Two extremely important coronal emission lines, λ 10,747 and λ 10,798, both Fe XIII, are too far in the infrared region of the spectrum to be photographed easily. Firor and Zirin (1962) have found it convenient to use an image-converter tube to study these lines. By accelerating the electrons with a potential of 18 kV and using an $f/1.5$ camera to photograph the phosphor they were able to decrease the time required for getting a photographic recording of the lines from about 30 minutes with direct photography on infrared-sensitized plates to about one minute with the image-converter.

Monochromatic Filters in Coronal Studies

One of the most difficult, and at the same time fruitful, methods of observing the corona is in the light of one of its emission lines only (Dollfus, 1962). This can be achieved by several techniques already mentioned. For example, with a coronagraph or at eclipse, a spectrum obtained with a slitless spectrograph shows the structure of the corona in each wavelength. Similarly, if the slit can be stepped above the limb, a composite monochromatic picture of the corona is achieved by placing the successive images of a given line side by side. In either case, however, if 1 Å on the spectrum corresponds to a significant height in the coronal image, there is confusion between extent in wavelength and extent in space, just as in the case of the Fabry–Perot interferometer pictures already mentioned.

This difficulty is avoided by photographing the corona in a limited wavelength interval of the spectrum containing an emission line. During a total eclipse the interval may be several ångstroms wide, since the brightness of the coronal continuum is much less than that of the stronger emission lines. With a coronagraph, however, because of the sky-scattered light, the wavelength band must be limited to not more than 1 Å. Thus whereas interference filters are adequate at an eclipse, birefringent filters or very narrow bandpass multilayer filters must be used at other times.

Birefringent filters have been described in detail in a number of books (e.g. Evans, 1953), so we shall not repeat the description here but present a simple outline of how they work for the benefit of the casual reader who is not already familiar with their operation.

When a piece of quartz or calcite crystal is cut with its faces parallel to its optic axis, then placed in a beam of plane polarized light so that its axis makes an angle of 45° with the plane of polarization of the incident light, the light is resolved into two components in the quartz, equal in intensity but oppositely polarized, traveling with different velocities through the quartz. Thus, when the light arrives at the exit face of the crystal, the two waves may be in phase, and if so, will recombine to give light polarized in the same plane as the incident light; or they may be 180° out of phase, in which case they will recombine to give light polarized at right angles to the plane of the incident light. If the two beams exit with some intermediate phase relationship, they will recombine to form elliptically or circularly polarized light. The phase relation between the outgoing waves that results in a given case depends on the thickness of the crystal and also the wavelength of the light, since the difference between the speeds of the two waves is different at different wavelengths. If, for a given crystal, the two waves of a given wavelength arrive in phase, those of an adjacent wavelength will arrive out of phase; and for a wavelength even farther removed, the waves will be in phase again. Thus, light from a continuous-spectrum source, after passing through a polaroid, crystal, polaroid combination—the two polaroids being oriented with their transmission axes parallel and at 45° to the crystal axis—is found upon analysis by a spectroscope to consist of alternate bright and dark bands. The distance between these bands is inversely proportional to the thickness of the crystal. Thus, if for a crystal of a given thickness the bright bands are 1 Å apart, a second unit with a crystal of the same material as the first but half as thick will remove every other band from the spectrum of the first unit. Similarly a third unit of half the thickness of the second removes every other remaining band. Addition of further units results in more and more widely separated bands. In the final spectrum of narrow, widely separated bands the breadth of each band depends on the thickness of the thickest unit; the separation of the bands, on the thickness of the thinnest unit. A sufficient number of units are placed in the filter to separate the bands to the extent that one of them may be isolated by an ordinary glass filter. A birefringent filter requires very precise workmanship in making each piece of crystal exactly the correct thickness. Furthermore, its temperature must be maintained to a fraction of a degree, and the filter must therefore be surrounded by a well-constructed thermostatically controlled heating unit. Finally, it will not operate properly in light that departs much more than $1°$ from parallel. Hence the speed of the optics to which it is attached is considerably limited, a fact that explains the large f-ratio on many coronagraphs.

Birefringent filters are generally about a foot long, and with their attached temperature controls are quite complex instruments. Furthermore, because of the several polaroids, their transmission is considerably restricted. As a result, when photographing the faint corona through a filter, a considerable exposure time—typically one or two minutes—is required. The transmission is never perfectly monochromatic: side bands are not completely surpressed, and light entering at an angle with the axis broadens the transmission band. Nevertheless, very excellent photographs of the corona in the two strongest visible emission lines, λ 5303 and λ 6374, have been taken on a survey basis for several years, both at Pic du Midi and at Sacramento Peak (Fig. 2.11).

Monochromatic photographs, projected cinamatographically at a speed several hundred times the rate at which they are photographed, give a vivid picture of the structure and motions in the inner corona. Certain care must be employed in viewing and interpreting these pictures, however. In the first place, since the pictures are monochromatic, they record the radiation from one coronal ion only. Hence apparent changes may be actual motions in the corona, or changes in the degree of ionization. Thus a bright object moving through the photographs may either be matter in motion or a state of ionization progressing through the corona. Furthermore, in order to bring out the details, very high contrast photography is generally employed. The result is a fictitiously sharp upper boundary of the monochromatic corona. Also, since the features are optically thin, the intersection of two loop structures will appear as a very bright spot. Thus, if the two loop structures are displaced only slightly along the line of sight and undergo small weaving motions, their points of intersection will move rapidly, giving a completely spurious impression of rapidly moving bright material.

C. Coronal Observing from Above the Earth's Atmosphere

Balloon and Satellite Coronagraphy

Even at the high altitudes at which most coronagraph stations are located, the sky is generally many times brighter than the white-light corona. At an altitude of 40,000 ft the two are of comparable brightness,

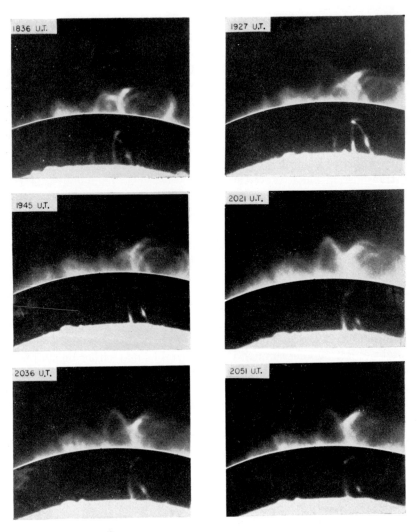

CORONA (5303 Å) AND LIMB (Hα) ϕ =170° 22 NOV. 1956

Fig. 2.11. Filtergrams of the λ 5303 monochromatic corona. The coronal pictures are shown in the upper part of each frame, with the corresponding Hα prominence photographs directly underneath. The similarity but lack of identity between the loop systems in the two wave lengths is quite apparent. Not quite so apparent is the correspondence between the long, low quiescent prominence to the left of the center of the arc in each frame and the gap in λ 5303 emission. Courtesy, Sacramento Peak Observatory, Air Force Cambridge Research Laboratories.

and at 100,000 ft the corona is definitely brighter than the sky. Newkirk has recently achieved considerable success in photographing the corona with a balloon-mounted coronagraph carried to about 100,000 ft, and with Eddy is constructing a satellite-mounted coronagraph.

In order to take advantage of the higher altitude a new set of coronagraphic techniques had to be devised (Newkirk and Bohlin, 1963) (Fig. 2.12), the basic innovation being an occulting disk external to the coronagraph objective. The need for such an occulting disk is apparent when one considers that the scattered light from the objective of a ground-based coronagraph is comparable to that from the sky. An occulting disk that could be placed at a very large distance in front of the coronagraph objective would be ideal: its image would fall in approximately the same place as the solar image, and nearly perfect occulting could be achieved. For obvious practical reasons, however, the disk cannot be more than a few feet in front of the objective. When the prime requirement that the objective lie entirely within the umbra of the disk is met, the objective receives unvignetted light only from the part of the corona at a greater angular distance from the limb than the angle subtended by the objective at the disk. A certain amount of vignetting of the inner corona is not undesirable, since the result is a photograph of more uniform exposure. However, one generally wishes to observe the corona beyond some distance from the limb—this distance depending on the purpose of the study—with maximum clarity. This requirement has limited balloon-borne coronagraphs to date to quite small objective apertures, the first being only a few millimeters in diameter and the second about 30 millimeters.

The presence of the external occulting disk introduces problems also for the optics beyond the objective. For example, a considerable diffraction pattern surrounds the image of the occulting disk and must be removed by diaphragms without removing the coronal image at the same time. The diffraction-image brightness may also be reduced by designing "teeth" on the occulting disk, which inhibit constructive interference within the shadow of the disk. During the development of several balloon coronagraphs, many of the problems introduced by external occulting have been solved, but the techniques can hardly be considered to be standardized as in the case of ground-based coronagraphs.

Ultraviolet and X-Ray Spectroscopy

Since an important fraction of solar radiation of wavelengths shorter than 500 Å comes from the corona, and wavelengths shorter than 100 Å

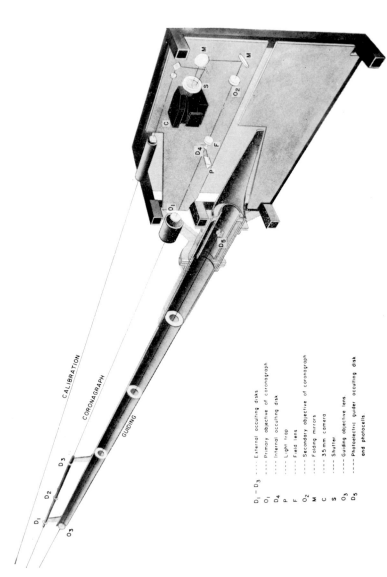

$D_1 - D_3$ ---- External occulting disks
O_1 ---- Primary objective of coronagraph
D_4 ---- Internal occulting disk
P ---- Light trap
F ---- Field lens
O_2 ---- Secondary objective of coronagraph
M ---- Folding mirrors
C ---- 35 mm camera
S ---- Shutter
O_3 ---- Guiding objective lens
D_5 ---- Photoelectric guider occulting disk and photocells

Fig. 2.12. Schematic diagram of Coronascope II. This instrument has been used several times for observing the corona from a balloon, at an elevation of about 100,000 feet. It is designed to take advantage of the low sky brightness at such altitudes by placing external occulting disks to shade the primary objective lens. The sequence of occulting disks reduces the diffracted light to less than that from a single disk. Courtesy High Altitude Observatory.

may be considered purely coronal in origin, observations of the sun in the very short wavelengths of the solar spectrum are essentially observations of the corona. One possible exception to this statement is the observation of very-short–wavelength radiation during a flare, at which time radiation even shorter than that generally coming from the corona is observed. Even here, however, it is likely that the locus of the flare, or at least that part of the flare from which the high energy radiation comes, is in the corona. These short-wavelength radiations are completely absorbed by the earth's atmosphere and must be observed from about 200 km above the earth's surface, or higher, by rockets, satellites, or space probes.

To date three general approaches have been used for observing the very short wavelength spectrum of the sun: photographic, photoelectric, and ion chamber or counter. Of these, the photographic method has been useful primarily with rockets, because the film must generally be recovered. Since techniques for returning satellites have now been developed, however, the use of photography in orbit may be increasingly important. In space probes the use of photography requires the automatic development and analysis of the photographs, and the telemetry of the data, as used by the Soviets in the study of the far side of the moon. Such techniques might be desirable for recording the entire X-ray spectrum of a flare not visible from the earth, but for most space-probe studies of solar X rays, photography is an unnecessarily difficult technique.

Much of the photography of very short wave ultraviolet spectra to date has made use of grazing-incidence spectrographs (Rense, 1961), since grating surfaces tend to be transparent for short UV radiation that strikes at an angle with the surface of more than one or two degrees. Similarly, a special photographic material must be used, since the gelatin that holds the silver halide grains together in an ordinary emulsion is highly absorbing to these wavelengths. One photographic technique is to coat the film with a fluorescent material that converts the energetic ultraviolet photons into photons that are not so badly absorbed by the gelatin. This is an inefficient process, however, and somewhat better success has been obtained by the use of very thin emulsions in which there is practically no binder.

In rocket observations photographic methods have the advantage over photoelectric methods that during the brief time the rocket is above the earth's atomsphere all of the grains in the emulsion are absorbing quanta of light. Thus, although the quantum efficiency is not generally as high as in a photoelectric device, all lines in the spectrum are being recorded at once, rather than one at a time. Tousey (1962) estimates that in the 170–300 Å range photographic techniques are in use that achieve the same precision in wavelength determination as a photoelectric scan and can d so in about one tenth the time, and that the spectrograph can be made t resolve a few hundredths of an ångstrom in this spectral region. Photc graphic techniques, as of 1963, had been used successfully to wavelength as short as about 120 Å.

A very simple photographic device for analysis of solar X radiation tha has been used successfully by the British (Willmore, 1961; Boyd, 1962) a set of emulsion detectors. One such system consists of five foils of alum num and beryllium overlying layers of emulsion. The degree of attenuatio in going from layer to layer gives information on the distribution of th radiation in wavelength, while the amount of exposure indicates the in tensity of the radiation.

Photoelectric devises for operation in the very-short–wavelength regio are not difficult to achieve, since almost any material becomes photc emissive with such radiation. The technical problems are the choice c photoemissive surfaces that will have the desired long-wave cutoff, th obtaining of the desired short-wave cutoff, the avoidance of stray photc electrons, and the measurement of intensity with wavelength in the ad mitted region. The most successful device so far employed for scannin grating-dispersed radiation is the Bendix magnetically focussed photo multiplier (Heroux and Hinteregger, 1960). This device takes advantag of the near vacuum in which it operates and the high photoemissivity o metals to X rays. In it, photoelectrons ejected from the cathode are ac celerated by the electric field and deflected back toward the cathode stri by a magnetic field. Thus they move in trochoidal paths, increasing i number with each impact. The dark current in this system may be as lov as the cosmic-ray background.

Photon counters become spectroscopic devices either when they are pro portional counters (Pounds et al., 1966), giving pulses that are propor tional to the photon energy, or when they are equipped with windows tha transmit only one predetermined band of radiation. Much of our knowledg of the variation of the solar X-ray spectrum with time comes from sets o counters of the latter type (Friedman, 1960). In such counters the tech nical problem is the proper choice of window. It is not easy, for example, t prepare windows of sufficient mechanical strength for use in rockets tha will transmit in the range 100 to 11 Å. Nitrocellulose films about 1000 Å thick are reasonably satisfactory. For shorter wavelengths aluminun windows are useful but have the disadvantage of very complex transmis sion curves, with several transmission peaks that cut off sharply at th ionization energy of the various inner electron shells. For the wavelength range 100–1100 Å, free-flow windowless counters may be used. In these, the radiation enters through a very small aperture, through which the gas flows out at a constant pressure. There is, of course, no wavelength discrimination in such a counter.

We should note that when counters are used for X-ray detection they must be suitably shielded magnetically from particle radiation, particularly if they are to operate in the Van Allen radiation belts.

Ultraviolet and X-Ray Photography

As of January 1, 1963, there had been six successful photographs of the sun taken in the short ultraviolet and X-ray region. Two of these were in Lyman-α radiation, and since these show the upper chromosphere, they are not of concern to us here. The third was a pinhole-camera photograph of the corona taken April 19, 1960 (Chubb *et al.*, 1961). The use of a pinhole camera was necessary because X rays cannot be focused by lenses or mirrors according to usual optical technique. (Bent-crystal and zone-plate focusing devices are now being developed.) The dimensions of the camera were $6 \times 4 \times \frac{3}{8}$ inch, and the pinhole, 0.005 in. in diameter, was covered with a thin plastic filter to cut out the visible light. The resulting image, only 0.1 in. in diameter, was badly smeared because of the rotation of the rocket about the axis pointing toward the sun. In spite of these difficulties, the picture gives information concerning the distribution of emission on the disk compared to the limb, the relative emission in active and quiet regions, and the approximate location of the major emitting sources of the sun. Three comparable pictures, also made with a rotating camera, were obtained June 21, 1961 (Blake *et al.*, 1963).

Since the first X-ray coronal photograph was taken, X-ray spectro-helioscopes have been designed and used. In a British design (Boyd, 1962) the focusing mechanism is the frustrum of a very deep paraboloid, 3 cm in aperture and of 30-cm focal length, with a proportional counter at its focus. 12-Å X rays striking the walls of the paraboloid at incidence of less than 2° are reflected with an efficiency of about 10%. With this design the field of view can be limited to one minute of arc, so that by the introduction of proper scanning motion and the counting only of pulses of a predetermined intensity, a picture of the sun in one X-ray wavelength may be obtainable. The grazing-incidence imaging technique has also been used quite successfully by Giacconi et al. (1965) for photographing the sun in the 8–12 Å range.

A simple and elegant device for viewing the solar disk in coronal X radiation was first used in a rocket on May 10, 1963, by Purcell (Tousey 1963). The device was a simple single-grating slitless spectrograph. Radia tion through a metallic filter, falling almost normally on the 40-cm grating ruled with 2400 lines/mm, produced a first-order spectrum covering 17 to 350 Å with a dispersion of 20 Å/mm. Solar images 1.8 mm in diameter in the stronger emission lines, gave monochromatic details with a resolu tion of 1′ of arc in He II (303.78 Å), Fe XV (284.2 Å) and Fe XVI (335. Å). In Fe XVI the plage region was very bright, but little emission ap peared elsewhere on the disk. Note that spectroheliograms are possible with this device only because it is being used in a wavelength region in which line emission completely dominates continuum emission.

Particle Detection

The detection and the measurement of the number and velocity of particles moving outward from the sun into the solar system is, in a very real sense, a form of observation of the corona. Any steady particle flux that can be identified as a solar wind yields information concerning the temperature and temperature gradients in the corona. The aggregates of particle flux that constitute M-region storms may be considered to be ex tensions of the corona sweeping past the earth. Flare-associated particles such as the soft cosmic radiation of flare proton events or the much more slowly moving clouds of particles in sudden-commencement magnetic storms, may or may not have their origin in the corona, but they certainly pass through the corona on their way to the earth; hence knowledge of them contributes to our understanding of the state of the corona during times of great solar activity. Also, the late arrival of the cosmic-ray par ticles, as frequently observed, gives evidence of a storage mechanism in the corona. Indirect particle observation, carried out from the surface of the earth, includes the relatively few cases in which cosmic-radiation de tectors at the surface of the earth have been activated by secondary cosmic ray particles resulting from solar flares. Other earth-based indicators of solar particles are riometers measuring the transparency of the polar sky to cosmic radio noise—large decreases indicating streams of high-energy solar protons reaching the earth—and magnetometer measurements, indi cating the disturbance of the earth's outer atmosphere by clouds of slower moving particles from the sun.

Many more flare cosmic-ray events can be detected at altitudes of 25–40 km then at sea level. Consequently, balloons are now being used exten sively to monitor the presence of such radiation. At the balloon altitudes the cosmic radiation is sometimes detected directly, and sometimes by the presence of X radiation produced by the interaction of the primary particles with the earth's upper atmosphere. The detection devices in such balloons are standard cosmic-ray equipment—counters and ionization chambers, equipped with magnetic deflecting devices to shield the detectors from charged particles and permit the electromagnetic radiation to pass, or to direct charged particles of a certain magnetic rigidity into the detector. Combinations of Cerenkov and scintillation counters have also been used to distinguish between alpha particles and protons.

Our most direct information concerning particles from the sun comes from deep-space probes, operating beyond the Van Allen radiation belts. The particle-detecting equipment on the early probes was relatively simple. *Pioneer III*, for example, had two Anton 213 Geiger-Mueller tubes. *Pioneer IV* had identical equipment, except that one of the tubes was shielded so that the penetrating power of the radiation could be determined. *Explorer X* carried a plasma probe into which positive and negative particles entered through a large aperture, then passed through a series of grids to a collector. This probe was designed to measure the density, direction, and flow velocity of particles of velocities in the range 10–1500 km/sec.

Compared to these three probes, *Explorer XII* was a space-going high-energy particle laboratory. It contained, in all, twelve particle measuring or detecting devices. One of these was a proton analyzer, consisting of a bent tube through which the particles would have to pass across an adjustable electrostatic field in order to reach the detector. Four Geiger tubes and three CdS cells made up the "trapped-radiation detector," measuring the energy flux of both protons and electrons. The cosmic-ray package on *Explorer XII* contained scintillation-counter telescopes, which measured the total cosmic-ray flux and the differential energy spectrum over various energy ranges. Finally, for measuring the flux, types, and energies of low-energy particles, an ion–electron detector was installed. It consisted of a photomultiplier tube activated by a powder phosphor placed behind a stepping absorber wheel. Counts registered by the tube indicated the particle flux, whereas the total phototube current measured the energy flux.

Later space probes, notably *Mariner II* in transit from the earth to Venus, and Interplanetary Monitoring Platforms *IMP I* and *II*, contain equipment similar to that of *Explorer XII* for measuring the velocity, direction, and flux of various particles from the sun. In addition they are equipped with rubidium vapor and fluxgate magnetometers. The magnetic fields thus measured are as important in interpretation of the extended corona as any particle observations, for these fields are so oriented as to be readily explained as coronal fields, carried outward from the sun in the configuration of Archimedes spirals by outward-flowing solar-wind particles (Ness and Wilcox, 1964). Furthermore, their structure is so well correlated with the photospheric magnetic fields that a well-defined transit time for the outflowing particles may be computed.

D. Radio-Frequency Techniques

Radio Astronomy

Solar radiation at wavelengths in the 10-cm range comes in part from the corona and in part from the chromosphere, but the contribution of the corona is secondary to that of the chromosphere from all portions of the sun except regions of enhanced coronal density. With increasing wavelength the relative contribution of the corona increases, and is dominant for wavelengths of 60 cm and longer. Radiation in the dekameter range originates at about one solar radius above the photosphere.

Since a major part of radio astronomy deals with radiations originating in the corona, and several books have been written on the subject (e.g. Pawsey and Bracewell, 1955), we will not attempt here to give a detailed discussion of electronic techniques that have been employed, but rather will summarize those aspects of the science that are important in the evaluation of the state of our knowledge of the corona. Antennas used in coronal radio astronomy may be mounted at the focus of parabolic reflectors (usually for wavelengths of 30 cm or less) or mounted in end-on or transverse arrays. They may be of the Yagi type to provide fairly sharp wavelength discrimination, or they may be of rhombic or some similar design to admit a wide band of wavelengths. They may be used singly, or in a two-antenna interferometer configuration, or in a multiantenna-array interferometer. The two-antenna interferometer locates the source in one of a large number of narrow bands of the interference pattern crossing the sky; the multiantenna array locates it in one of a greatly reduced number of bands. Greater definition is obtained by arranging the antennas in a crossed configuration, which limits the source to small rectangular regions defined by the crossing of two interference patterns. Simple dipole antennas respond only to one component of polarization of the incident radiation, but combinations of dipoles can distinguish between linear, circular, elliptical, and random polarization.

The phase relationships imposed by the circuits that join the various antennas of an interferometer array to a receiver can be varied to alter

he position of the various lobes of the interferometer pattern on the sky,
or the receiver may passively respond to the sun as it crosses the pattern
n its daily motion. Similarly, if two dipoles are oriented to receive orthog-
onally-polarized signals, the phase of the coupling can be varied to analyze
he characteristics of elliptical polarization in the radiation.

Rather than enter into a more detailed consideration of the instrumenta-
ion of radio astronomy, we shall classify the assembled apparatus accord-
ng to (1) whether it is a fixed-frequency or sweep-frequency apparatus,
(2) whether it integrates the radiation of the entire corona, or whether it
an resolve gross coronal features, and (3) whether it can or cannot dis-
riminate one state of polarization from another.

One might expect that a fixed-frequency apparatus that receives signals
rom the entire sun and does not analyze their state of polarization would
ontribute a minimum of information compared to more versatile instruments. In actuality, the contribution of such instruments to solar astronomy
as been of major importance. Such equipment, maintained in continuous,
ighly stable operation over many years, has yielded extremely valuable
nformation concerning the long-term behavior of the radio corona. Fur-
hermore, it has been used in conjunction with solar eclipses (Covington,
1947, 1963; Christiansen *et al.*, 1949) to locate centers of bright emission
n the corona with considerable precision. Similarly, through statistical
orrelation of signals from such receivers with the presence and positions
of optical features, a considerable amount of information concerning the
structure and lifetime of radio-emitting sources in the corona has been
deduced (Piddington and Minnett, 1951; Piddington and Davies, 1953).
Such techniques are difficult and uncertain at best, however, and are being
replaced by interferometer observations for the identification of sources of
hermal radio emission in the corona.

For the study of nonthermal radiation the situation is somewhat different,
since one may generally surmise from optical observations the region from
which a burst originates. As a burst progresses upward through the solar
atmosphere, its frequency, being proportional to the square root of the
electron density at the origin, decreases with time. This change in frequency, its most interesting property, can be followed by a sweep-frequency receiver. In the rare cases in which simultaneous observations with
a crossed interferometer array are also available, one can make a three-
dimensional plot of the motion of the source of the disturbance. An array
of fixed-frequency receivers with closely spaced frequencies is comparable
to a sweep-frequency system, and can give a somewhat higher time
resolution.

One of the most productive interferometers to date for resolving the detailed structure of radio emission in the solar corona has been the 9.1-cm Mills Cross arrangement of the Stanford Radioscience Laboratory (Swarup, 1961). In this arrangement thirty-two 10-ft parabaloids are arranged in crossed E–W and N–S arrays. With the 25-ft spacing the fringes of the two crossed interferometers are 41' apart. Since the two interferometers are alternately connected in phase, then out of phase, the resulting power in the alternating signal measures only the radiation from the source located at the intersections of the two systems of fringes. These intersections constitute pencil beams that are about 3' wide, and sufficiently widely spaced that only one is considered to be on the sun at any time. Prior to 1961, phase shifters had not been introduced into the N–S array so as to make possible latitude shifts in the pencil beams. Consequently, pencil beam maps of the radio sun were made by taking advantage of the circumstance that the motion of the sun was not, in general, parallel to the E–W fringes. As a consequence, the various pencil beams crossed the sun along different chords, and in the course of about one hour covered all latitudes. Obviously, maps so constructed could not portray highly variable solar features, but could give an accurate picture of the slowly varying sources of emission that dominate 9.1-cm radiation anyway. These maps were represented in contour form, with as many as 15 different brightness levels portrayed (Fig. 2.13). If features of too great a variability for the slow building up of a map were present, they could be studied by simply cutting out the N–S array and observing the sun as it drifted across the N–S fringes of the E–W array. The half power width of the fan beam is somewhat narrower than that of the pencil beam. Hence, if only one feature at a given longitude on the sun was of interest, its E–W dimensions could be determined more precisely with the fan beam than with the pencil beam, and a highly variable signal could be studied. Obviously, since 9.1-cm radiation can originate either in the chromosphere or the corona, the Stanford device could not be considered strictly a radio coronameter. However, with the type of resolution available it was possible to determine the height of an emitting source that was fixed in the solar atmosphere by its rate of passage across the solar disk, thereby determining to what extent it should be considered as coronal.

Sweep-frequency equipment now covers the entire range from 7.6 to 580 Mc/sec. The first such receiver, in Australia (1954), covers the range 40–240 Mc/sec (Wild et al., 1954). Shorter wavelengths are covered by the Fort Davis (Maxwell et al., 1959) radio spectrographs (25–580 Mc/sec) and the Michigan ones (200–600 Mc/sec), and longer wavelengths are

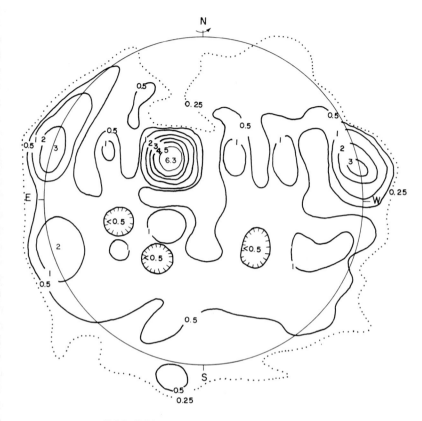

1960 JULY 15, 19:30 U.T.

CONTOUR BRIGHTNESS UNIT = 7.1 x 10⁴ °K

Fig. 2.13. An isophotal map of the 9.1-cm radio corona, from the 3′ pencil beam of the Mills Cross of the Stanford Radioscience Laboratory. Courtesy, Stanford Radio Astronomy Institute.

covered at Boulder (7.6–41 Mc/sec) (Boischot *et al.*, 1960) (Fig. 2.14). Frequency is typically varied in these instruments by a motor-driven variable condenser in the intermediate-frequency oscillator. Antennas vary with the wavelength range being studied. The Australian system uses a rhombic antenna; the Fort Davis uses three different types of antennas for three frequency ranges, all fed by a 28-ft parabaloid reflector; and the Boulder system consists of dipoles in corner reflectors, the two antennas being arranged as a steerable interferometer. Unfortunately, the geographic

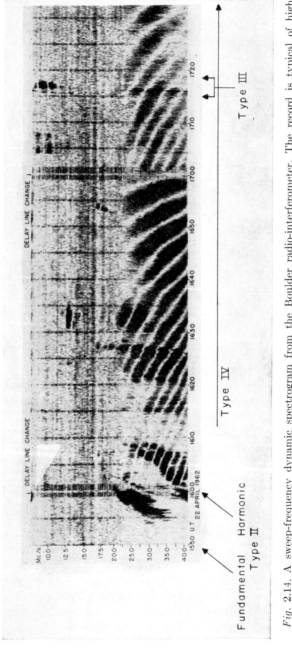

Fig. 2.14. A sweep-frequency dynamic spectrogram from the Boulder radio-interferometer. The record is typical of high solar activity. The first event is a slow-drift Type-II burst, accompanied by its harmonic. Continuum emission begins at about 1615 UT and continues to the end of the record. A fast-drift burst is seen to be superimposed upon the continuum at about 1716 UT. As the detector sweeps through its range of frequencies, the antenna pattern moves across the sky. The passage of nodes of the pattern across the source gives a minimum in the intensity record. As the sun moves relative to the interferometer, the positions of these nodes change in wavelength. The result is the sequence of alternate bright and dark bands on the record. The noise from terrestrial sources at 15–16 Mc/s shows no such drifting-band structure. (Courtesy, High Altitude Observatory.)

locations of the three stations is such that bursts observed over the entire range of wavelengths are rare. Furthermore, the stations differ in sensitivity, and different frequency bands at each station differ in sensitivity, to the extent that it is difficult to determine over how wide a frequency range bursts emit—i.e., whether they all originate low in the solar atmosphere and terminate at great heights, or whether some originate higher or terminate lower than others. Nevertheless, the quantity of useful data from sweep-frequency receivers is enormous.

An ideal radio technique for probing the corona would employ a combination of interferometric, sweep-frequency, and polarization observations. Burst phenomena originate conveniently at about the greatest depth in the corona from which signals can reach the earth. If we could follow the progress of the sources—not only upward through the corona by sweep-frequency observation, but across the disk by interferometers—and at the same time observe evidence of Faraday rotation (Akabane and Cohen, 1961) of the plane of polarization by the overlying magnetic field, we could use bursts much more effectively than at present for analysis of the structure of the corona.

No discussion of radio-astronomy techniques for study of the corona would be complete without mention of the investigation of the very outer solar atmosphere through its occultation each year of discrete astronomical radio-noise sources. Of more than a dozen sources that come sufficiently close to the sun to experience some scattering (Slee, 1961) of their radiation by the corona, one source—the Crab Nebula—has yielded much more information than all of the other combined (Hewish, 1958; Vitkevich and Panovkin, 1959). Besides being one of the brightest radio sources in the sky, the Crab Nebula passes within about 5 solar radii of the sun. Occultation is first observed at distances of more than 100 solar radii; hence the annual passage provides information over a remarkable range of distances. Occultation is attributed to scattering by irregularities in the corona, rather than to absorption, and anisotropic scattering (Högbom, 1960) gives evidence of the shape and orientation of the scattering elements. The degree of scattering is a function both of electron density and electron-density variation. By making certain assumptions concerning the variations, it is possible to draw conclusions concerning the electron density out to great distances from the sun. At its closest approach to the sun, the Crab Nebula is very near the projection of the solar axis on the sky. Hence the close-in information that it gives is appropriate to the polar regions in the corona. At the greatest distances at which occultation is observed it approaches but never reaches the equator. Since each source traverses the same path through the corona each year, observations of several sources must be combined when the technique is used in making a two-dimensional density map of the corona.

Radar Astronomy

No technique for observing the corona has more exciting prospects than radar. Within half a decade a small group of radar astrono;ners (Eshleman *et al.*, 1960; Abel *et al.*, 1961; Chisholm and James, 1964) have demonstrated that they can not only reflect signals from the corona, but draw conclusions concerning its temperature, density, state of expansion, state of random motion, and state of rotation.

The Massachusetts Institute of Technology installation at El Campo, Texas, has made some of the most significant radar observations of the corona to date. From this installation, 38.25-Mc/sec signals are broadcast by a rectangular array of 1024 dipoles in a pattern with an E–W extent of 110 ft and a N–S extent of 1750 ft. The effective gain of the array compared to an isotropic radiator is 34 dB for a vertical beam. The resulting beam width (measured at half-power points) is $0.75°$ in the N–S direction and $15°$ in the E–W direction. The narrow dimension can be directed to the latitude of the sun by phasing each dipole, whereas the broader dimension permits 16 minutes of transmission and 16 minutes of reception each day.

The signal is separated from noise by transmitting a set of pulses that differ in frequency from the central frequency by a fixed amount (4 kc/sec in early operation, 20 kc/sec later), the frequency of the various pulses succeeding one another in a pseudo-random fashion. The outputs of two receivers tuned to the two frequencies are then combined in subtraction, and the resulting signal is compared to the transmitted signal with various time delays. The most effective time delay, corresponding to reflection at $1.5 R_\odot$ with two additional seconds introduced to care for a retardation of group velocity in the coronal gas, typically gives a signal of 6–8 standard deviations, whereas the signals with other delay times, differing in steps of 8 seconds, fall well within one standard deviation. By varying the frequencies of the receivers, a spectroscopic analysis of the reflected signal can be carried out and the Doppler frequency shifts computed.

The physical state of the corona is manifest in the following manner: The absorption of the radar signal depends on the temperature of the coronal gas; the optimum delay time indicates the height above the photosphere of the coronal layer of appropriate density for optimum reflection of the transmitted frequency; a shift from the transmitted frequency of he center of the distribution of received frequencies indicates a general notion of the corona, such as a solar wind. A broadening of the distribution results from a combination of distributed macroscopic velocities and olar rotation. The two effects can be separated, in principle, by a comparison of the reflected frequency spectrum with two different delay times— ne that observes the subterrestrial point, and the other, a coronal annulus. The process is complicated in practice by the wide range of depths in the orona over which a reflection takes place. Also, the macroscopic motions re not necessarily radial to the sun. There is evidence from optical line profiles that the macroscopic motion is primarily radial, however, and ince the problem of reflection at various heights is subject to analysis, adar offers a most promising means of determining rotational properties f the outer corona.

REFERENCES

bel, W. G., Chisholm, J. H., Fleck, P. L., and James, J. C. (1961). Radar reflections from the sun at very high frequencies. *J. G. R.* **66,** 4303.

kabane, K., and Cohen, M. H. (1961). Polarization of Type III bursts and Faraday rotation in the corona. *Ap. J.* **133,** 258.

llen, C. W. (1956a). Coronal photometry of the eclipse of 1954 June 30, *M. N. R. A. S.* **116,** 69.

llen, C. W. (1956b). Spectrophotometry of the outer corona. *M. N. R. A. S.* **116,** 413.

ly, M. K., Evans, J. W., and Orrall, F. Q. (1963). A photometric study of the continuum and seveenteen emission lines in the inner solar corona. *Ap. J.* **136,** 956.

thay, R. G., and Roberts, W. O. (1955). Coronal line intensities at the Khartoum Eclipse. *Ap. J.* **121,** 231.

lackwell, D. E. (1955). A study of the outer corona from a high-altitude aircraft at the eclipse of 1954 June 30. *M. N. R. A. S.* **115,** 629.

lake, R. L., Chubb, T. A., Friedman, H., and Unzicker, A. E. (1963). Interpretation of X-ray photograph of the sun. *Ap. J.* **137,** 3.

oischot, A., Lee, R. H., and Warwick, J. W. (1960). Low frequency solar bursts and noise storms. *Ap. J.* **131,** 61.

oyd, R. L. F. (1962). A program for astronomical studies by rocket-borne instruments, *in* "Space Age Astronomy" (A. J. Deutsch and W. B. Klemperer, eds.). Academic Press, New York.

harvin, P. (1963). The new photoelectric coronameter used at the Paris Observatory. *Compt. rend.* **256,** 368.

hisholm, J. H., and James, J. C. (1964). Radar evidence of solar wind and coronal mass motion. *Ap. J.* **140,** 377.

hristiansen, W. N., Yabsley, D. E., and Mills, B. Y. (1949). Measurements of solar radiation at wave lengths of 50 Cal during the eclipse of 1 November 1948. *Aust. J. sci. Res.* **A2,** 506.

hubb, T. A., Friedman, H. Kreplin, R. W., Blake, R. L., and Unzicker, A. E. (1961). I. X-ray and U. V. measurements during the eclipse of October 12, 1958. II. X-ray solar disk photograph. *Mém. Soc. Roy. Sci. Liége* **4,** 228

Covington, A. E. (1947). Microwave solar noise observations during the eclipse of November 1946. *Nature* **159**, 405.

Covington, A. E. (1963). Microwave radio emission from limb coronal condensation for the eclipse of February 5, 1962. *J. Roy. Astr. Soc. Can.* **57**, 253.

Dollfus, A. (1962). Properties of monochromatic emission of the solar corona. *Compt rend.* **255**, 3369.

Dollfus, A., Martin, M., and Leroy, J. L. (1961). Observation of the solar corona before during and after the total eclipse of 15 February 1961. *Compt. rend.* **252**, 3402.

Eshleman, V. R., Barthle, R. C., and Gallagher, P. B. (1960). Radar echoes from the sun. *Science* **131**, 329.

Evans, J. W. (1953). Birefringent filters. *In* "The sun" (G. P. Kuiper, ed.), p. 626. Univ of Chicago Press, Chicago, Illinois.

Firor, J., and Zirin, H. (1962). Observations of five ionization stages of iron in the sola corona. *Ap. J.* **135**, 122.

Friedman, H. (1960). The sun's ionizing radiations. *In* "Physics of the Uppe Atmosphere" (J. A. Ratcliffe, ed.), p. 133. Academic Press, New York.

Giacconi, R., Reidy, W. P., Zehnpfennig, T., Lindsay, J. C , and Muney, W. S. (1965) Solar x-ray images obtained using grazing incidence optus. *Ap. J.* **142**, 1274.

Heroux, L., and Hinteregger, H. E. (1960). Bendix magnetically focused photomultiplier *Rev. Sci. Inst.* **31**, 280.

Hewish, A. (1958). The scattering of radio waves in the solar corona. *M. N. R. A. S* **118**, 534.

Högbom, J. A. (1960). The structure and magnetic field of the solar corona. *M. N. R. A. S* **120**, 530.

Hyder, C. L. (1965). The polarization of coronal emission lines. *Ap. J.* **141**, 1382.

Jarrett, A. H., and von Klüber, H. (1961). Interferometric investigation of emission lines of the solar corona during the total eclipse of 12 October 1958. *M. N. R. A. S* **122**, 223.

Karimov, M. G. (1961). Polarization measurements of the solar corona outside eclipse *Izv. Astrofiz. Inst., Akad. Nauk Kaz SSR* **11**, 64.

Laffineur, M., Bloch, M., and Bretz, M. (1961). On the procedure for photographing of the solar corona during a total eclipse. *Compt. rend.* **25**, 2180.

Maxwell, A., Howard, W. E., III, and Garmire, G. (1959). Solar radio interference a 125, 200, 425, 500 Mc/s. *Harv. Univ. Radio Astr. Sta. Sci. Rept.* No. 14.

Mitchell, S. A. (1935). The corona. *In* "Eclipses of the Sun," 4th ed. Columbia Univ Press, New York.

Mogilevskii, E. I., Nikolskii, G. M., and Nikolskaya, K. I. (1960). The polarization o coronal emission lines. *Sov. Astr. A. J.* **4**, 225.

Ness, N. F., and Wilcox, J. M. (1964). Solar origin of the interplanetary magneti field. *Phys. Rev. Lett.* (1963). **13**, 461.

Newkirk, G., Jr., and Bohlin, D. (1963). Reduction of scattered light in the coronagraph *Applied Optics* **2**, 131

Ney, E. P., Huch, W. F., Kellogg, P. J., Stein, W., and Gillett, F. (1961). Polarization and intensity studies of the eclipse of October 2, 1959. *Ap. J.* **133**, 616.

Pawsey, J. L., and Bracewell, R. N. (1955). "Radio Astronomy." Oxford Univ. Press London and New York.

Piddington, J. H., and Davies, R. D. (1953). Thermal Radio emission from the sun and the source of coronal heating. *M. N. R. A. S.* **113**, 582.

Piddington, J. H., and Minnett, H. C. (1951). Solar radio-frequency emission from localized regions at very high temperature. *Aust. J. Phys.* **4**, 131.

Pounds, K. A., Willmore, A. P., Bowen, P. J., Norman, K., and Sanford, P. W. (1966). Measurements of the solar spectrum in the wavelength band 4-14Å. *M. N. R. A. S.* (in press).

Rense, W. A. (1961). Solar ultraviolet photospheric and coronal lines. *Mém. Soc. Roy. Sci. Liége* **4**, 272.

Rush, J. H., and Schnable, G. K. (1966). High altitude observatory's new coronagraph and spectrograph. *Applied Optic* **3**, (in press).

Saito, K. (1948). Polarigraphic observations of the corona at the eclipse on February 5, 1943. *Tokyo Astr. Bull.* **2**, 63.

Slee, O. B. (1961). Observations of the solar corona out to 100 solar radii. *M. N. R. A. S.* **123**, 223.

Swarup, G. (1961). Studies of solar microwave emission using a highly directional Antenna. AFOSR-265, Radioscience Lab., Stanford.

Tousey, R. (1962). Techniques and results of extraterrestrial radiation studies from the ultraviolet to X-rays. *In* "Space Age Astronomy" (A. J. Deutsch and W. B. Klemperer, eds.), p. 000. Adacemic press, New York.

Tousey, R. (1963). The extreme UV spectrum of the sun. *Space Sci. Rev.* **2**, 3.

Vitkevich, V. V., and Panovkin, B. N. (1959). On the structure of the non-uniformities of the solar super-corona. *Astr. Zhurn.* **36**, 544.

von Klüber, H. (1958). Intensities, polarization and electron density of the solar corona from photographs taken at the total eclipse of 1952, February 25. *M. N. R. A. S.* **118**, 201.

Waldmeier, M. (1951). "Die Sonnenkorona," Vol. I. Birkhäuser, Basel.

Wild, J. P., Murray, J. D., and Rowe, W. C. (1954). *Aust. J. Phys.* **7**, 439.

Willmore, A. P. (1961). Observations of the L-α and X-ray Emissions of the sun. *Mém. Soc. Roy. Sci. Liége* **4**, 103.

Wlerick, G., and Axtell, J. (1957). A New instrument for observing the electron corona. *Ap. J.* **126**, 253.

Wood, R. W. (1905). *Pub. U. S. Naval Obs.* **4**, D116.

CHAPTER 3

OBSERVATIONAL ASPECTS OF THE CORONA

A. Introduction

What is the appearance of the corona? To the eye it is the pearly halo of light surrounding the eclipsed sun, as vividly described by Bailey and Young (Chapter 1). But the corona is observed in many different ways, and with each observing method it has a unique manifestation. Only by white-light eclipse photographs and, roughly, by monochromatic photography does it have the same appearance as by direct observation. Through the optical spectrograph the corona is a set of broad, widely spaced emission lines (Fig. 3.1), most of which are so faint as to be barely perceptible, superimposed on a background of faint continuous emission. If the corona has been imaged on the slit of the spectrograph, the lines and occasionally the continuum in the spectrum show an intricate pattern of intensity variation (Prokofyeva, 1963) (Fig. 3.2).

The corona photographed by an X-ray camera above the earth's atmosphere appears as a disk somewhat larger than the disk of the visible sun, bright around the edges and marked by large bright spots. Examined by an extreme ultraviolet spectrograph it is a large number of closely spaced bright lines, with the lines more separated at the long-wavelength end of the spectrum and a less bright continuum at the short-wavelength end.

Its appearance at radio frequencies varies greatly with the type of instrument used. The radio corona may appear as the tracing of the signal from an antenna when the sun is in its reception pattern, the violence of the fluctuations in the signal being greater for greater wavelengths and also for greater solar activity. If an interferometer is used, the tracing of the radio corona may appear to be an irregular plateau, as the sun drifts through a fringe in the antenna pattern. If the antenna has a pencil beam,

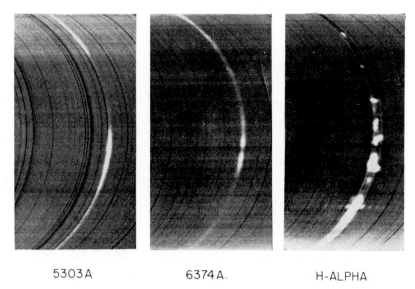

5303 A   6374 A   H-ALPHA

Fig. 3.1. The green (λ 5303) and red (λ 6374) coronal emission lines, and the prominence Hα line. Each line is shown on a background of about 30 Å of sky-scattered photospheric continuum. Wavelength increases from left to right. Fraunhofer lines in the
continuum provide a convenient wavelength reference, but distort the profiles of several
coronal lines, notably λ 5303, λ 5694 and λ 4086. One can see at a glance that the cornal
lines are many times broader than the Fraunhofer lines. The spectrogram whose sections
are shown here is from the Climax 5-in. coronagraphy-spectrograph, dispersion about
2 Å/mm. Courtesy, High Altitude Observatory.

a number of such tracings can be combined to give a disk picture of the
corona, which, although poorly resolved, shows the major bright radio-
noise–emitting features. If a sweep-frequency receiver is being used, the
corona appears on a two-dimensional display of wavelength vs time. On
such a display events rather than features stand out. The more violent the
event, the brighter the display; the more rapidly it moves through the solar
atmosphere, the steeper the trace on the display.

To a radio receiver following a discrete source of emission in the sky as
it passes near the sun, the corona is an extended curtain that both dims
and diffuses the radio beam. To a radar beam it is a fuzzy, expanding,
squirming mirror. Finally, to a space probe it is a stream of very dilute,
hot gas flowing outward from the sun with considerable velocity, accompanied by a complex magnetic-field pattern.

In this chapter we shall describe each of these aspects in more detail,
giving thereby a picture of the corona as it appears through more or less

Fig. 3.2. Detailed structure in the green coronal line in a Climax spectrogram. Although λ 5303 on spectrograms generally appears to be much more uniformly distributed over wide regions of the limb than the λ 6374, a close inspection under good observing conditions frequently reveals much detail in its brightness from one portion of the limb to another. The four bright knots shown near the middle of the arc in this picture are probably the intersections of the slit with the image of two bright loops in the monochromatic corona.   Courtesy, High Altitude Observatory.

direct use of the instruments described in Chapter 2. In Chapter 4 we shall discuss procedures for a more sophisticated analysis of some of these observations. Finally, in subsequent chapters we try to fit the data together to give a single physical picture of this largest object in our solar system, the solar corona.

B. The White-Light Corona

As described in Chapter 2, the corona has been viewed, sketched, photographed, and scanned photoelectrically in white light. Of the many observations that have been made, the composite of all eclipse photographs constitutes one of the most important bodies of coronal data. Visual observations can be considered auxiliary to these in providing awareness of the filamentary structure of the corona, and photoelectric scans for giving precise quantitative measurements during eclipses or more crude information outside of eclipses.

Spectroscopic analysis shows the white light to have a distribution of energy with wavelength almost identical to that of the solar photosphere. There is a slight suggestion of reddening (Allen, 1956b), but this is difficult to detect within the limits of spectrophotometric accuracy (Allen, 1956a). Blackwell (1952), by extending measurements into the infrared to 1.9 μ, did detect a considerable reddening with distance from the sun, which he attributed to the scattering of sunlight by interplanetary dust—i.e., to the F corona. The continuum radiation from the K corona appears to be the color of the integrated radiation from the photosphere, as it should be if it is due to electron scattering of photospheric radiation (see Chapter 6).

Conversely, since the K corona is due to electron scattering, and since every free electron scatters radiation in proportion to its illumination, the white-light corona will give a rather faithful picture of the distribution of matter along various lines-of-sight by which it is viewed. Complications arising from polarization effects and decreasing illumination of the electrons with distance from the sun will be considered in detail in Chapter 6.

From the intercomparison of photographs and sketches of the corona as seen at many eclipses a concept has evolved (Secchi, 1875; Mitchell, 1935; Mustel, 1962) of structural forms that are typical of various phases of the solar cycle. At sunspot maximum—i.e., at times when sunspots are most numerous—the coronal brightness is rather uniformly distributed around the solar limb (Fig. 3.3). To phrase the concept more quantitatively, isophotes—i.e., contours of equal brightness—are nearly circular. The circular symmetry is disturbed by the presence of local bright features that extend like bright shafts or plumes of light more or less radially outward from the limb, and also by dark lanes in which the corona is notably low in brightness; but these features seem to be distributed randomly around the sun.

At sunspot minimum, the configuration is very different (Fig. 3.4). In its extreme form the minimum corona can be described completely by two features: equatorial streamers and polar plumes. The polar plumes, which we shall describe in more detail later, generally appear to follow the lines of force from an extended bar magnet with its axis lying along the axis of rotation of the sun. The threads making up the high-latitude extremes of the equatorial streamers likewise leave the sun as though following

Fig. 3.3. A sunspot-maximum corona. This 16-second exposure was made at Mina
Bronces, Chile, with the Lick Observatory 40-ft focal-length eclipse camera. The year,
1893, was the peak year of a rather strong sunspot maximum. Courtesy, Lick Observatory.

lines of force of the same dipole, then inflect at about one solar radius from
the limb to approach the extended equator tangentially. The equatorial
streamers are bounded by these graceful curves. In each quadrant at
about 65 to 70° latitude (van de Hulst, 1950), between the polar plumes
and the equatorial streamers, lies a well-defined region of diminished

brightness. Prior to the year 1954 the equatorial streamers in the sunspot corona were typically represented as being slightly cleft at their outer extent, as though each was the superposition of two streamers, the axis of one being a little to the north, and of the other, a little to the south of the equator. Such splitting was not evident at the eclipse of 1954, which occurred in coincidence with a very extreme minimum of sunspot activity. Photographs from that eclipse (Fig. 3.5) show the equatorial streamers to be not only entirely without cleavage but very diminished in intensity as

Fig. 3.4. A sunpsot-minimum corona. This photograph was made by the same camera, with the same exposure time, as that of Fig. 3.3. The observing site was Thomston, Georgia, and the year, 1900—at the time of a sharp minimum in solar activity. Courtesy, Lick Observatory.

Fig. 3.5. The eclipse of June 1954 took place under the most minimum conditions of solar activity of any eclipse that has ever been studied. For weeks prior to the eclipse the disk had been clean of spots and plage. Even the quiescent filaments had diminished and practically disappeared. The green coronal line became unobservable on the corona-graph spectrographs. The red-line emission dwindled to four faint tufts around the disk, one on each pole, and one on each limb at the equator. Courtesy, Washburn Observatory.

well (Waldmeier, 1955). One is tempted to postulate that in an even more extreme minimum the corona might disappear entirely.

The evolution of the corona from sunspot-maximum to sunspot-minimum type is marked by a decrease in brightness, by the gradual change of the isophotes from circular to elliptical, and by the clearer definition of streamer features and polar plumes. The evolution is probably a consequence of the streamer-type features becoming less numerous, hence less overlapping, particularly in the polar regions. The eclipse of 1962 (Fig. 2.3) is interesting in that one limb was rather characteristic of sunspot maximum, with many bright features distributed widely over the hemicircle, whereas the opposite limb was already of near-minimum type. The eclipse of 1952 (Fig. 3.6) illustrates a somewhat later type, in that one limb is clearly minimum, whereas the other contains two strong streamers, both well displaced from the equator.

Up to this point we have used the word *streamer* to identify any coronal feature other than a polar plume extending outward from the limb. Even a causal examination of eclipse photographs reveal that such features exist in a variety of forms, however. Furthermore, some are most noticeable close to the limb only, whereas others become identified at greater distances. Also, certain forms are found in association with sunspot groups, others with quiescent prominences well removed from sunspots. During the past century a vocabulary has evolved for the description of these various forms, but there has been some confusion in terminology. Consequently,

Fig. 3.6. An intermediate type eclipse. The February 1952 eclipse was photographed from Khartoum, Sudan, by the Naval Research Laboratory expedition, using the 18-ft focal-length Gardener camera.   Courtesy, Naval Research Laboratory.

we shall attempt to identify and define here a number of different coronal forms and adhere to this terminology throughout the book. We have omitted from our lexicon a number of descriptive names such as fans, arches, and fountains, since these are difficult to associate with noncoronal aspects of solar activity. Arches in the corona, for example, occur both over sunspot groups and over quiescent prominences. We consider those in the former location to be parts of coronal enhancements, or if very intense, to be coronal condensations, whereas those over quiescent prominences are part of the more complex features, helmets.

With due recognition of the difficulty in the use of a few words to describe any object as complex as the solar corona, we submit the following terminology for the designation of coronal features:

Condensation. Our *condensation* corresponds to Waldmeier's (1956b) *sporadic condensation.* A condensation is found only over active sunspot groups, and is always quite close to the solar surface. Its density is relatively very high—one or two orders of magnitude more than that of the surrounding corona. Its lifetime is limited to the duration of intense activity in the active region, and its extent is never more than a few ten-thousands of kilometers. It may be a small bright white knot at the top of an active prominence loop, or at the top of a system of such loops; or it may itself have a loop-like configuration. It is readily apparent in white light, looking like a white prominence (Waldmeier, 1962). In monochromatic light it is even more apparent; and on coronal spectrograms it shows as a marked bright streak of continuum in which such emissions as Ca XIII and Ca XV (to be discussed in Section C of this chapter) are generally to be found.

Enhancement. We apply the word *enhancement* to a class of phenomena that Waldmeier (1956b) has described as *permanent condensations.* An enhancement, though resembling a condensation in that it lies close to the sun and has a higher density than the surroundings, differs in that it is of significantly lower density than the condensation, has a longer life, and occupies more space. Enhancements appear over sunspot groups of all levels of activity and last throughout the life of the spot group, or perhaps one or two solar rotations longer. They also appear at polar latitudes at times of high solar activity. It is reasonable to describe the inner, very dense portion of the coronal region overlying a very active sunspot group as a "condensation," but the more extensive portions of the region as an "enhancement." The condensation may last only days or hours, but the enhancement may persist for months.

Streamers. Streamer-like structures become recognizable at heights of

50,000–100,000 km above the solar limb, and have been distinguished out to many solar diameters. Two types of such streamers have been clearly identified: those situated over active regions, and those extending above prominences. The difficulty in determining whether a streamer seen on the limb is in the plane of the sky, or seen in projection from in front or behind the limb has rendered it impossible to say whether or not these two classifications include all streamer-like objects, but for lack of evidence to the contrary, we shall assume that they do (see Vsekhsvayatskii and Ivanchuk, 1962). Furthermore, since the word *helmet* describes very aptly the coronal structures overlying quiescent prominences, we shall reserve the word *streamer* for extensions of the corona overlying active regions. Streamers, so defined, are generally rather structureless, although they may have a cusp-like configuration near their base. The more extended portions maintain a fairly uniform cross-section, or spread out somewhat with increasing distance from the sun. Some streamers that appear to be long, thin jets from our point of view may actually be thin disks with their narrow dimension normal to the line of sight. Dollfus *et al.* (1961) observed such a jet with a white-light photometer for so many days after the eclipse of 1961 that they concluded it must have had a significant longitudinal extent.

Helmets. As indicated in the discussion of *streamers*, helmets are the extensions of the corona overlying quiescent prominences. Typically, when these features are observed the prominence has reached sufficient maturity that it is oriented along a solar latitude, and is therefore seen edge-on at the limb. The overlying helmet has a very characteristic appearance: a broad spade-shape with the prominence at the axis of symmetry. The broadest part of the helmet is often one-half a solar radius or more across, and the upper end draws toward a sharp point at one or two solar radii from the limb. One of the more striking features of a helmet is a very dark region immediately surrounding the prominence, succeeded by alternate bright and dark arches concentric with the prominence (see Obashev, 1961). Helmets are among the more striking features of the corona out to one or two solar radii, but do not appear to have as great extent as the streamers.

Polar Plumes. During the minimum period of solar activity the polar regions (latitudes greater than 70°) are characterized by an absence of streamers or helmets, but by the presence of the polar plumes. These plumes appear to be small, cylindrical features of high density compared to their surroundings, of about 7000 km cross section. They are more clearly resolved on some occasions than others, and the question is still open as to whether they are imbedded in a general structureless polar corona, or whether the background against which they are viewed is itself unresolved plumes. It is conceivable that individual plumes are never actually observed, but that the enhanced scattered light that is called a plume is a statistical fluctuation of the number of electrons along a line of sight resulting from the chance alignment of more plumes in some cases than in others. Arguing against this speculation is the observation that the plumes appear to outline a dipole magnetic field in which the poles are separated by about two-thirds of a solar diameter. If the plumes were the result of chance alignment of many smaller features along the line of sight, and if the smaller features themselves followed a dipole configuration, two features at some distance from the pole, one on the limb and one well in front of the limb lying along the same line of sight near the limb, would certainly diverge at greater heights. Hence it would seem unlikely that polar plumes could maintain their identity out to about a solar radius, as they do, unless that identity is real.

An important question, yet to be resolved, is whether the coronal structures of polar-plume dimensions are a unique feature of the polar regions at sunspot minimum or whether they are the basic structures of the entire corona, recognized as individuals only under special circumstances, but at other times so numerous as to be clumped into larger features (see Nesmyanovich, 1962).

In the vocabulary that we have just defined, we describe the white-light corona at sunspot maximum as a spherically symmetric confusion of plumes, streamers, and helmets, so numerous that only a few features can be distinguished. As the cycle progresses streamers and helmets become easier to distinguish, the helmets being most in evidence in the latitude zones of greatest filamentary development—poleward of the spot zones— with the streamers most abundant over the spot zone. Polar plumes become distinguishable. Finally, at sunspot minimum there are few large quiescent prominences and few helmets. The residue of solar activity of the cycle is near the equator, and the streamers extending above it fuse to form a disk-shaped concentration of coronal material that we recognize in pro- jection against the sky as the equatorial streamers. Polar plumes, no longer obscured by other coronal features, follow the lines of force of the polar magnetic fields, which, having reversed at sunspot maximum, exhibit maximum coherence and intensity at sunspot minimum.

C. The Visual Monochromatic Corona

A bright-line spectrum is superimposed on the continuous spectrum of the corona. Near the sun and at time of high sunspot activity the more intense of the lines may be fifty to one hundred times as bright as the coronal continuum, which in turn is a few millionths of the brightness of the photospheric continuum. The study of these lines—their identification, their variation in brightness with position in the corona and with the solar cycle, and the explanation of their presence and behavior—constitutes a major part of coronal science. Specifically, observation of these lines has been an important objective of many eclipse expeditions (Allen, 1946; Michard *et al.*, 1954), and their study has been the prime occupation of the coronagraph stations (see Appendix I). Daily measurements of intensities of some of these coronal lines are published in the *IAU Bulletin of Solar Activity*, and indices summarizing the characteristics of one of the lines, λ 5303 of Fe XIV are reported in the *F-Series* publications of the United States Central Radio Propagation Laboratory. Finally, extensive libraries of daily coronal spectrograms are available for further study, the most complete probably being the Climax photographic observations housed at the High Altitude Observatory Laboratory, Boulder, Colorado.

We give in Appendix II a list of optical coronal lines that have been identified to date, indicating the ion from which each line arises and its ionization potential, the transition that produces the line, and the transition probability. The list is based on the table in the 1963 edition of Allen's *Astrophysical Quantities*, supplemented from the more recent list by Pryce (1964) and further supplemented from Rohrlich and Pecker (1963). There are some rather striking differences in wavelength between the tables of Allen and Pryce, one of the most remarkable being a difference of 1 Å for the coronal green line. The value given by Pryce appears to be a typographical error. Discrepancies are also present in the wavelengths of the two coronal yellow lines. In Appendix II we give our own wavelengths for these two lines, measured from High Altitude Observatory spectrograms by Mr. William Boardman (Boardman and Billings, 1965).

Aly *et al.* (1963) add a measurable but unidentified line λ 3454 for which they suggest the ionization potential is less than 200 V, and raise doubts concerning the identifications of λ 3534 and 3643. The former, they point out, is too bright for the accepted vanadium abundance in the sun, and the latter behaves as though from an ion of lower excitation potential than Ni XIII.

The list is by no means complete. Aly (1955) gives seven additional lines that were detected by him and Lyot on spectrograms of the 1952 eclipse, and 25 more lines from a later reexamination of the same plates. Most of these faint lines had been observed in previous eclipses, so may be considered as established but unidentified. Also, some yet-unobserved lines have been predicted (Collins, 1964).

An examination of the table of coronal lines reveals that the greater part arise from forbidden transitions of the type $\Delta L = 0$, $\Delta J = \pm 1$. Thus, they are magnetic transitions between levels within the ground state of the ions. In neutral atoms or ions of small charge these levels lie so close together that the radiation resulting from transitions between them appears far in the infrared or radio region of the spectrum. Indeed the 21-cm line of neutral hydrogen, so important in radio astronomy, is just such a transition. With increasing ionic charge these levels are more and more widely separated, however. Finally, in the case of coronal ions, such transitions result in visible radiation.

Direct identification of the lines, as carried out primarily by Edlén (1942), begins with a laboratory determination of the ultraviolet spectrum of an ion. The difference between the wave numbers of resonance-line multiplets then gives the term splitting of the ground state. Such laboratory identifications are available for only a few coronal lines, however. The remainder have been found by Edlén, Rohrlich, and others by methods of extrapolation. Ideally (Rohrlich and Pecker, 1963) the extrapolations are carried out by determining the atomic parameters that describe Coulomb and spin interactions for members of an isoelectronic sequence of ions whose spectrum has been analyzed. These parameters are then extrapolated under the knowledge that they should approach a hydrogen-like dependence on the ionic charge Z for large Z. In practice the necessary data for a precise determination of these parameters are frequently not available. In such cases the energy differences between the levels in the ground state in any isoelectronic sequence are considered to be smooth functions of Z whose asymptotic behavior is approximately known. Thus the wavelengths are determined directly by extrapolation along isoelectronic sequences. The identification has been materially assisted by the realization that lines from ions of similar ionization potential are found in association in the corona. Thus the distribution of line brightness with position angle around the limb is more nearly the same for the two lines λ 6374 of Fe X and λ 7892 of Fe XI than for λ 6374 compared to λ 5303 of Fe XIV (Mitchell 1935; Athay and Roberts, 1955).

Transitions producing optical coronal lines, although forbidden, are not highly forbidden. Transition probabilities range from about ten to a few hundred, thus are about one millionth the probability of ordinary dipole transitions.

A fortuitous set of circumstances makes the forbidden coronal lines accessible to our observation. The temperature of the corona favors the production of ions whose ground-state level separations give visible transitions. The density of the corona is sufficiently low that collisional deexcitation does not depopulate the upper levels for coronal emission during the hundredth of a second, more or less, between excitation and radiation. Finally, the corona is sufficiently immense that the emission, though weak, adds up along vast lines of sight to be readily detectable.

Out of the entire list of lines, three are particularly useful for following the day-by-day changes in the corona. These are the red line, λ 6374 of Fe X; the green line, λ 5303 of Fe XIV; and the yellow line, λ 5694 of Ca XV. The three are in a very accessible part of the spectrum for visual observation or photography. The red and green lines are the most intense of any in the visible range, and the yellow line on occasions is of comparable intensity. Finally, the three lines come from widely separated states of ionization. The ionization potential for Fe X is 233 V, for Fe XIV, 355 V, and for Ca XV, 814 V. Thus the red line gives information on the cooler portions of the corona, the green line on those regions of intermediate temperature, and the yellow line, on the hotter regions. Regions in the corona cooler than those emitting the red line certainly do exist, prominences being an outstanding example. Regions too hot to emit the yellow line may also exist, but evidence for their presence is much less definitive. However, according to the terminology of solar astronomy, prominences are not usually considered a part of the corona. Solar gas is coronal gas only if it is at a temperature high enough to produce coronal ions. Therefore, by definition, the three lines—red, green, and yellow—cover quite well the range of coronal temperatures.

Several studies have been based on long-term daily intensity measurements of the red, yellow, and green coronal lines. These have included relation to other solar features; variation with the solar cycle; changes in latitude of zones of activity; changes in shape of the monochromatic corona; changes in longitude and latitude of specific features with time; and relation of specific coronal to specific photospheric and chromospheric features.

Although the publication of coronal intensities in the *IAU Bulletin of Solar Activity* was meant to expedite the use of data from various stations in studies of this sort, most of the long-range analyses have utilized the data of one station only. The most notable are Waldmeier's many exhaustive studies of the Arosa observations, which are described in the book *Die Sonnenkorona*, Volume II (Waldmeier, 1957), and in numerous journal articles. Trellis (1957) has similarly analyzed the Pic du Midi data, Behr (1951) the Wendelstein data, Bretz and Billings (1959) the Climax data, and Nagasawa (1961) the Norikura data. Bell has carried out a number of studies using Climax and Sacramento Peak data combined.

In many cases the investigators named above have reported a number of different synoptic aspects of the corona in a single report. In this summary we shall attempt, instead of outlining the various reports individually, to separate out specific topics on which the investigations have thrown light.

The red, green, and yellow emission lines have been followed in sufficient detail to yield conclusions concerning their relation to other specific active solar features. Concerning these three lines we can make the generalization that λ 5694 is closely related to intense solar activity, λ 5303 is generally related to all solar activity, and λ 6374 is often related to solar activity, but the relationship is much less clearly delineated than in the case of the other two lines.

During the early days of coronagraphy, Lyot, Waldmeier, and Roberts all recognized the close association of the coronal yellow line with intense solar activity. Waldmeier (1956a) concluded that when observing conditions are favorable the line will almost certainly be observable over an F-type spot group, but gives some evidence (1959) that high-latitude spots at a given phase in the sunspot cycle are better producer of λ 5694 emission than low-latitude spots. Dolder *et al.* (1954a,b) made a statistical study of its relations to flares and to the characteristics of sunspot prominences, concluding that regions displaying strong yellow-line emission are characterized by limb flares and strongly curved, active-region prominences with highly focused downward streaming material. Waldmeier (1959) pointed out that the λ 5694 emission in an active region lies closer to the center of the region than either the λ 5303 emission or the λ 6374 emission, often being concentrated near the top of the small, tight loops of the sunspot prominence. Finally, Waldmeier (1957), Trellis (1957), Billings (1957), and Zirin (1959) have all noted strong continuum radiation with intense yellow-line emission. Billings (1957) has pointed out that only in regions of unusually high electron density could we expect to have enough calcium ions to give the observed yellow-line intensity. Thus regions that emit a bright yellow line are "condensations" as defined earlier in this chapter.

The latitude zone of most intense green-line emission is the zone of sunspot activity, with maxima in emission in the vicinity of spot groups (Waldmeier, 1940, 1957; Nagasawa, 1961). However, emission maxima are frequently displaced from spot groups or are present at the locus of former spots (Waldmeier, 1957), and occasionally appear removed from the spot zone, as in the polar zones (Cooper and Billings, 1962; Waldmeier, 1957). Both Waldmeier (1957) and Trellis (1957) find a much closer correspondence of green-line emission with faculae than with other disk phenomena. Typically, if a spot group becomes apparent before the plages are well developed the λ 5303 emission will be weak; but if at the next rotation the plages are bright the green-line emission will also be bright. Similarly, if the plage remains after the spot group has disappeared, the coronal regions will also remain. Nagasawa (1961) finds that the duration of the region will not be more than one-fourth revolution after the spot disappearance, but this may be longer than the duration of the plage. Trellis concludes that every plage has an associated coronal "jet," but that not every coronal "jet" has an associated plage. Plages, in turn, are highly correlated with photospheric magnetic fields.

Charvin (1963) has noted an observation that may be of considerable significance in relation to geomagnetic phenomena. He points out that whereas the λ 5303 emission close to the sun is intensified over active regions, that farther from the sun appears to be intensified between active regions.

The association of λ 6374 emission with disk activity is less clearly defined than that of the yellow and green lines. In many cases bright emission in both λ 5303 and λ 6374 are evident over an active region. In such cases they identify coronal "enhancements." In other cases there will be a minimum in λ 6374 emission coincident with a maximum in λ 5303 or λ 5694. Also, a great deal of λ 6374 emission appears in the absence of any coronal region. As a general rule, a region of moderate activity, especially during the early years of a sunspot cycle, is likely to have strong emission in both λ 5303 and λ 6374. A region of more intense activity shows some emission in λ 5694, a maximum in λ 5303, and a minimum in λ 6374, although this minimum may be surrounded by heightened λ 6374 emission. An even more intense region might show intense λ 5694 emission near the center of the region, heightened λ 5303 emission in the vicinity of the region but with a minimum directly over the region, and a marked minimum in λ 6374. Finally, Waldmeier (1950) has reported one extremely active region in which even λ 5694 experienced a minimum directly over the sunspot. This rather typical pattern of events is easily explained if we postulate that the more violent the activity in a region, the greater the heating of the corona over the region. Unfortunately, it is not always followed. On occasions, for example, very brilliant red-line emission will appear in the same active region as yellow-line emission. Also, if we assume that extremely active regions are very hot throughout, or if they are hot at the center and cooler toward their periphery, it is difficult to explain the presence of the active-region prominences near the very center of the coronal region. Trellis (1957) carried out a statistical study that suggests a more complex temperature structure in the coronal regions. He finds that whereas bright "jets" of λ 5303 emission tend to lie near the east and west periphery of plages, the λ 6374 "jets" are either near the centers of the plage or well east or west of its periphery. The temperature structure implied by this observation is one in which the region is cooler in its center, higher near the periphery of the plage, and cooler again further out. This picture would be in contradiction to the observation of yellow-line emission near the centers of active regions, unless we take into account that λ 5694 frequently reaches its maximum brightness at a greater height than λ 5303 and λ 6374 (Dollfus, 1953). Thus we must consider a three-dimensional temperature model in order to completely describe the situation.

As we might expect from its close association with spot activity, yellow-line emission is the coronal feature most sensitive to changes in the sunspot cycle. Near sunspot maximum the line can be observed almost every day of low sky brightness; near minimum, not at all. The zone in which it is observed follows the sunspot zone precisely, and heliographic maps of yellow-line emission locate clearly the regions of greatest activity. Unfortunately, the observation of the line is too dependent on observing conditions to make it very useful for statistical studies.

The long-range variations in λ 5303 emission have been studied much more thoroughly, and by a greater variety of techniques than those of any other line. Three aspects of emission that have been studied extensively are: (1) variation of the total emission in the line with the solar cycle; (2) latitude zones of heightened emission; and (3) changes in the shape of the monochromatic corona with the sunspot cycle.

The total emission in λ 5303 has been found to follow the sunspot number in considerable detail, although the relative importances of different short-period increases and decreases are not always the same in the two phenomena (Fig. 3.7). Bretz and Billings (1959) did not confirm Waldmeier's (1960b) report of a one-year lag of coronal minimum in the equatorial zone behind the sunspot minimum.

When yearly averages of λ 5303 emission at each latitude are plotted against latitude, as has been done by Waldmeier (1957), Trellis (1957), and Bretz and Billings (1959), the outstanding features are large maxima north and south of the equator that appear near the sunspot latitudes, move equatorward with the progression of the solar cycle, merge at the equator, and diminish almost to the point of disappearance by sunspot minimum. These maxima are to be expected as a consequence of the bright λ 5303 emission in active regions.

In addition to the strong maxima at sunspot latitudes, however, there are small maxima, frequently almost completely lost in the wings of the strong maxima in intensity plots, but of a great deal of interest. Waldmeier

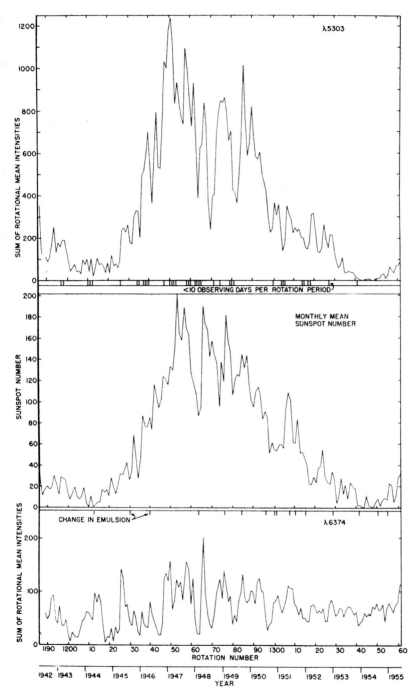

Fig. 3.7. The variation in green- and red-line intensity during one solar cycle, as determined by Bretz and Billings (1959) from Climax observations. The monthly mean sunspot number is included for comparison. Courtesy, High Altitude Observatory.

(1957) and Bell (1963) have studied these secondary maxima in detail, and both have found that they become much more apparent if the number of maxima per observation period per latitude rather than the mean intensity is plotted against latitude. Two very interesting aspects of these small maxima have emerged.

(1)   A zone of enhanced λ 5303 emission in each hemisphere appears at a high latitude several years before the beginning of the sunspot cycle and migrates equatorward, reaching the 40° latitude in coincidence with the appearance of new-cycle spots at this latitude. The polar birth of this zone, about the time of one sunspot maximum, is the first evidence of the succeeding activity cycle. As far as the green-line corona in this zone is concerned, the only effect of the appearance of new sunspots is the dramatic brightening of emission in the zone; but no interruption whatsoever takes place in its steady 15-year progress from the latitude of origin to the equator. Trellis (1957, 1963) also has pointed out evidence of such a coronal precursor to the sunspot zone.

(2)   Waldmeier (1957) has also distinguished a north and a south polar coronal zone. These zones originate at about 50° early in the sunspot cycle and migrate poleward, reaching the poles about sunspot maximum, then disappear. Their disappearance seems to coincide with the reversal of the polar magnetic.

The general form or outline of the green-line corona (Waldmeier, 1957, 1960a), as compared to that of the white-light corona observed at eclipse, shows that coronal emission is more sensitive than electron density to the presence of active regions. The maximum ellipticity of the green-line corona occurs about two years after sunspot maximum, after the polar corona disappears but while there is still strong emission overlying the sunspot latitudes. This is in strong contrast to the behavior of the white-light corona, which has its greatest ellipticity at sunspot minimum.

Although there is a general correspondence of red-line to green-line emission during the solar cycle, the differences are quite striking. For one thing, the variation of total red-line emission during the cycle is not nearly so pronounced. Waldmeier (1957) found evidence of a double periodicity in the emission, with maxima occurring both at sunspot maximum and again near sunspot minimum. Bretz and Billings (1959) did not confirm this double periodicity, nor did Trellis (1957), who found a stronger correspondence of total λ 6374 emission with sunspots than either Waldmeier or Bretz and Billings.

The red line, like the green line, has, on the average, more emission near the sunspot latitudes than elsewhere around the limb. However, as found by Trellis (1957) and confirmed by Bretz and Billings, the latitude of maximum red-line emission preceeds that of maximum green-line emission by about 5° as the zones progress toward the equator. Red-line emission lingers longer at the equator than green-line emission following the completion of a solar cycle, and also appears at the poles during sunspot minimum. A very significant observation made by Waldmeier (1957) is that during years of sunspot maximum the heliographic maps of green- and red-line emission show a general but not detailed correspondence, whereas at sunspot minimum they tend to be complementary.

The structure of the monochromatic corona is best compared to that of the white-light corona through photographs taken by narrow-band filters that admit only one coronal emission line (see Fig. 2.11). Pic du Midi has carried out an extensive program of photographing the corona in this manner, using both red-line and green-line filters. Also, Sacramento Peak has carried out a program of daily cinematography, weather permitting, through a green-line filter. The two most striking differences between monochromatic pictures and white-light pictures are: (1) the monochromatic brightness drops off more rapidly with distance from the sun and (2) the features appear in stronger contrast (Michard *et al.*, 1954). Both differences are a consequence of the fact that a considerable part of the excitation for emission of the coronal lines is collisional, hence the emission is roughly proportional to the square of the electron density, whereas the scattering of photospheric light to produce the white-light corona is proportional to the first power of the electron density.

There is a rough correspondence between red-line, green-line, and white-light structure in the corona, indicating that regions of higher density contain an enhanced amount of material of both low and intermediate temperatures. The correspondence between the red- and green-line features breaks down when the two are compared in sufficient detail (Dollfus, 1962), but at the limit of resolution of present pictures many features still appear identical in both lines.

In addition to accentuating the structural features, the monochromatic corona has the major advantage over the white-light corona of being accessible from a coronagraph station on any good observing day, not just during a total eclipse. Consequently, changes in the monochromatic corona may be studied from minute to minute, hour to hour, day to day, or limb passage to limb passage. Such studies reveal that the corona is remarkably quiet most of the time. Intricate features often show no clear change from day to day and very little from one limb passage to the next. On widely

separated occasions some rather striking motions do occur (Kleczek, 1963)
These typically have the appearance of twitches of single small features
A loop may suddenly break and whip outward, then reform, for example
while adjoining material remains undisturbed. However, the continued
restless motion that one finds in active prominence regions is very rare
indeed in the corona.

D. The Ultraviolet Corona

Permitted coronal emission lines are all in the ultraviolet and X-ray
regions of the spectrum. The longest of these are interspersed among
prominence lines at about 1000 Å. They become increasingly numerous
with decreasing wavelength, and shorter than the Lyman limit of ionized
Helium, 228 Å, we may consider the entire solar spectrum (except during
flares) to be made up of coronal emission plus Lyman continuum of Hydrogen and Helium and a small amount of free–free emission. In this
region we encounter a problem in nomenclature. Shall we call the radiation
ultraviolet, extreme ultraviolet, or X ray? *Extreme ultraviolet* (EUV) is
generally now used in preference to *ultraviolet* for wavelengths of less than
200 or 300 Å (Zirin, 1962; Tousey, 1963), hence is more appropriate than
ultraviolet for most of the coronal radiation in the range now under discussion. However, the designation *X rays* or *soft X rays* has been used
extensively for wavelengths of a few angstroms (Chubb *et al.*, 1961;
Willmore, 1961; Mandel'shtam, 1963), and has been extended to 50 or
100 Å. Since there is no physical demarcation between EUV and X-ray
coronal emission, we adopt the scheme of Hinteregger and collaborators
(1964) and designate all coronal radiation of wavelengths shorter than
about 1000 Å by the symbol XUV.

The exploration of the XUV coronal spectrum has constituted one of the
major activities of solar physics during the past decade. The longer-
wavelength portion has been investigated, in the United States, by the
Naval Research Laboratory group (Tousey, 1963; Detwiler *et al.*, 1961;
Austin *et al.*, 1962) and by the Colorado group (Violett and Rense, 1959;
Rense, 1961) as short-wave extension of solar ultraviolet exploration. The
Air Force Cambridge group (Hinteregger, 1960, 1961a,b; Hinteregger
et al., 1964) has concentrated on the region from a few hundred angstroms
to 50 angstroms. A second Naval Research Laboratory group (Friedman,
1960; Acton *et al.*, 1963; Blake *et al.*, 1964, 1966) and a NASA group
(Lindsay, 1964; White, 1964) have concentrated on the wavelengths of a

few angstroms. Outside the United States, a British group (Willmore, 1961; Bowen *et al.*, 1964) and a Soviet group (Mandel'shtam *et al.*, 1963) have made important contributions to the short-wave portion of the spectrum.

From the above observations it has become apparent that the coronal XUV spectrum to wavelengths at least as short as 13 Å is almost entirely an emission-line spectrum. Hinteregger *et al.*, (1964) describe the entire spectrum between 310 and 55 Å as made up of close-spaced lines. The same description applies to the 14–25 Å range explored by Blake *et al.* (1964, 1966). Whether the spectrum below 12 Å is primarily line or continuum is still a matter of debate. Many of the ions that give longer-wavelength lines have reached their resonance-radiation series limits for wavelengths as short as 12 Å, so should be contributing free–bound emission to the continuum. In confirmation of the idea that the continuum dominates, Blake *et al.* (1966) looked for such lines in the 2–8 Å range in 1963, without success. However, Lindsay and White (Lindsay, 1964) found that the total flux less than about 10 Å was much too high to be explained by continuum emission, even from a 3,000,000° corona, so invoked line emission. Finally, Shklovskii (1965) explained the observed flux as line emission from excited inner-shell electrons from a corona of moderate temperatures.

Lines in the XUV spectrum are so dense that many are not clearly resolved, and many that are resolved are not yet identified. The process of identification is proceeding rapidly, to the extent that the list given in Appendix III will undoubtedly be obsolete by the publication of this book. It is included only to indicate the type of ions and transitions involved. In the list we have arbitrarily limited the lines to those from ions of more than 100 V ionization potential. Ions of lower ionization potential can hardly be called coronal, although they are of interest in regard to the theory of the production of the corona, since many of them probably originate in the chromosphere–corona interface. An important study, yet to be made, is the spectroscopic observation of the XUV corona during a total eclipse in order to determine which of the ions really are found well above the chromosphere.

XUV coronal radiation is highly variable. In general, the variability increases with decreasing wavelength and with the degree of ionization of the emitting ion. The flux at one astronomical unit from the quiet sun at wavelengths of less than 10 Å, for example, is about 10^{-4} ergs cm^{-2} sec^{-1} (Lindsay, 1964; Manson, 1964), but even small flares will increase this flux by a factor of 5 or more, and large flares by orders of magnitude.

Furthermore, fluctuations of a factor of 2 are observed within as short a time interval as one second (Lindsay, 1964). In contrast, on one occasion during the orbiting of the satellite OSO-I, a Class-2 flare increased the Fe XV line λ 284 only 10% and the Fe XVI line λ 335 by 50%. The longer-wavelength lines appear to be more sensitive to overall changes in solar activity than to individual flares. During a time in which the sunspot number changed from zero to 94, λ 284 and λ 335 both changed in intensity by about a factor of 4. The 1–10 Å region, on the other hand, is particularly sensitive to flares.

The total XUV emission is an extremely important datum, since this emission is a major energy sink for the corona. At the time of writing this chapter we can say only that the quantity is obviously quite variable, perhaps changing by an order of magnitude or more during the solar cycle, and that a plausible range of fluxes may be from 1 to 10 ergs cm^{-2} sec^{-1} at one astronomical unit. The greater part of the energy comes from lines of wavelengths greater than 50 Å, but observations in this wavelength range have been carried out primarily by rockets, hence give brief samples that may not be representative of the phase of the solar cycle, and in many of these observations the calibration has been uncertain. The type of data on which our estimates of total emission are based is illustrated by a recent study by Elton *et al.* (1964) of the spectrum between 170 and 220 Å. From this small spectral range the observers tabulated 40 lines, all un-identified, most of which could be found in the spectrum of a Zeta-pinch to which iron had been added. The intensities of these lines are given on an arbitrary scale, but a correspondence between the scale and absolute units is suggested. It is interesting to note that if the intensities of the 40 lines are added together, their sum corresponds to 1 erg cm^{-2} sec^{-1}. Thus the total flux from the corona at one astronomical unit over all wavelengths must be several ergs cm^{-2} sec^{-1}.

A question of equal importance to that of the total energy radiated by the corona is: Where in the corona does the radiation originate? X-ray photographs (Blake *et al.*, 1963), spectroheliograms (Tousey, 1963), and fan-beam scanners (Blake *et al.*, 1966) all indicate that the greater part comes from active regions overlying calcium plages. The shorter the wave-length range being considered, the greater the per cent contribution from the active region. We shall consider the implication of these observations with regard to the temperature and density of coronal enhancements in a later chapter.

The technical problems connected with obtaining high-quality images of the sun in XUV radiation are now being solved. Such images are intrinsically capable of much higher resolution than optical images and can be expected to provide a wealth of detail concerning coronal structure. Certainly they will show the coronal condensations and enhancements in great detail, and by proper choice of wavelengths, should provide differentiation between hot and cold regions in the gas. Furthermore, if suitable time-resolution is available, such images should give us a new look at the more significant aspects of flares.

E. The Radio Corona

The corona as viewed by radio waves appears very different from either the optical or the XUV corona. In the first place, the energy received is many orders of magnitude lower than that at shorter wavelengths. In the second place, the image must always be a fuzzy one, because of the low resolving power associated with long wavelengths. Finally, the image is distorted by extreme refraction effects, particularly near the solar limb. In spite of such difficulties, however, the radio corona is a very exciting and instructive object. By choice of successively longer wavelengths it may be examined layer by layer outward from the sun. From the polarization of the radio noise a great deal may be learned about coronal magnetic fields (Kakinuma and Swarup, 1962; Cohen, 1959, 1961). By observation with proper time-resolution we are made aware of sudden, dramatic events whose counterparts, if any, in the optical or XUV corona are only partially understood.

Let us review briefly the various phenomena observed. At wavelengths of 20 cm or less the predominant emission either is constant or changes slowly with time, the time scale of the change being days or weeks. The steady component of this emission is readily explained as the thermal emission from the chromosphere and is of no further concern to us here. The slowly varying component, on the other hand, although also interpreted as thermal, has been identified through eclipse (Covington, 1947, 1963) and interferometer (Kislyakov and Salomonovich, 1963; Swarup *et al.*, 1963; Christiansen and Warburton, 1953) studies of the sun as originating from active regions in the lower corona. These regions, being of greater optical depth than the surrounding corona, enhance the radio noise by contributing emission more appropriate to coronal than chromospheric temperatures.

The radio emission from the entire sun has been observed daily at 10.9 cm wavelength over almost two solar cycles. The apparatus is of great stability, and the total record can be considered one of the best measurements of integrated solar activity available. As a record of coronal activity, it depends on the number of active regions on the earthward side of the lower corona, their density, and their temperature.

From daily interferometer scans of the sun one can separate the effects of the various active regions. The apparent temperature of each region still depends jointly on its optical depth and its actual kinetic temperature. Casual studies of these regions to date indicate that their relation to general solar activity is similar to that of regions of bright emission in the coronal green line. They are brightest over regions of greatest sunspot and flare activity, they are apparent any time that significant activity is present, and they tend to persist about one solar revolution after the disappearance of the associated sunspot group. The correlation between 10-cm and green-line emission in an active region might be expected to disappear if the region becomes so hot that Fe XIV diminishes. Thus a joint study of the two phenomena should provide a supplement to the yellow coronal line observations for identifying very-high–temperature regions in the corona.

Because of the slowly varying component in the decimeter-range emission it is difficult to define with any great precision the level of the unchanging background. The usual process is to plot emission against sunspot number and extrapolate to zero sunspot number. Piddington and Davies (1953) found somewhat better correlation by including the spot number of the previous rotation in the plot.

At longer wavelengths the slowly varying component is not so much in evidence. The very violent short-lived burst and storm events are superimposed on a background that changes little from day to day. A significant change does take place over the solar cycle, however. In the wavelength range of 60 to 100 cm the increase in background with increasing solar activity can be explained by an increase in density of the overall corona— i.e., by an increase in the contribution of the corona relative to that of the chromosphere. However, an increase in background noise at sunspot maximum is also observed at wavelengths in which the corona should always be optically deep. The increase in background at these wavelengths indicates an increase in the overall coronal temperature. Since both density and temperature increase with increasing solar activity, it is paradoxical that the apparent radio-frequency temperature of the sunspot-maximum corona does not differ more than it does from that at sunspot minimum. In fact, the difference between the plots of apparent temperature vs frequency at maximum and minimum may be explained by a $1.5\times$ isothermal increase in density (Allen, 1957). This is a smaller increase than the 1.8× indicated by the white-light corona. The solution to the paradox lies in the remarkable fact that an increase in temperature actually decreases the apparent radio temperature over quite a range of wavelengths. The optical depth for thermal emission is proportional to the square of the electron density and inversely proportional to the $\frac{3}{2}$ power of the temperature. Thus, since the emission is proportional to the product of temperature and optical depth for optically thin layers, the apparent temperature is proportional to $N_e^2/T_e^{1/2}$. If a change in electron density by a factor of 1.8 accompanied by a change in electron temperature results in the same increase in apparent temperature that would result from a change in density by a factor of 1.5 without temperature change, the actual temperature would change by a factor of $(1.8/1.5)^4 = 2.1$, which is consistent with the observed change from dominant red-line to dominant green-line emission.

Whereas the slowly changing component of solar radio emission indicates activity that may often be identified with enhanced λ 5303 emission, the more transient radio features observed at longer wavelengths—the nonthermal emissions—indicate the most violent events known to take place in the corona. Of the various nonthermal features that have been distinguished by the use of sweep-frequency radio spectrographs, only one —the Type-II bursts (Fig. 3.8) (Wild *et al.*, 1954)—has a plausible optical counterpart. These bursts are observed at frequencies less than 300 Mc/sec and are characterized by no polarization and by a frequency drift, toward lower frequencies, of about 0.2 Mc/sec. The frequency drift indicates that the source is moving upward through the corona at a speed of a few hundred kilometers per second, which is suggestive of optical surges. Similar lateral motions of the sources have been detected by interferometer observations (Wild *et al.*, 1959). Furthermore, Type-II bursts, like large surges, accompany optical flares. Finally, quite a number of Type-II bursts have actually been identified time wise with observed flare surges (Giovanelli and Roberts, 1958; Lowman and Billings, 1960). The identification would be considered complete, were it not that the apparent velocity of the burst sources, as determined both from frequency-shift rate and from displacement in interferometer pattern, is about twice as great as that of the optical surges. This discrepancy appears both in the mean burst velocities (Maxwell and Thompson, 1962) and in the intercomparison of specific bursts with corresponding optical surges, and suggests that the source of the burst precedes the optical surge as a shock front (Uchida, 1960). In any case, the existence of Type-II bursts indicates surge-induced kinetic disturbances in the corona, and the frequency of these disturbances is a good indicator of the amount of violent activity in the solar atmosphere.

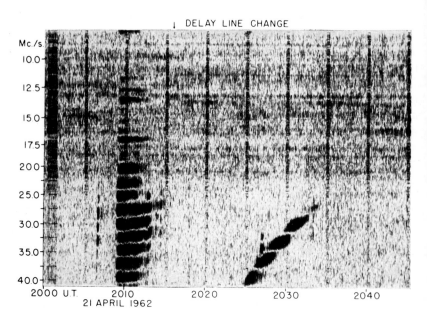

Fig. 3.8. Excerpt from the Boulder radio-noise dynamic spectrograph record showing a Type-II burst at right. Several Type-III bursts and continuous emission also appear on the record. Courtesy, High Altitude Observatory.

   Type-IV bursts are indicative of even more violent activity. They follow Type-II or Type-III bursts (fast-drift bursts, to be discussed later) (Boischot, 1960) and are characterized by circularly polarized emission over a wide band of frequencies. The source of the emission moves through the corona with velocities of hundreds of kilometers per second, then stops moving at a distance of about 1 $R_\odot$, but may continue to emit for one or more hours. These bursts have a strong correlation with high-energy protons at the earth, and may therefore be considered as among the most violent events in the solar corona. Type-V bursts are similar, but have a much shorter duration.

   The longer-wavelength radio phenomenon most closely associated with the presence of large sunspot groups is the noise storm. It is an enhanced, circularly polarized emission of duration of several hours to several days, covering a wide range of wavelengths greater than 50 cm. Superimposed on the high but rather steady emission are numerous short pips of much more violent emission (storm pips or Type-I bursts) (Goldstein, 1959) of duration of a fraction of a second to a few seconds. The emitting centers for noise storms have dimensions of 1–10 minutes of arc, and although they may be with sunspot groups, they are frequently displaced somewhat from directly over the spots. Furthermore, the wavelength range of the emission requires that they be at a considerable height in the corona.

The emission pips in noise storms may be related to Type-III bursts, the difference being that in the latter the emission is identified to be lying in a definite frequency band (Fig. 3.9) that drifts rapidly to lower frequencies (Wild *et al.*, 1954). Type-III bursts are found from 560 Mc/sec to the lowest frequencies that have been studied. The frequencies commonly drift at about 20 Mc/sec^2 toward lower frequencies, although in some cases the direction of drift reverses (Inverted U burst) (Boischot, 1960). This extremely rapid change of frequency corresponds to a passage of the source through the corona with a velocity of one-tenth to one-third the velocity of light, and must indicate the presence in the corona of very fast particles.

The relation of Type-III bursts to optical phenomena in the corona, or to solar activity in general, is not yet clearly understood. During the course of a flare many Type-III bursts may occur, but their prevalence varies strongly from flare to flare. Also they may occur when no flare is in progress, and, as a matter of fact, when no very significant active region—as judged by optical standards—is on the disk. Malville (1961) has studied some of the characteristics of flares with which Type-III bursts are associated, and has found that the occurrence of either a surge with a flare or a noise-storm center over the spot group associated with the flare approximately doubles the flare's probability producing Type-III bursts. Sometimes Type-III bursts appear to emerge from Type-II bursts, as though the latter, although moving fairly slowly, has very-high–energy particles confined in its magnetic field (Roberts, 1959).

In general it appears that the long-range changes in the corona, as observed by radio-frequency measurements, follow those observed by optical measurements; but that at radio frequencies several phenomena appear that would not be expected from optical observations—notably, the high-velocity particles indicated by the Type-III bursts and the very disturbed conditions high in the corona during noise storms and Type-IV and Type-V bursts. Finally, whereas to an optical astronomer the corona is remarkably serene most of the time, to the radio astronomer it is a much more violently disturbed medium than the photosphere or chromosphere. Some of this discrepancy arises as a result of nomenclature rather than fact. If a flare occurs just above the chromosphere, or strong loop prominences connect sunspots, or a surge is seen in Hα, we are accustomed to think of

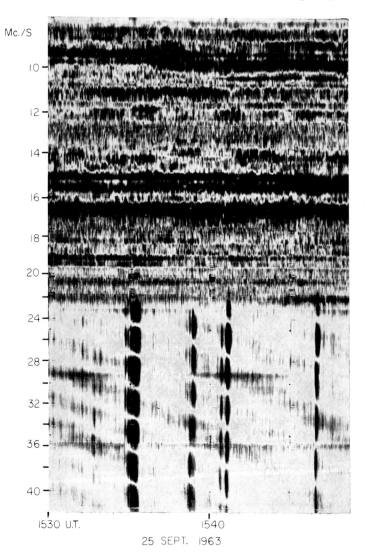

Fig. 3.9. Type-III bursts in rapid succession, from the Boulder dynamic spectrograph. Note that the lower-intensity continuum background upon which the intense bursts are superimposed appears to have a fine structure of many small Type-III bursts. Courtesy, High Altitude Observatory.

the event as projected into the corona but not part of it, whereas the noise storms or bursts associated with these events are attributed to the corona. Semantics, however, can explain only a small part of the discrepancy. One of the major goals of coronal physics should be to evolve a concept of the corona into which both optical and radio observations fit comfortably. Will the picture be that of a corona that is normally quite stable, but is prodded into a violent outpouring of radio emission by the action of faster or slower aggregates of material introduced from chromospheric disturbances; or is it itself the seat of the most violent events of the solar atmosphere?

The general shape of the radio corona corresponds to that of the white-light corona. This is confirmed by Tiainen (1964) for the 3.5-meter sun during the 1954 eclipse, and by Avignon and Squaren-Malinge (1961), who followed the changes in ellipticity during a solar cycle, using 169-Mc/sec observations. Hewish (1958) found that similar changes in ellipticity could be observed at 8 $R_\odot$ from the occultations of the crab nebula, but not at 16 $R_\odot$. Slee (1961), however, using occultations from thirteen discrete sources, determined an elliptical distribution of scattering elements out to 55 $R_\odot$ at the equator with a corresponding scattering effect at 40 $R_\odot$ at the poles. Since his observations were made near sunspot maximum, we might expect an even more pronounced ellipticity near sunspot minimum.

Occultation observations by a number of observers have also yielded some information as to the size, shape, and orientation of the structural irregularities in the very outer corona. There is fairly general agreement (Hewish, 1958; Vitkevich and Panovkin, 1959; Högbom, 1960; Vitkevich, 1964; Erickson, 1964) that the irregularities are elongated, with the long axis of the irregularities predominately radial. Vitkevich and Panovkin have found some evidence that the orientation departs from radial as though following a dipole field, but such departures are difficult to establish because the nearest approach of the Crab Nebula to the sun is in the polar regions, where dipole fields are nearly radial anyway. Hewish and Wyndham (1963) found evidence of deflection of the orientations from radial toward the equator in 1961–1962, but in 1959, at sunspot maximum, the orientation was radial. Such a solar-cycle effect would be consistent with white-light observations in which the polar plumes at sunspot minimum follow a dipole configuration, whereas at sunspot maximum the various structural features of the corona appear to be oriented radially, or depart from radial in a rather random fashion.

Although there is general agreement on the form of the very outer corona, there is no agreement on the size of the structures. Slee found evidence of very large structures, 3.5 $R_\odot$ across, from time variations in the scattering, but noted that scattering irregularities must be much smaller. Hewish and Wyndham gave an upper limit for the cross section of a scattering feature at 60 $R_\odot$ as 5000 km, and as lower limits, 10 km at 20 $R_\odot$ and 50 km at 90 $R_\odot$. A feature of the upper-limit diameter, extrapolated back to the sun by a $1/r$ law has a cross section of 100 km—i.e., granular dimensions. Although the validity of such an extrapolation is questionable, the result is interesting. Finally, Basu and Castelli (1963) working at much shorter wavelengths than used by other observers, found evidence of scattering irregularities of less than 1 km cross section.

One of the major limitations of solar radio astronomy is that the sun provides no signal of a well-defined frequency for determination of Doppler shifts. With radar, not only the frequency but the time of sending the pulse is known. Both data greatly increase the effectiveness of radio-frequency observations of the corona. Chisholm and James (1964), from the reflection of 38.25-Mc/sec pulses, have concluded that at 1.5 $R_\odot$ the corona has a directed motion outward of 16 km/sec superimposed on a random motion of 35 km/sec. The interpretation of these motions in relation to the expansion and heating of the corona will be discussed in much more detail in Chapter 7.

F. The Probed Corona

Earth satellites operating in orbits that carry them to ten or more earth radii—i.e., beyond the earth's magnetosphere—or space vehicles en route to other parts of the solar system pass through the extended solar corona and thus provide information through direct contact with it. Even though this method of observation of the corona is only a few years old, the information gained is already being extrapolated theoretically to the sun, and conclusions are being drawn from it as to the physical characteristics of the entire corona—even the part very close to the sun, which has been under optical observation for over a century (Brandt et al., 1964). The probed observations are of two basic types: observation of particles, and observations of magnetic fields. The particle observations give particle fluxes over various energy ranges—hence, particle density and velocity—and some information concerning temperature through the distribution in particle velocities (Neugebauer and Snyder, 1963; Gringauz et al., 1961). Magnetometers determine the direction and magnitude of the magnetic ield at the location of the probe (Coleman *et al.*, 1961; Heppner *et al.*, 1963; Ness *et al.*, 1964).

The space probes operating at about one astronomical unit from the sun see the corona as a very tenuous gas of a few particles per cubic centimeter moving outward from the sun at a velocity of several hundred kilometers per second (Neugebauer and Snyder, 1963), a velocity that apparently decreases with decreasing solar activity. These particles are at a temperature of a few hundred thousand degrees Kelvin. They have velocity fluctuations that correlate with geomagnetic activity (Snyder *et al.*, 1963) and carry with them a magnetic field of a few hundred-thousandths of a gauss that quite accurately maps the field at the central meridian of the sun four days earlier (Ness and Wilcox, 1964). The transit time implied is appropriate for particles of the observed velocity.

Thus the space-probe observations complete our picture of a corona that extends from just above the solar surface to distances beyond the radius of the earth's orbit, an expanding corona in which the particles move outward from the sun at a speed that increases with distance from the sun. These outward-moving particles carry with them a magnetic field that passes outward through the solar photosphere, distorts the lower corona into a multitude of concentrations and configurations, then extends continuously outward into space.

In summary, we can say that by all observing techniques the corona is very hot, completely ionized, and permeated by a magnetic field that becomes increasingly radial with distance from the sun. All techniques also show evidence of marked irregularities in temperature and density, particularly in the inner corona. In the past there has been a strong inclination of observers using different techniques to name and characterize these irregularities in terms of the observational features as seen by their own equipment. The important goal of identifying observational features as seen by various techniques has been only partially achieved.

REFERENCES

Acton, L. W., Chubb, T. A., Kreplin, R. W., and Meekins, J. R. (1963). Observations of solar X-ray emission in the 8-20Å band. *J. G. R.* **68**, 3335.

Allen, C. W. (1946). The spectrum of the corona at the eclipse of 1950 October 1. *M. N. R. A. S.* **106**, 137.

Allen, C. W. (1956a). Coronal photometry of the eclipse of 1954 June 30. *M. N. R. A. S.* **116**, 69.

Allen, C. W. (1956b). Spectrophotometry of the outer corona. *M. N. R. A. S.* **116**, 413.

Allen, C. W. (1957). The quiet and active sun. "*I.A.U.* Symposium No. 4, Rad Astronomy." Cambridge Univ. Press, London and New York.

Allen, C. W. (1963). "Astrophysical Quantities," 2nd ed. Oxford Univ. Press (Athlone London and New York.

Aly, M. K. (1955). Preliminary note on measures of coronal emission lines observed the total eclipse, February 25, 1952, by B. Lyot and M. K. Aly. *Ap. J.* **122**, 43

Aly, M. K., Evans, J. W., and Orrall, F. Q. (1963). A photometric study of the continuu and seventeen emission lines in the inner solar corona. *Ap. J.* **136**, 956.

Athay, R. G., and Roberts, W. O. (1955). Coronal line intensities at the Khartou Eclipse. *Ap. J.* **121**, 231.

Austin, W. E., Purcell, J. D., and Tousey, R. (1962). A. Spectrum of the sun from 1¢ to 700 Å (abstract). *Ap. J.* **67**, 110.

Avignon, Y., and Squeren-Malinge, A. (1961). Dimensions of the quiet sun in 1¢ Mc/sec. *Compt. Rend.* **253**, 2859.

Basu, S., and Castelli, J. (1963). Occultation of the Crab Nebula by the solar corona June 1962. *Science* **197**, 885.

Behr, A. (1951). The intensity variation of the green coronal line 1943-1950. *Z. Ap.* **28** 296.

Bell, B. (1963). Private communication.

Billings, D. E. (1957). Profile of the yellow coronal line. *Ap. J.* **125**, 817.

Blackwell, D. E. (1952). A comparison of the intensities of infra-red radiation from th solar corona at the eclipse of 1952 February 25. *M. N. R. A. S.* **112**, 562.

Blake, R. L., Chubb, T. A., Friedman, H., and Unzicker, A. E. (1963). Interpretatio of X-ray photograph of the sun, *Ap. J.* **137**, 3.

Blake, R. L., Chubb, T. A., Friedman, H., and Unzicker, A. E. (1964). Solar X-ra spectrum below 25 angstroms. *Science* **146**, 1037.

Blake, R. L., Chubb, T. A., Friedman, H., and Unzicker, A. E. (1966). Spectral an photometric measurements of solar X-ray emission below 60Å. *Ap. J.* (in press).

Boardman, W. J., and Billings, D. E. (1965). Wave-lengths of the yellow coronal line *Ap. J.* **141**, 1289.

Boischot, A. (1960). "La radioastronomie. Masson, Paris.

Bowen, P. J., Norman, K., Pounds, K. A., Sanford, P. W., and Willmore, A. P. (1964 Measurements of the solar spectrum in the wavelength band 4-14Å, *Proc. Roy. Soc* **A281**, 538.

Brandt, J. C., Michie, R. W., and Cassinelli, J. P. (1964). Interplanetary gas X corone temperatures, energy deposition and solar wind. Contribution from the Kitt Pea National Observatory.

Bretz, M. C., and Billings, D. E. (1959). Analysis of emission corona 1942-1955 from climax spectrograms. *Ap. J.* **129**, 134.

Charvin, P. (1963). The measurements and study of intensity gradients in the corona ray λ 5303. *Compt. rend.* **256**, 1078.

Chisholm, J. H., and James, J. C. Radar evidence of solar wind and coronal mass motion *Ap. J.* **140**, 377.

Christiansen, W. N., and Warburton, J. A. (1953). The distribution of radio brightnes over the solar disk at a wavelength of 21 CM. *Aust. J. Phys.* **6**, 262.

Chubb, T. A., Friedmann, H., Kreplin, R. W., Blake, R. L., and Unzicker, A. E., (1961 I. X-ray and Y. V. measurements during the eclipse of october 12, 1958. II. X-ra solar disk photograph. *Mém. Soc. Roy Sci. Liége* **4**, 228.

Cohen, M. H. (1959). Linear polarization in Type III bursts. *Ap. J.* **130**, 221.

Cohen, M. H. (1961). Microwave polarization and the coronal magnetic field. *Ap. J.* **133**, 978.

Coleman, P. J., Jr., Sonett, C. P., and Leverett, D., Jr. (1961). On the interplanetary Magnetic storm: Pioneer V. *J. G. R.* **66**, 2043.

Collins, P. D. B. (1964). Relativistic calculations of the Z-dependence of atomic energy levels with application to the Identification of some coronal emission lines. *Ap. J.* **140**, 1206.

Cooper, R. H., and Billings, D. E. (1962). A long-lived polar coronal region. *Z. Ap.* **55**, 24.

Covington, A. E. (1947). Microwave solar noise observations during the eclipse of 1 November 1946. *Nature* **159**, 405.

Covington, A. E. (1963). Microwave radio emission from limb coronal condensations for the eclipse of February 5, 1962. *J. Roy. Astr. Soc. Can.* **57**, 253.

Detwiler, C. R., Purcell, J. D., and Tousey, R. (1961). The extreme ultraviolet spectrum of the sun. *Mém. Soc. Roy. Sci. Liége* **4**, 253.

Doler, F. P. Roberts, W. O., and Billings, D. E. (1954a) Solar flares and the yellow coronal line. *Ap. J.* **119**, 120.

Dolder, F. P., Roberts, W. O., and Billings, D. E. (1954b). Active region prominences and the yellow coronal line. *Ap. J.* **120**, 112.

Dollfus, A. (1953). Observation of coronal emission associated with prominences, Convegni Volta, Rome, Problemi della fisica solare, p. 219, Academia Nazional dei Lincei.

Dollfus, A. (1962). Properties of monochromatic emission of the solar corona. *Compt. rend.* **255**, 3369.

Dollfus, A., Martin, M., and Leroy, S. L. (1961). Observation of the solar corona before, during and after the total eclipse of 15 February 1961. *Compt. rend.* **252**, 3403–3404.

Edlén, B. (1942). Identification of coronal lines. *Z. Ap.* **22**, 30.

Elton, R. C., Kolb, A. C., Austin, W. E., Tousey, R., and Widing, K. G. (1954). Origin of certain solar emission lines between 170 and 220Å. *Ap. J.* **140**, 390.

Erickson, W. C. (1964). Radio wave scattering properties of the solar corona. *Ap. J.* **139**, 1290.

Friedman, H. (1960). The sun's ionizing radiations, *in* "Physics of the Upper Atmosphere" (J. A. Ratcliffe, ed.), p. 133. Academic Press, New York.

Giovanelli, R. G., and Roberts, J. A. (1958). Optical observations of the solar disturbances causing Type II radio bursts. *Aust. J. Phys.* **11**, 353.

Goldstein, S. J., Jr. (1959). The angular size of short-lived solar radio distrubances. *Ap. J.* **130**, 393.

Gringauz, K. I., Bezrukikh, V. V., Ozerov, V. D., and Rybchinskii, R. E. (1961). A study of interplanetary ionized gas, high energy electrons and corpuscular radiation of the sun, employing three-electrode charged particle traps on the second soviet space rocket. *Artificial Earth Satellites USSR* **6**, 101.

Heppner, J. P., Ness, N. F., Scearce, C. S., and Skillman, T. L. (1963). Explorer 10 magnetic field measurements. *J. G. R.* **68**, 1.

Hewish, A. (1958). The scattering of radio waves in the solar corona. *M. N. R. A. S.* **118**, 534.

Hewish, A., and Wyndham, J. D. (1963). The solar corona in interplanetary space. *M. N. R. A. S.* **126**, 469.

Hinteregger, H. E. (1960). Interplanetary Ionization by solar extreme UV radiation. *Ap. J.* **132**, 801.

Hinteregger, H. E. (1961a). Solar extreme UV radiation. *J. G. R.* **66**, 2367.

Hinteregger, H. E. (1961b). Monochromatic measurements of lyman series emissions of solar H and He+. *Mém. Soc. Roy. Sci. Liége* **4**, 111.

Hinteregger, H. E., Hall, L. A., and Schweitzer, W. (1964). Solar XUV spectrum from 310 Å to 55 Å. *Ap. J.* **140**, 319.

Högbom, J. A. (1960). The structure and magnetic field of the solar corona. *M. N. R. A. S.* **120**, 530.

Kakinuma, T., and Swarup, G. (1962). A model for the sources of the slowly-varying component of microwave solar radiation. *Ap. J.* **136**, 975.

Kislyakov, A. G., and Salomonovich, A. E. (1963). Radio emission from solar active regions in the millimeter range. *Sov. Astr.-A. J.* **7**, 177.

Kleczek, J. (1963). Regular structures in the green solar corona. *Astr. Soc. Pacific* **75**, 9.

Lindsay, J. C. (1964). The extreme ultraviolet radiation (1–400 Å) *Planetary Space Sci.* **12**, 379.

Lowman, K. M., and Billings, D. E. (1960). Study of the flare-surge event of September 7, 1958. *Aust. J. Phys.* **13**, 606.

Malville, J. M. (1961). Study of fast drift radio bursts and related phenomena. Ph.D. Thesis, University of Colorado.

Mandel'shtam, C. L., Tindo, I. P., Voron'ko, Yu. K., Shurygin, A. I., and Vasil'en, B. N. (1963). Investigation of the sun's X-radiation. *Planetary Space Sci.* **2**, 61.

Manson, J. E. (1964). Solar X-rays from 3 to 12 angstroms as measured with a proportional counter spectrometer. Air Force Cambridge Environmental Research Papers No. 68, AFCRL–64–932.

Maxwell, A., and Thompson, A. R. (1962). Spectral observations of radio bursts. II. Slow-drift bursts and coronal streamers. *Ap. J.* **135**, 138.

Michard, R., Dollfus, A., Pecker, J. C., Laffineur, M., and d'Azambuja, M. (1954). Optic and radio observations of the total eclipse of the sun of 25 February 1952. II. Monochromatic photographs. *Ann. d'Astrophys.* **17**, 345.

Mitchell, S. A. (1935). "Eclipses of the sun," 4th ed., Chapter XX. Columbia Univ. Press, New York.

Mustel, E. R. (1962). The spatial structure of the solar corona. *Sov. Astr.-A. J.* **6**, 333.

Nagasawa, S. (1961). Some relations between the intensity of the green coronal line and sunspot groups. *Publ. Astr. Soc. Japan* **13**, 384.

Nesmyanovich, A. T. (1962). The structure of the solar corona on February 15, 1961 from observations at Dzhankio. *Sov. Astro.-A. J.* **6**, 210.

Ness, N. F., and Wilcox, J. M. (1964). Solar origin of the interplanetary magnetic field. *Phys. Rev. Letters* **13**, 461.

Ness, N. F., Scearce, C. S., and Seek, J. B. (1964). Initial results of the IMP-1 magnetic field experiment, *J. Isophys. Res.* **69**, 3531.

Neugebauer, M., and Snyder, C. W. The mission of mariner II preliminary observations. *Science* **138**, 1095.

Obashev, S. O. (1961) On the structure of the corona over prominences. *Izv. Astrofiz. Inst. Akad. Nauk Kaz. SSR* **12**, 78.

Piddington, J. H., and Davies, R. D. (1953). Thermal radio emission from the sun and the source of Coronal Heating, *M. N. R. A. S.* **113**, 582.

Prokofyeva, I. A. (1963). Solar corona in active regions from Rlkovo Observations of the green and red lines, *in* "The Solar Corona" (J. W. Evans, ed.), p. 89. Academic Press, New York.

Pryce, M. H. L. (1964). The origin of coronal emission lines. *Ap. J.* **140**, 1192.

Rense, W. A. (1961). Solar ultraviolet photospheric and coronal lines. *Mém. Soc. Roy. Sci. Liége* **4**, 272

Roberts, J. A. (1959). Solar radio bursts of spectral Type II. *Aust. J. Phys.* **12**, 327.

Rohrlich, F., and Pecker, C. (1963) Highly ionized atoms: The configurations S^2p^n ($n = 1, 2, 4, 5$). *Ap. J.* **138**, 1246.

Secchi, P. A. (1875). "Le Soleil," 2nd ed. Gauthiers-Villars, Paris.

Shklovskii, I. S. (1965). Nature of solar X-ray emission. *Sov. Astr.-A. J.* **8**, 538.

Slee, O. B. (1961). Observations of the solar corona out to 100 solar radii. *M. N. R. A. S.* **123**, 223.

Snyder, C. W., Neugebauer, M., and Rao, U. R. (1963). The solar wind velocity and Its correlation with cosmic ray variations and with solar and geomagnetic activity. *J. G. R.* **68**, 6361.

Swarup, G., Kakinuma, T., Covington, A. E., Harvey, G. A., Mullaly, R. F., and Rome, J. (1963). High-resolution studies of ten solar active regions at wavelengths of 3-21 CM. *Ap. J.* **137**, 1251.

Tiainen, P. O. (1964). Solar corona on meter wavelengths according to observations made during the eclipse of June 30, 1954. *Ann. Acad. Sci. Fennicae: Ser. A VI.* (1957), No. 149.

Tousey, R. (1963) The extreme UV Spectrum of the sun. *Space Sci. Rev.* **2**, 3.

Trellis, M. (1957). Contribution to the study of the solar corona, Chapter IX. *Ann. d'Ap.* Suppl. 5.

Trellis, M. (1963). Distribution of coronal jets as a function of latitude in the course of the solar cycle. *Compt. rend.* **257**, 52.

Uchida, Y. (1960). One the exciters of Type II and Type III radio bursts. *Publ. Astr. Soc. Japan* **12**, 376.

van de Hulst, H. C. (1950). Polar rays of the corona. *B. A. N.* **11**, 150.

Violett, T., and Rense, W. A. (1959) Solar emission lines in the extreme ultraviolet. *Ap. J.* **130**, 954.

Vitkevich, V. V. (1964). A. two-component model of the solar super-corona. *Astr. Zhurn.* **41**, 684.

Vitkevich, V. V., and Panovkin, B. N. On the structure of the non-uniformities of the Solar super-corona. *Astr. Zhurn.* **36**, 544.

Vsekhsvayatskii, S. K., and Ivanchuk, V. I. (1962). Overall structure of the solar corona of February 15, 1961, *Sov. Astr.-A. J.* **5**, 655.

Waldmeier, M. (1940). Comparative observations of the coronal lines 5303, 5694 and 6374 Å. *Z. Ap.* **20**, 172.

Waldmeier, M. (1950). The coronal structure in the vicinity of a great spot group. *Z. Ap.* **27**, 73.

Waldmeier, M. Results of the Zurich eclipse expedition 1954. I. Preliminary photometry. *Z. Ap.* **36**, 275.

Waldmeier, M. (1956a). The variation of the monochromatic general emission of the solar corona in the 11 Year Cycle. III. The line 5694 Å. *Z. Ap.* **39**, 219.

Waldmeier, M. (1956b). Analysis of a coronal condensation. *Z. Ap.* **40**, 221.

Waldmeier, M. (1957). "Die Sonnenkorona" Vol. II. Birkhäuser, Basel.

Waldmeier, M. (1959). Observation of the coronal line 5694 Å. *Z. Ap.* **47,** 105.

Waldmeier, M. (1960a). Form and outward extent of the monochromatic corona. *Z. Ap.* **50,** 35

Waldmeier, M. (1960b). The variation of the monochromatic corona in the 11 year cycle. *Z. Ap.* **50,** 145.

Waldmeier, M. (1962). The Zurich eclipse expedition of 1962. *Astr. Mitt.,* Zurich, No. 248.

White, W. A. (1964). Solar X-rays, A comparison with microwave radiation. "AAS–NASA Symposium on the Physics of Solar Flares, 1963." NASA., Washington D. C.

Wild, J. P., Murray, J. D., and Rowe, W. C. (1954) Harmonics in the spectra of solar radio distrubances *Aust. J. Phys.* **7,** 439.

Wild, J.P., Sheridan, K.V., and Trent, G. H. (1959). The tranverse motion of the sources of solar radio bursts. "Paris Symposium on Radio Astronomy, Bracewell." Stanford Univ. Press, Stanford, California.

Willmore, A. P. (1961). Observations of the Lα and X-ray emissions of the sun. *Mém. Soc. Roy. Liége* **4,** 103.

Zirin, H. (1959) Physical conditions in limb flares and active prominences. *Ap. J.* **129,** 414.

Zirin, H. (1962). Coronal observations and rocket solar ultraviolet results. *Amer. Rocket Soc. Meeting.* Paper 2679-62.

CHAPTER 4

SPECIAL METHODS OF DATA ANALYSIS

A. Introduction

Data analysis is the bridge by which we pass from observation of the corona to knowledge concerning it. With every method of observation special techniques have been developed. Although these techniques are frequently quite elaborate, they are usually discussed only briefly in scientific-journal reports on the observations. More detailed procedures are to be found in special bulletins and memoranda, or are a part of the lore of the research groups that have developed them.

A thorough discussion of the analysis techniques associated with all of the observing methods listed in Chapter 2 or the observations discussed in Chapter 3 would be a very ambitious undertaking. For example, the analysis that goes into the interpretation of telemetered satellite observations, the calibration of radio telescopes, and the computations involved in the separation of radar signals from noise are all very intricate processes. Instead of attempting to present all pertinent methods we have chosen only a few procedures in the analysis of optical data with which we have had some personal experience. These we are describing in some detail for various reasons. In the case of the analysis of eclipse photographs we are attempting to provide for the reader a fairly complete account of the steps by which information on the density distribution in the corona is obtained. The method of analysis of the coronameter data gives considerable insight into the use of the instrument. The measurement of coronal line intensities is discussed in detail to aid in the evaluation of the largest single body of published coronal data. Finally, we are using this chapter as a medium for recording the techniques that we have developed over a number of years for the analysis of line profiles.

B. Analysis of Eclipse Photographs

The bright halo of white light that is observed to surround the moon at the time of a total eclipse is made up of two parts: sunlight scattered by electrons in the hot outer atmosphere of the sun—the true corona (commonly called the K corona)—and sunlight scattered or reflected by the minute solid particles in interplanetary space, which also produces the zodiacal light. The latter light is said to come from the F corona, *F* designating "Fraunhofer," since its spectrum contains the absorption lines of radiation from the solar photosphere. Before any conclusions concerning the physical state of the corona can be deduced from a white-light eclipse photograph, these two sources must be separated. Since there are no characteristics of the photograph that distinguish one source of light from the other, additional data, obtained either polarimetrically or spectroscopically, must be used in the separation.

The separation by polarization techniques is based on the assumption that the polarization in the observed corona comes entirely from the K corona, and that the degree of such polarization may be computed theoretically. This assumption must be somewhat qualified as a result of the observation by Blackwell and Ingham (1961) that although at great distances from the sun the zodiacal light is highly polarized, the analysis of its spectrum indicates the scattering to be due to particles rather than electrons. The discovery at first cast some doubt on the entire process of separation of the F and K coronas by polarimetry. However, a more thorough analysis of the problem by Ingham (1961) disclosed that the polarized part of the particle scattering is due to reflection of radiation, and that this effect is greatest at large elongations; whereas the light scattered by particles at small elongations is due primarily to diffraction and the component of coronal light so arising is completely unpolarized. Thus the method of separation by polarization is acceptable, but out to a distance of about five solar radii only. At greater distances the F corona may no longer be considered to be unpolarized.

In general, both the plane of polarization of the continuum coronal light and the degree of polarization might be considered to be unknown quantities, although unless synchrotron radiation in very strong magnetic fields is present we would expect polarization to be radial—i.e., the electric vector to be tangential to the solar limb—as will be shown theoretically in Chapter 5. Observations have confirmed this expectation to within their limit of error, but the possibility exists that synchrotron emission may yet be found in very active regions.

If we assume that the polarization is radial, only two photographs through polaroids oriented at right angles to each other are adequate for separation of the F from the K corona. Suppose the two polaroids are oriented with their transmission planes parallel to X and Y axes of a co-ordinate system. Then, at a point in the corona on a radius that makes an angle θ with the X axis, the intensity of the light through the X polaroid is

$$I_x = I_p \cos^2 \theta + \frac{I_u}{2}$$

(1)

and through the Y-polaroid,

$$I_y = I_p \sin^2 \theta + \frac{I_u}{2}.$$

(2)

where I_u is the intensity of the unpolarized component of the radiation, and I_p that of the polarized component. Thus,

$$I_p = \frac{I_x - I_y}{\cos^2 \theta - \sin^2 \theta}$$

(3)

and

$$I_u = I_x + I_y - I_p.$$

(4)

For values of θ near $45°$ the method is indeterminate, but for other positions in the photograph the polarized and unpolarized components of the radiation are separable. Next, given a coronal model, the theoretical value for the polarization P_k of K-coronal radiation at the point in question may be computed, according to the theory of Chapter 5, from the density distribution of electrons in the corona. Then, since

$$P_k = \frac{I_p}{I_p + I_{u_k}},$$

(5)

where I_{u_k} is the unpolarized component of the coronal light and

$$I_u = I_{u_k} + I_F,$$

(6)

we have, from (5),

$$I_{u_k} = \frac{I_p(1 - P_k)}{P_k}$$

(7)

and, from (6),

$$I_F = I_u - \frac{I_p(1 - P_k)}{P_k}$$

(8)

and

$$I_k = I - I_F.$$

(9)

We see, therefore, that a completely logical separation of the F and K corona by polarization techniques requires a knowledge of the density distribution of electrons in the corona—a distribution that can be found only from the intensities of the K corona after the F corona has been subtracted away. Obviously, then, the problem is one of iteration. We can begin with a set of polarizations as a function of height, as for example, those computed by van de Hulst (1953) (see Appendix IV). Using these we compute the first approximations for the F and K corona by Eqs. (8) and (9), then from this first approximation for the observed corona determine an appropriate electron-density model, in accordance with the theory of Chapter 5. Next, from this new model, we compute the expected polarizations as a function of height, obtain a new separation of F and K corona, and repeat until further iterations no longer lead to significant changes in the coronal model. After this tremendous labor is completed, the question remains whether the *form* of the coronal model is correct or not. In other words, if spherical symmetry has been assumed for the electron distribution, the results will remain in doubt because the obvious streamer structure of the corona has been ignored. It is not surprising, in view of the difficulties in the computations and the uncertainties in the results, that the number of eclipse observations in which the polarized and the unpolarized components of the corona can be separated is considerably greater than the number of tables of coronal electron densities.

At least three observations, through polaroids oriented at various angles, are necessary for determining both the degree and plane of polarization at any point. One procedure is to orient the polaroids at 0, 60, and 120° from an arbitrary reference direction. Suppose, then, that the plane of polarization of the coronal radiation makes an angle θ with the reference direction. If the transmission of the polaroid is perfect, the intensities of radiation through the various positions of the polaroid are

$$I_{0°} = I_A = \frac{I_u}{2} + I_p \cos^2 \theta, \tag{10}$$

$$I_{60°} = I_B = \frac{I_u}{2} + I_p \cos^2 (60° - \theta), \tag{11}$$

$$I_{120°} = I_C = \frac{I_u}{2} + I_p \cos^2 (120° - \theta). \tag{12}$$

These equations simplify to

$$I_A = \frac{I_u}{2} + I_p \cos^2 \theta, \tag{13}$$

$$I_B = \frac{I_u}{2} + \frac{I_p}{4} (\cos^2 \theta + 3 \sin^2 \theta + 2\sqrt{3} \sin \theta \cos \theta), \tag{14}$$

$$I_C = \frac{I_u}{2} + \frac{I_p}{4} (\cos^2 \theta + 3 \sin^2 \theta - 2\sqrt{3} \sin \theta \cos \theta), \tag{15}$$

from which

$$I_B - I_C = \frac{\sqrt{3}}{2} I_p \sin 2\theta, \tag{16}$$

$$I_A - I_C = \frac{I_p}{4} (3 \cos 2\theta + \sqrt{3} \sin 2\theta), \tag{17}$$

$$I_A - I_B = \frac{I_p}{4} (3 \cos 2\theta - \sqrt{3} \sin 2\theta), \tag{18}$$

giving, from (17) and (18),

$$2I_A - I_B - I_C = \tfrac{3}{2} I_p \cos 2\theta. \tag{19}$$

From (16) and (19),

$$\theta = \tfrac{1}{2} \operatorname{arc\,cot} \frac{2I_A - I_B - I_C}{\sqrt{3}(I_B - I_C)} \tag{20}$$

and

$$I_p = \tfrac{4}{3}[(I_A + I_B + I_C)^2 - 3(I_A I_B + I_A I_C + I_B I_C)]^{1/2}. \tag{21}$$

From (13) and (16),

$$I_u = 2I_A - I_p \pm [I_p^2 - \tfrac{4}{3}(I_B - I_C)^2]^{1/2}. \tag{22}$$

An alternative procedure is the orientation of the polaroids at angles of 45° relative to each other. This has the advantage of leading to simpler working equations and—if camera facilities are available for four polaroid orientations—of providing one redundant piece of data for checking the others (Saito and Yamashita, 1962).

Let us designate the four polaroid positions as A, B, C, and D, with the polarized component of the radiation oriented at an angle θ to position A. Then

$$I_A = \frac{I_u}{2} + I_p \cos^2 \theta, \tag{23}$$

$$I_B = \frac{I_u}{2} + I_p \cos^2 (45° - \theta), \tag{24}$$

$$I_C = \frac{I_u}{2} + I_p \cos^2 (90° - \theta), \tag{25}$$

$$I_D = \frac{I_u}{2} + I_p \cos^2 (135° - \theta), \tag{26}$$

which simplify to

$$I_A = \frac{I_u}{2} + I_p \cos^2 \theta, \tag{27}$$

$$I_B = \frac{I_u}{2} + \frac{I_p}{2} (1 + \sin 2\theta), \tag{28}$$

$$I_C = \frac{I_u}{2} + I_p \sin^2 \theta, \tag{29}$$

$$I_D = \frac{I_u}{2} + \frac{I_p}{2} (1 - \sin 2\theta), \tag{30}$$

from which we conclude

$$\tan 2\theta = \frac{I_B - I_D}{I_A - I_C} = \frac{2I_B - I_A - I_C}{I_A - I_C}, \tag{31}$$

$$I_p = [(I_A - I_C)^2 + (I_B - I_D)^2]^{1/2}, \tag{32}$$

$$I_A + I_C = I_B + I_D = I_u + I_p. \tag{33}$$

The operational procedure, then, is to photograph the corona simultaneously through three or four identical cameras with the axes of the transmitted light oriented either in 60 or 45° intervals. In the event the cameras cannot be made identical, calibration factors must be introduced into the above equations.

The reduction of a set of such eclipse photographs involves the point-by-point measurement of the photographic density on each photograph, and evaluation of light intensity from density through the calibration procedure for the photographs.

The spectroscopic method of separation of F from K corona (first used by Grotrian, 1934) is based on the assumption that the high thermal velocities of the coronal electrons will completely obliterate the Fraunhofer lines in the radiation that they scatter. This assumption may be verified readily by noting that a line scattered by million-degree electrons would be broadened to about 200 Å.

The principle of the method is very simple. Suppose the total emission appearing on a microphotometer tracing of the coronal spectrum is the sum of the F and K components. We shall assume that deflections in the tracing are proportional to intensities. If h is the depth of a given Fraunhofer line, and F the intensity of the continuum in the spectrum of the F corona, the relative central intensity of the line in the Fraunhofer spectrum is

$$r_0 = \frac{F - h}{F} = 1 - \frac{h}{F}, \tag{34}$$

whereas in the coronal spectrum it is $r = (F + K - h)/(F + K) = 1 - [h/(F + K)]$. Thus

$$\frac{F}{F + K} = \frac{1 - r}{1 - r_0} \tag{35}$$

or

$$\frac{K}{F + K} = \frac{r - r_0}{1 - r_0}. \tag{36}$$

The quantity r_0 is measured from a spectrum of the solar disk, whereas r is determined for the same line in the coronal spectrum.

The method has the advantage that it can be applied repeatedly for many lines in the spectrograms, that it is simple, and that only minor questionable assumptions are involved. A serious difficulty in its use, which has not been fully appreciated, is that most spectroscopes introduce polarization, thereby attenuating one component of the K corona. Waldmeier (1958) has raised the point that instrumental smearing of Fraunhofer lines reduces the continuum levels of both K and F, and that when this effect is taken into account, better agreement with polarization techniques is obtained. The range of application of the spectroscopic method during any eclipse is rather limited. The intensity of the corona decreases so strongly with distance from the sun that beyond one or two solar radii there is not enough light to expose a spectrographic plate during eclipse totality. Furthermore, if the entire duration of the eclipse is needed for obtaining a single spectrogram, information for separation of the F and K components is available over a single narrow strip of corona only.

A procedure sometimes used is to orient the spectrograph slit along a solar radius and determine from the resulting spectrogram the fraction of F corona as a function of distance from the sun. Then, from a calibrated photograph taken during the same eclipse, the intensity of the combined F and K corona may be determined. This, in conjunction with spectroscopic data, gives the F corona as a function of distance along the radius of the spectrograph slit. Finally, the F corona is assumed to have radial symmetry, and its appropriate value is subtracted from the total emission at each radial distance to determine the K corona. The obvious difficulty with this method is the assumption of a symmetrical F corona. Waldmeier (1956) concluded from polarization methods that this assumption is not correct, but that the F corona is most intense near the equator—as one might expect from its identity with zodiacal light.

Finally, we should note that many fine eclipse photographs have been made without calibration, and that many calibrated photographs have no accompanying data for separation of the F and K coronas. As a result a number of expediencies have been used in the analysis of such photographs. Isophotes from some uncalibrated plates have been calibrated with considerable certainty, for example, by comparison with the data from calibrated plates of the same eclipse (von Klüber, 1961). In other cases, larger approximations have been made. Van de Hulst (1950), for example, in order to use an excellent 1900 uncalibrated plate to study polar structures, assumed that the distribution of brightness in the polar regions was the same as that from calibrated plates of several other eclipses.

In cases in which calibrations are present but no provision has been made to separate the F and K corona, the F corona is frequently assumed to have the same intensity as at other eclipses.

C. Analysis of K-Coronameter Observations

The use of a K coronameter is complicated by the presence in the earth's atmosphere of polarization in singly and multiply scattered sunlight, by gradients in the scattered radiation, and by polarization in the coronameter.

Some of these complications are also present in eclipse polarimetry, but to a considerably diminished extent. For example, the sky near the eclipsed sun receives some illumination from the ground and the atmosphere outside the path of totality, which must be taken into account in precise eclipse photometry. The effects of scattering and instrumental polarization are of secondary importance during an eclipse, however, but are of major concern with the coronameter.

We may expect the singly scattered illumination from the sky to be polarized symmetrically to the solar disk, and the secondary scattered light to have a polarized component in the plane of the zenith that increases with the zenith angle. Thus, as the coronameter encircles the sun, measuring the difference, β, between the radially and tangentially polarized light (and on another recorder, B, the total intensity), the β record will contain a constant component due to the polarization of the primary halo, a second harmonic arising from the polarization in the secondary scattering, and a first and a third harmonic from the gradient in secondary scattering. When the effects of atmospheric polarization and of instrument polarization are removed, the deflections in the β record come entirely from the corona. The B deflections are due almost entirely to the sky and are used only in computing corrections for the β record.

The contribution of the sky to the High Altitude Observatory coronameter is evaluated by making scans at three solar radii—a distance from the center of the sun at which the contribution of the K corona is considered negligible compared to that of the sky. Each β-record scan is then subjected to Fourier analysis by an electronic computer to determine the contributions of the various atmospheric scattering mechanisms. The amplitudes found in the analysis are then used in determining correction terms by assuming that the contribution of the primary scattering halo to β is proportional to the distance of a scan from the center of the sun, that gradients are uniform throughout the scan, and that both primary and secondary scattering are proportional to the secants of the zenith angle. In practice the effect of gradients across the scan is nearly negligible compared to the polarization in the primary and secondary scattering. The contribution to β of secondary scattering has also been found to be surprisingly independent of the albedo of the earth. Apparently, although snow on the ground increases greatly the amount of secondary scattered light, its effect on β is quite small because of the uniformity of the white surface. There is some indication that a body of water near the coronameter may prove to be a more variable source of secondary sky polarization than the land, perhaps because of its dielectric reflecting surface.

Instrumental polarization arises both from the polarizing characteristics of the transmitting optics and from polarizing reflections of the scattered light within the instrument. Such polarization may be detected by admitting light to the occulting-disk aperture from the center of the solar disk, then attenuating it by appropriate filters before it reaches the detector. A part of the instrument polarization is conveniently canceled out by introduction of a fixed tilted glass plate into the optical path, while a major part of the remainder can be eliminated by the calibration procedure.

In the calibration, a controlled degree of polarization is introduced into light from the center of the solar disk by adjustment of the tilt of a second glass plate. The quantity of light is controlled by choice of aperture at the occulting disk and by attenuating filters. The product of degree of polarization and quantity of light gives the difference between the two orthogonally polarized beams. From the tabulation of this product vs deflections of the β recorder, one may in principle determine a factor for converting β-record scans of the corona into units of brightness of the solar disk.

In practice, β-record deflections must be measured from a background deflection due to uncompensated instrumental polarization. The background deflection, in turn, is a function of the intensity of the light in the coronameter. Consequently, one of the objectives of the calibration procedure is to determine the parameters of this function. These parameters, as well as the conversion factor mentioned above, are all determined by least-squares analysis of the data from a single calibration routine.

When the corona is scanned, the incident-light intensity from the B record is used to compute the background deflection of the β record; the net β-record deflection is converted to units of solar-disk brightness, is then corrected for sky polarization as discussed above, and finally is corrected for atmospheric attenuation to give the difference between the radially and tengentially polarized components of coronal radiation.

D. Emission-Line Intensity Measurements

In a statement dated September, 1947, d'Azambuja introduced the first inclusion of coronal-line–brightness measurements into the *Quarterly Bulletin of Solar Activity* of the International Astronomical Union. He pointed out that the brightness was being measured regularly at 5° intervals around the limb at Arosa, Climax, Pic du Midi, and Wendelstein; Pic du Midi was making the measurements photometrically in equivalent ångstroms, whereas Arosa, Climax, and Wendelstein were estimating the brightness in arbitrary scales running from 0 to 40 or 0 to 50. Finally, for the only day in the January–March quarter of 1947 for which all four stations had observations, d'Azambuja drew a polar diagram showing the measurements of the four stations superimposed. It is interesting that the agreement among the stations was as good as that found by Hansen (1958) after ten years of effort on the part of the coronagraph stations to improve their photometry. This comparison does not give a really accurate picture of the situation, however. The agreement found by d'Azambuja was fortuituously good. Subsequently, Behr (1951), Bell and Glazer (1953), Bruzek (1955), and Hansen found very poor correlation between the measurements at the various stations. Much of the correspondence was so bad that coronagraphers were inclined to ask one another if they really were looking at the same sun. In spite of their inconsistencies, the crudeness of their scales, and the difficulties in obtaining unambiguous physical meaning from them, the line-brightness data describe the only day-by-day observations of the corona extending over many years. Consequently, we examine in some detail the manner in which they have been obtained, in an attempt to evaluate their significance.

Techniques for line-brightness measurements vary widely from station to station, falling into three general classes: (1) direct visual observation on the coronal spectrum; (2) measurements on coronal spectrograms; and (3) direct photoelectric measurements. In each of these classes we find various degrees of sophistication and precision.

The earliest attempts to express coronal intensities were made by visual observers who, after looking at the spectrum on various days for some time, set up in their memory an arbitrary scale for expressing the intensity of the line they wished to measure. The disadvantages of such a procedure in addition to the vicissitudes of memory are quite evident. The scales had no references for keeping their meanings constant with time or relating them to other similarly devised scales. Also they had no basis for linearity. The most serious handicap in the use of such scales, however, was the great variability of the apparent brightness of a coronal line with varying sky brightness. Thus early coronal-line–brightness measurements gave considerably more information about the condition of the sky than about the corona.

These difficulties were corrected to a large extent at Arosa and Norikura by the introduction of a comparison line into the spectrum. For green-line measurements light from a thallium lamp was introduced into the spectrograph along with coronal light, so that the two spectra were superimposed. Then the amount of light from the lamp was adjusted by an optical wedge to bring the thallium line λ 5350 to the same brightness as the coronal line λ 5303. Arosa has used a similar technique with a neon lamp for measuring the λ 6374 line. In each case the lamp has been calibrated from time to time against a suitably attenuated image of the solar disk. A similar procedure, used at Pic du Midi, has been to divert some of the photospheric light from in front of the occulting disk, use it to illuminate a piece of chalk that is imaged on the spectrograph slit near the coronal image, and then view the resulting spectrum with an eyepiece so designed that 1 Å of the chalk image appears superimposed on the coronal spectrum near the line to be measured. Thus, through a knowledge of the relative efficiencies of the coronal and auxiliary optical systems and the amount of attenuation required to make the portion of the photospheric spectrum match the coronal line, the brightness of the line is determined. This procedure has an advantage over the thallium lamp in that changes in the transparency of the sky are automatically compensated for. However, the determination of the efficiency of the auxiliary optics used for the photospheric light has proved to be a very difficult problem.

With either of the two methods described above it is possible to express the brightness of a coronal line in equivalent angstroms. If a line brightness is unit equivalent angstroms, the same amount of energy enters the spectrograph in radiation in that line as in a wavelength interval 1 Å broad from the center of the solar disk centered at the wavelength of maximum emission in the line. Coronal-line brightness generally falls in the range from 0 to 200×10^{-6} equivalent angstroms. The above definition needs a slight qualification, since it assumes that the disk emission contains no Fraunhofer lines within the specified 1-Å band. In the case of the many coronal lines for which this assumption is not true we must rephrase the statement: A line of unit equivalent angstroms is of such brightness that the same amount of energy enters the spectrograph from that line as from a wavelength interval 1 Å broad from an idealized source having the same continuum brightness as the center of the solar disk, but no Fraunhofer lines. In actual practice, if a Fraunhofer line lies within 0.5 Å of the center of the emission line, the emission line can be compared with a nearby 1-Å interval of the disk spectrum in which no absorption lines are present.

Photographic, like visual, coronal line photometry was carried out by rather crude techniques during the first decade of coronal patrol. At Climax, the only station to photograph the coronal spectrum daily, the intensity of the line was measured at a given point by successively placing several different comparison lines on the spectrogram beside the coronal line and determining which comparison line matched the coronal line in blackness. The comparison lines were identified from one another by an arbitrary scale from 1 to 50. This photographic method had several advantages over the visual-memory method. The comparison lines could be preserved from year to year. Also some compensation for varying sky brightness was effected by viewing the comparison line against the background of the sky spectrum when comparing it with the coronal line. The compensation was only partial, however, since the method involved equating the photographic density of the comparison line plus the density of sky spectrogram to the density resulting from the combination of coronal emission and scattered skylight. In such an equality the contribution of the sky can cancel out only in the unusual circumstance that the photographic density is a linear function of the intensity of light exposing the photographic plate. In general this condition is not met, and for very bright skies errors of a factor of 2 or 3 are introduced into the method of measurement. The method also requires very rigorous photographic controls. These were achieved at Climax by impressing on each plate a series of sensitometric spots from a carefully controlled source. If the spot densities fell within a specified range, the plate was considered to be of standard photographic quality. If the spot densities fell outside that range, it was necessary to regard the line intensity determinations of low weight, although the plate might contain a perfectly adequate, calibrated photographic record of coronal emission. Finally, we note that the comparison-line method of measuring spectrograms, like the visual determination of intensity on a memory scale, did not express coronal intensities in absolute units.

Before describing improved methods of measurement of coronal intensities from photographic plates, we should note one difficulty in all of the photometric methods mentioned above which depend on the visual comparison of one line with another. For a precise visual comparison, the coronal line and the comparison line must have similar profiles. Since the coronal lines are very broad, the comparison with a line from a thallium lamp is feasible only if the spectrograph has such low dispersion that almost the entire profile of the line results from the width of the slit. The arrangement used at Pic du Midi will tolerate larger dispersions, since the 1-Å aperture band of photospheric spectrum is made to be about the same width as a coronal line. However, the former has a rectangular and the latter a Gaussian profile. It is possible to produce a photographic comparison line whose profile resembles that of a coronal line, but the techniques are difficult. In general, also, the difficulties increase with increased dispersion.

Greatly improved photographic photometry is now carried out on Climax and Sacramento Peak spectrograms by photoelectric analysis of the spectrograms, and similar techniques are used at Kislovosk. For several years Climax and Sacramento Peak spectrograms have been traced by microphotometer, tracings being made across the line at $2\frac{1}{2}°$ intervals around the solar limb. The intensity at the center of the line is then determined by a comparison of the deflection on the tracing with deflections for various steps in a comparison spectrogram.

The comparison spectrogram, in turn, is that of a suitably attenuated image of the center of the solar disk. At Climax, attenuation of the solar image is achieved by use of a very dense piece of "neutral" glass filter, which has a transmission of about 14×10^{-6} at 5303 and 33×10^{-6} at 6374 Å. A gradation in exposure on the spectrogram is produced by replacing the spectrograph slit by a triangular slit. At Sacramento Peak the attenuator is an opalized glass used in conjunction with a special rectangular slit on which a silvered step wedge is mounted. A difficulty in the use of the triangular slit is that in the spectrum from its wide end the Fraunhofer lines are spread out so that their wings overlap, thus depressing the entire continuum. Absorption lines are not sufficiently abundant in the vicinity of λ 6374 to cause any difficulty, and in the vicinity of λ 5303 the maximum effect of about 10% can be eliminated by computation. Near the violet end of the spectrum, however, they introduce a serious problem. The aluminized step wedge used at Sacramento Peak is free from this difficulty, but has the disadvantage that the metal is subject to deterioration from pin pricks and discoloration, whereas the open triangular slit is highly stable.

Ideally, when microphotometer tracings are made, the brightness of the emission line should be determined by converting deflection to intensity at all points in the line profile and integrating under the profile. Thus the brightness is equivalent ångstroms is equal to the height in intensity units of a rectangular profile 1 Å in width having the same area as the area under the intensity profile. However, since coronal lines generally differ very little from Gaussian, it is adequate to multiply the maximum intensity by the width of the line at half maximum, and the product by the factor 1.06, common to all Gaussian profiles. In actual practice, the screw on the automatic carriage used in measuring Climax and Sacramento Peak spectrograms does not possess sufficient accuracy to distinguish between the widths of most profiles. Hence, except for profiles that are obviously very broad or very narrow, the practice is to measure only the maximum intensity and use a standard mean half width.

The daily measurement of line brightness at every $2\frac{1}{2}°$ position by means of a microphotometer is tedious even when an automatic carriage is available. For rapid reporting of data, a device has been set up at Climax similar to one used at Kislovosk, by means of which intensities are obtained from point photometry at the line centers. The method is applicable only if the spectrograms are of fairly high dispersion. An image of the spectrogram, enlarged by about a factor of 20/1, is projected on a protractor. The detector element of an Ansco densitometer, with an aperture sufficiently narrow that the illumination over it will be nearly uniform, is held at the image of the line center and the densitometer deflection recorded. A similar reading is made in the image of the adjacent background continuum. The line intensities are obtained from these two readings by comparison with the calibrating spectrogram. Intensities thus measured agree quite well with those obtained by microphotometer tracings.

There are advantages in the use of photoelectric techniques directly on the solar spectrum rather than on photographic images of the spectrum. A number of errors can creep into photographic photometry. The photographic characteristics of the plate may vary from one portion of the plate to another, or the microphotometer response may change somewhat between the tracing of the line and the tracing of the calibrating spectrogram. Furthermore, there is an inevitable degradation of information because of the finite size of film grains. These difficulties are avoided if a photometer is used to scan the line in the spectroscope. Making such scans at 5° intervals, however, is very time consuming, particularly if the coronagraph observations must be made between passing clouds. The photographic process has the advantage that an entire spectrum can be recorded in a minute or less, and analyzed at leisure. An ultimate device would have the advantage of both photographic and direct photoelectric photometry by making direct photoelectric measurements simultaneously on all parts of the entire line spectrum. Such a device has been under consideration at Sacramento Peak Observatory. In its operation, a portion of the spectrum would fall on an image tube with storage capacities. Associated electronic gear would measure the brightness in all parts of the raster. One technique that has been considered for displaying the results is by an isophotal map of the image on the tube.

Although the scatter diagrams plotted by Hansen (1958) for comparison of measurements by one station with those of another show considerable scatter, significant improvements have been made over earlier observations. Present photometric techniques eliminate the seasonal effect of sky-brightness variation. They also eliminate the variations of one station with regard to another from year to year, as found by Bell and Glazer in 1953. Earlier studies, as those by Behr (1951), did not bring these difficulties out, since they compared stations with similar climatic conditions over short periods of time.

One of the present causes of variation in measurements from station to station is the absence of uniformity in the choice of observing distance from the limb. The observers at Pic du Midi, in using a spectrograph slit oriented radially to the sun, integrate the observed intensity from the edge of the occulting disk (about 30″ from the sun's limb) outward. Thus the observed brightness depends on both the intensity at 30″ and the emission gradient. Arosa and Sacramento Peak use tangential slits at 40″ from the limb. The distance of the Climax curved tangential slit from the limb is about 30″. There is also a tendency for visually measured intensities at Arosa to fall below those determined by photographic photometry at the higher end of the intensity scale. This tendency is readily explained, since although the visual scale is immediately calibrated by the thallium lamp, as described above, the maximum-intensity level on the scale designates all lines above a certain brightness and may include lines that differ from one another by a factor of 2.

Some discrepancies are apparently the result of rapid local changes in the corona with time. Occasionally, for example, two sets of observations by different stations will agree quite well for all but one point on the limb. At that point a minor peak in brightness may be reported by one station, a major peak a few hours later by the other. Rösch, during the years 1959 and 1960, arranged for simultaneous observations by different stations. Although the number of such observations were too few to lead to any strong conclusions, it appeared that intensities were significantly less discrepant when measured simultaneously.

Rapid variations in seeing conditions at a station are more likely to occur than rapid variations in the coronal brightness, however, and these can produce serious changes in the apparent intensity of the coronal lines. In recent experiments at Climax we have kept the spectrograph slit on the same portion of the corona for the photographing of as many as 50 spectrograms in rapid succession. During one such sequence the seeing conditions evidently deteriorated considerably, as indicated by a loss of resolution of bright features in the spectral lines, and at this time the measured brightness of a small feature changed by about 50%.

A final observational problem is introduced by the polarization, at times, of certain coronal lines. Coronagraph spectrographs are frequently rather strongly polarizing devices, with mirrors, image-rotators, and gratings in their optical systems. Thus the lines may be attenuated by an unknown amount by the polarization in the optics. Some evidence of this effect is frequently apparent in different intensities of the same feature for different positions of the image rotator. The phenomenon of coronal-line polarization has been recognized only during the past few years, but because of it, the validity of more than 20 years of coronal data has been questioned. However, the fact that observations of the unpolarized λ 6374 line show as much or more scatter from station to station than the λ 5303 line, which may be 40% polarized, is evidence that the problem is no more important than other difficulties. Furthermore, most of the recorded observations are made so close to the limb that line polarization is well below the theoretical value it can reach at greater distances from the limb.

A very basic cause for discrepancies still existing is the inadequacy of the practice of reporting line brightness at 5° intervals around the limb. The structure of the emission corona is much more detailed than can be described by such reporting, the features as seen by present observing techniques being more nearly 1° than 5° in dimensions, with the line brightness frequently dropping to one-half its peak value between such features. As a consequence, one would expect large differences among stations, some of which report the maximum within each 5° interval, others, the intensity precisely at the 5° mark, and others, the average over each 5° interval. Even if all followed the practice of giving the maximum intensity occurring within the 5° interval, large differences would arise because of variation in the quality of seeing. Thus it appears that the present photometric processes are about as good as is justified by existing methods of day-by-day reporting.

E. Line-Profile Analysis

There are three quantities of interest to be found from the study of coronal line profiles: the half-width or width at half-maximum, the departure of the actual profile from Gaussian, and the position of the line maximum. The first gives a measure of thermal and statistically random motion, the second gives evidence of the presence of motions that are not statistically random, and the third indicates the net nonrandom motion directed toward or away from the observer. Most coronal-line profiles are distorted by irregularities due to film grain or phototube noise, and by Fraunhofer lines in the sky background spectrum (Fig. 4.1). The fundamental difficulties in coronagraphy leading to these distortions are: (1) The corona is too faint for high signal–noise analysis in the time available. One cannot use fine-grained films or photoelectric scanning devices with

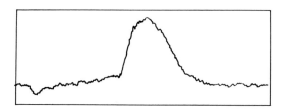

Fig. 4.1. A typical microphotometer tracing of the λ 5303 line, from a spectrogram
made by the 5-in. Climax coronagraph. The dispersion on the spectrogram is approximately 2 Å/mm. The assymmetry introduced by the Fraunhofer λ 5302 line is one of
the major annoyances in the study of the coronal green line. Courtesy, High Altitude
Observatory.

long time-constants; and   (2) Except at a time of total eclipse, the corona
must be viewed against the background of scattered light containing all of
the Fraunhofer lines. Because of these two difficulties it is generally impossible to determine the half-width with a precision of better than about
5% or to detect small departures of the shape from Gaussian. Furthermore,
since the coronal lines are quite broad, a precise determination of the
wavelength position of their maxima is difficult.

There are various techniques for decreasing the distorting effects of film
grain and background absorption lines. One of these is simply to smooth,
by eye, through the film grain and across the absorption lines. Another is
to fill in the absorption lines by point-by-point addition of the inverted
absorption-line profile to the observed profile, then to smooth by eye
through the resulting points and film grains. This latter process calls for a
detailed knowledge of the absorption-line profile as observed by the coronagraph and microphotometer—a piece of auxiliary information that is not
easily obtained, since the absorption line is always distorted by the presence of the emission line. A fairly good approximation may be found from
tracings at points where the emission is weak. Also, the inverted absorption-
line profile must be applied at precisely the correct wavelength position.
The positions of adjoining absorption lines provides a reference for locating
the point of application, but small errors in their location or small errors
in the microphotometer screw can lead to a serious distortion of the coronal-
line profile.

There is a technique for elimination of the effect of the λ 5302.3 absorption line on the half width of λ 5303 that is useful when profiles covering a
range of intensities, as in a graded-height sequence of observations, are
available. One plots the actual measured half width as a function of the

ratio *background intensity/line central intensity*. Such a plot will show strong fluctuations arising from observational effects, actual fluctuations in the line width, and the effect of Doppler displacements of the emission relative to the absorption line. However, if enough data are available, a mean curve may be drawn through the points that can be extrapolated to zero background/line ratio, giving the mean half width at zero background. The ratio of the mean half-width at zero background to the various mean values at nonzero background is now used as a factor for correcting all of the profiles used in the study. This is the most effective technique we have found for determining the variation of half width of a coronal line with height.

One can probably make about as good an evaluation of the characteristics of an individual line profile by smoothing through film-grain noise and small absorption lines by eye as by any more elaborate technique. The danger of introducing small systematic effects through personal bias is high, however, and if line widths are to be used in a statistical analysis, it is desirable to determine them individually by a statistical procedure. Billings and Lehman (1962) have outlined a least-square method for computation of the Gaussian parameters that give best fit to an observed line profile. By their method, if the intensity at line maximum can be taken as known, both the position of the line maximum and the width of the line can be computed by least-square methods. Or, if the position of the line maximum can be taken as known, its magnitude and the line width can be computed.

More specifically, they write the Gaussian equation

$$I = A \exp\left[-(\lambda - \lambda_0)^2/\sigma^2\right]$$

in the form

$$(\ln A - \ln I)^{1/2} = \frac{\lambda}{\sigma} - \frac{\lambda_0}{\sigma}, \qquad (37)$$

for the case where the maximum intensity A is considered known, or in the form

$$\ln I = \ln A - \frac{(\lambda - \lambda_0)^2}{\sigma^2}, \qquad (38)$$

for the case where the line position is considered known. In the former case the observed quantities

$$(\ln A - \ln I)^{1/2}$$

are fitted with a straight-line function by a least-square computation. A is evaluated by smoothing through the peak of the profile, whereas I corresponds to the actual unsmoothed microphotometer deflections. In the latter case the best straight-line fit is found for the observed $(\ln I)$ as a function of $(\lambda - \lambda_0)^2$. In either case only the portions of the profiles that are completely free from absorption lines are used.

In fitting Eq. (37) to a profile, each point has the weight

$$w = I^2(\ln A - \ln I), \tag{39}$$

whereas for Eq. (38) the weight is simply

$$w = I^2. \tag{40}$$

Profiles from an optically thin corona can depart from Gaussian only as a result of macroscopic motion within the coronal gas or the presence of more than one temperature along the line of sight. Motions that destroy the symmetry of the profiles are easy to detect and interpret. Motions that leave the profiles symmetric are much more difficult to deal with. For example, macroscopic motions that have a statistical distribution are completely indistinguishable from thermal motions. Their effect is to broaden the profiles but leave them strictly Gaussian. Other forms of motion that produce neither displacements nor asymmetry in the profile are: (1) circulatory motion, in which each observation includes whole numbers of circulation systems; (2) oscillatory motion, in which whole numbers of oscillations are observed; (3) symmetric inflow or outflow of matter from each feature in the corona; and (4) inflow or outflow of matter in the entire corona. Yallop has investigated (4) for the case of a solar wind. He finds a characteristic type of distortion that increases with height above the limb and also broadens the profiles strongly with height. Since observed line profiles generally do not broaden with height, we conclude that the solar-wind velocity in the inner corona is not sufficiently great to make mechanism (4) of overwhelming importance. We shall discuss its effects quantitatively in Chapter 6.

The motion types (1), (2), and (3) all distort a thermal profile in very nearly the same manner. This distortion shows up most clearly if the profile is plotted in logarithmic form, as in Eq. (37) (Billings, 1964). For maximum distorting velocities of as much as three-tenths the thermal velocity of the emitting ions the shape of the profile is not detectably different from Gaussian, even though it is broadened significantly. For greater velocities the plot of $(\ln A - \ln I)^{1/2}$ vs λ becomes concave upward, with the curvature increasing strongly with increasing velocity. However, if there are a large number of oscillating, expanding, contracting, or circulating elements oriented at random to the line of sight, or possessing a random distribution of amplitudes, the observed profile again becomes indistinguishable from Gaussian. Consequently, a single bright feature is more likely to have a motion-distorted profile than is the summation of many features along the line of sight.

Viewing several features along a line of sight, on the other hand, is likely to superpose several profiles of different thermal half-widths. The super-position leads to a distortion in the resulting profile such that the loga-rithmic plots are concave downward—in a configuration almost precisely opposite that from motion distortion (Fig. 4.2). Consequently, we may use amplitude of the distorting motion as a "distortion parameter" and assign negative parameters to profiles that are distorted by superposition of profiles of various widths. We see that it is possible to have a purely

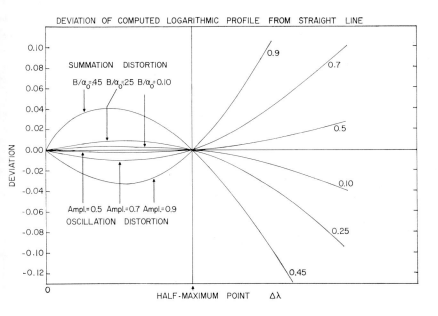

Fig. 4.2. The distortion of line profiles from Gaussian produced by harmonic oscillation of the source, compared to the distortion produced by a range of temperatures alone the line of sight. The quantity plotted is the departure of $(\ln A - \ln I)$ from a straight line, where A is the maximum intensity in a profile and I is the intensity at wavelength λ. Curves concave upward correspond to profiles that are broader in the shoulders, those concave downward indicate profiles are elevated in the wings. Courtesy, *Astrophysical Journal.*

Gaussian profile in which both motion distortion and temperature-range distortion are present, but in amounts to exactly cancel one another. Furthermore, if one or the other type of distortion is observed, it is impossible to specify the degree of the distorting influence, since an unknown portion of the distortion of one type may be canceled by distortion of the opposite type.

Some conclusions may be drawn from the shape of line profiles, however. For example, ionization theory places a fairly definite upper limit on the breadth of the temperature distribution that is likely to exist among any one ionic species along a line of sight (see Chapter 5). Broader distributions are possible only in the unlikely case that the distribution of coronal matter with temperature minimizes at the temperature at which the emitting ion should be the most abundant. This limit, in turn, provides an upper limit to the amount of distortion from coherent macroscopic motion that is being canceled by temperature-range distortion. No definite conclusion is possible about the amount of randomly oriented macroscopic motion that may be broadening the line profiles. Further progress becomes possible only through the comparison of shapes of profiles from single bright emission features with those from lines of sight averaging many features.

The limitations of present-day coronal spectrophotometry permit line-shape analysis only on bright lines observed against a sky background of low brightness. Furthermore, Fraunhofer lines in the scattered-light background can render a profile useless for shape analysis. In the case of the green coronal line, for instance, only the long-wavelength wing can be used, and this must be corrected for several minute Fraunhofer lines that distort it. When only one wing is thus used, it is difficult to distinguish between symmetric and asymmetric distortion. The line λ 6374 is excellent in the rare cases that it is of sufficient intensity to give adequate signal/ noise. It is doubtful if either of the yellow lines will ever be suitable for line-shape analysis unless a strongly emitting feature is photographed with a slit spectrograph during a total eclipse, or an externally occulted coronagraph of sufficient aperture for high resolution becomes available for use on artificial earth satellites. Finally, a fairly fine-grained film must be used for the observations. In the Climax 5-in. coronagraph the coarsest admissible film is Plus-X. With it an exposure of at least 30 sec is required for λ 5303. Consequently, if higher frequency motions are present in the corona we can hope to detect them only through the statistical residues in gross profile displacements, or through the type of profile distortions outlined above.

We have found that a very powerful procedure for determining the nature and magnitude of the distortion in an observed profile is to compute the variance of the profile from theoretical profiles with different distortion parameters. When the variance is plotted against distortion parameters it usually shows a well-defined minimum at the distortion parameter that best describes the profile. The computation is quite tedious, since the variance of an observed profile from a theoretical profile is the sum of the weighted variances of 50 or more observed points from calculated points, the weights being given by Eq. (39). Furthermore, care must be taken to match the two profiles being compared in half width, amplitude, and wavelength position before their shapes can be adequately compared. The entire process is practical only with an electronic computer.

REFERENCES

Behr, A. (1951). The intensity variation of the green coronal line 1943-1950. *Z. Ap.* **28,** 296.

Bell, B., and Glazer, H. (1953). Comparison of annual intensities of coronal emission lines. *Harv. Solar Sci. Rept.* No. 12.

Billings, D. E. (1964). The shape of coronal line profiles. *Ap. J.* **139,** 710.

Billings, D. E., and Lehman, R. C. (1962). Line-width temperatures of distinct coronal features. *Ap. J.* **136,** 258.

Blackwell, D. E., and Ingham, M. F. (1961). Observations of zodiacal light from a very high altitude station. II *M. N.* **122,** 129.

Bruzek, A. (1955) The coronal emission regions and their relation to sunspots and faculae. *Z. Ap.* **35,** 213.

d'Azambuja, L. (1947). New data on solar activity. *I. A. U. Quart. Bull. Solar Activity* No. 77.

Grotrian, W. (1934). Concerning the Fraunhofer Spectrum of the solar corona. *Z. Ap.* **8,** 124.

Hansen, R. T. (1958). Studies of coronal line intensities, a morandum. IGY World Data Center, Boulder, Colorado.

Ingham, M. F. (1961). Observations of zodiacal light from a very high altitude station, IV, *M. N.* **122,** 157.

Saito, K., and Yamashita, Y. (1962). Polarigraphic observations of the solar corona at the total eclipse on October 12, 1958 in the Southern Pacific. *Ann. Toyko Astr. Obs.* **7,** 163.

van de Hulst, H. C. (1950). Polar rays of the corona. *B. A. N.* **11,** 150.

van de Hulst, H. C. (1953). The chromosphere and the corona, *in* "The sun" (G. P. Kuiper, ed.), p. 207. Univ. of Chicago Press, Chicago, Illinois.

von Klüber, H. (1961). Inner solar corona. *M. N. R. A. S.* **123,** 61.

Waldmeier, M. (1956). Results of the Zurich eclipse expedition 1954. *Z. Ap.* **40,** 120.

Waldmeier, M. (1958). The components of the continuum coronal spectrum. *Z. Ap.* **46,** 17.

CHAPTER 5

THE NATURE OF THE CORONAL GAS

A. Kinetic Properties of the Gas

Let us imagine that we could examine one cubic millimeter of corona
gas in great detail. If the examination were carried out close to the sun
we would find within this volume several hundred thousand protons, about
1.2 times that many electrons, something less than 100,000 α particles
and a few hundred highly stripped ions of other elements. Not only would
our method of observation need to be impossibly sharp, but also remarkably
quick, for electrons would cross the cubic millimeter in about one-tenth of
a nanosecond. Protons would move about one-fortieth as fast, and each
heavy ion would spend about a microsecond in the volume. About one
hundred times each second an electron would pass close enough to another
particle to be deflected by as much as 90°, whereas among the slower-
moving protons such deflections would occur only once or twice a second.
An overwhelming majority of the particles would pass through the space
without experiencing any deflection that could be called a collision.

Were the sample chosen in a portion of the corona of weak to moderate
magnetic field, uniform over a mean free path of a particle, the various
particles would pass through the cubic-millimeter volume in nearly straight-
line trajectories. The distribution in speeds of each species of particle would
be nearly Maxwellian, and the distribution in directions, very nearly
isotropic.

The last two statements are not obvious. If we were to follow any
electron, proton, or ion for some distance beyond our sample, we would
see it executing a helical motion about magnetic lines of force, the radii of
the helices being a few centimeters for the electrons and a few meters for
the protons and α particles. We might expect that the confinement of the

116

ions to such helical paths would destroy their random velocity. In order to see that this is not the case, let us again fix our attention upon the cubic-millimeter volume of the corona, which is small compared to the radii of gyration of the various particles. Within this volume the various particles will obviously have a random distribution of velocities along the direction of the magnetic field, since a nearly uniform field does not interact on the longitudinal component of their velocities. Furthermore, they will have a random distribution of speeds normal to the field, since, again, the field does not act to change the speed. Finally, even in the plane normal to the magnetic field, the directions of motion will be isotropic, since the axes of the various helices that the particles describe will have a circularly symmetrical distribution about the element of volume (provided the magnetic field does not vary significantly within one radius of gyration). Thus the distribution of velocities within the element of volume will be appropriate to the temperature only, and will be completely unaffected by the presence of the magnetic field. Two important consequences of this generalization are that the collisional ionization and excitation processes will depend only on the temperature and density in the gas, and that the thermal Doppler broadening of emission lines will also be independent of the magnetic field. The interaction of the magnetic field and completely ionized gas, or plasma, is manifest primarily on a macroscopic rather than on a microscopic scale. We shall discuss the effect in detail in Chapter 7.

Although sufficiently close encounters between coronal particles to produce strong deflections are rare, each ion* is continually under the influence of the Coulomb attraction or repulsion of many neighboring ions. We need to consider the net effect of these electrostatic interactions in more detail in order to give meaning to such concepts as the mean free path of coronal particles. As in all plasmas, the electric field of one ion is modified by the presence of surrounding ions according to a well-known function—the Debye potential. We give below an elementary derivation for this function based on approximations that are well satisfied for the corona.

Suppose we consider, in a hydrogen plasma, a positive ion of charge e located at $r = 0$. Then if $U(r)$ is the electric potential at radius vector r, the density of positive charge, being governed by a Boltzmann distribution, is

$$\rho_+ = \bar{n}_e e \exp - \frac{Ue}{kT} \tag{1}$$

---

* Throughout the text we shall use the unmodified term *ion* to designate any charged particle of atomic dimensions—i.e., electron, proton, or heavy ion.

and that of negative charge

$$\rho_- = \bar{n}_e e \exp \frac{Ue}{kT}. \tag{2}$$

Thus, by Poisson's equation,

$$\nabla^2 U = 4\pi \bar{n}_e e \left[\exp\left(\frac{Ue}{kT}\right) - \exp\left(-\frac{Ue}{kT}\right) \right]. \tag{3}$$

Now if $Ue/kT \ll 1$ we can represent each exponential by the first two terms in a Maclaurin expansion. In the case of the corona this condition is fulfilled over a wide range of values of r. For example, if $T \sim 1{,}000{,}000°$K, $Ue/kT \leq 2 \times 10^{-9}/r$, which is much less than unity for all values of r greater than atomic dimensions.

Equation (3) has a solution in the form $U = (A/r) \exp[-(r/D)]$. Substitution in (3) gives

$$D = \left(\frac{kT}{8\pi \bar{n}_e e^2}\right)^{1/2},$$

and, since $U \to e/r$ as $r \to 0$, $A = e$. Hence the expression for the Debye potential is

$$U = \frac{e}{r} \exp\left(-\frac{r}{D}\right). \tag{4}$$

In the corona the Debye length D is typically a few millimeters. At distances from an ion greater than the Debye length the electric field is significantly less than the inverse-square electric field, because of the shielding effect of the surrounding ions, which tend to be predominantly of the opposite sign. Thus D represents the maximum distance from an ion at which the electric field of the ion is significant. The Debye length is intermediate between the mean distance between particles, which is of the order of 10^{-3} cm, and the mean free path of several kilometers.

If we consider the interaction of an ion with all of the ions in its vicinity to terminate at one Debye length, the ion interacts simultaneously with about one million other ions, positive and negative. We might expect that the net effect of interacting with such a large number of ions would be zero, since the amount of positive and negative charge is always very nearly balanced. In actuality, however, an ion, in executing its thermal motion, comes particularly close to certain other ions in the field, with the effect that it undergoes a sequence of smaller and larger deflections from its straight-line path. The successive deflections tend to cancel, but because of statistical fluctuations the ion under consideration will generally experience a residual deflection. The problem is thus essentially that of a random walk.

The deflection per encounter in a Coulomb field, as measured in a center of mass system, is given by

$$X = \pi - 2 \tan^{-1} \frac{Mpu^2}{ZZ_1e^2}, \tag{5}$$

where u is the velocity of one ion relative to the other, Ze and Z_1e are the charges on the two ions, and p, the "impact parameter," is the distance between the straight lines that define the paths of the two ions before encounter. It is convenient to express deflections in terms of the ratio of p to p_0, the impact parameter that would have resulted in a $90°$ deflection of the ion. Thus it can be shown that

$$X = 2 \tan^{-1} \frac{p_0}{p}, \tag{6}$$

which for large values of p gives

$$X = \frac{2p_0}{p}. \tag{7}$$

We now approximate the actual situation in which all ions are in motion with one in which an electron is moving with speed u through a field of fixed protons. In this case, $p_0 = e^2/m_e u^2$. The number of encounters per second of impact parameter lying between p and $p + dp$ will be $2\pi pnu\, dp$. As a second approximation we take the deflection for each such encounter to be $2p_0/p$ radians, according to Eq. (7), but in a random direction. Thus, if we observe the ion normal to its initial path, we will see it wander from that path in steps of magnitude $2p_0/p$ in a two-dimensional random walk. The deflection per second in either coordinate of the plane of the walk resulting from encounters of impact parameter between p and $p + dp$ is equal to $1/\sqrt{2}$ times the product of the deflection per encounter and the square root of the number of encounters:

$$\frac{1}{\sqrt{2}} \cdot \frac{2p_0}{p} (2\pi pnu\, dp)^{1/2}.$$

Hence the mean value, per unit time, of the square of the deflection is

$$\langle X^2 \rangle_{x,dp} = 4\pi p_0^2 nu \frac{dp}{p}, \tag{8}$$

and for all impact parameters lying between p_1 and p_2,

$$\langle X^2 \rangle_x = 4\pi p_0^2 nu \ln \frac{p_2}{p_1}. \tag{9}$$

The resultant mean deviation per second is

$$\langle X^2 \rangle = \langle X^2 \rangle_x + \langle X^2 \rangle_y = 2\langle X^2 \rangle_x = 8\pi p_0^2 nu \ln \frac{p_2}{p_1}. \tag{10}$$

We have given reasons for placing the outer limit of the impact parameter at the Debye length, D. We see from Eq. (10) that we would have an infinite deflection if we put the lower limit at zero. If, instead, we place the lower limit at p_0, the effect of ignoring closer encounters exactly compensates the effect of the approximation of Eq. (7). The reader can verify this by comparing our derivation with the more exact one given by Spitzer (1956), on which we have been leaning heavily. In the corona $\ln D/p_0 = \ln \Lambda$ may be set equal to 20, within the limit of other approximations that have been made in this derivation.

Since the charged particles undergo a continuing sequence of deflections from their initial path, rather than occasional sharp collisions, the concepts of collision time and mean free path are quite different from those for a gas of neutral molecules. Following Spitzer (1956), we define the time between collisions, t_D, as the time required for a particle to undergo a net deflection of 90°. Thus

$$t_D = \frac{\pi^2/4}{\langle X^2 \rangle}. \tag{11}$$

If the electron maintains essentially the same speed u while being diverted by 90° from its original path,

$$t_D = \frac{\pi m_e^2 u^3}{32ne^4 \ln \Lambda}. \tag{12}$$

The average of t_D over a Maxwell distribution in u is

$$\bar{t}_D = \frac{(\pi m_e)^{1/2}}{ne^4 \ln \Lambda} \cdot \left(\frac{kT}{2}\right)^{3/2} = \frac{0.58\, T^{3/2}}{n \ln \Lambda}, \tag{13}$$

which will be of the order of one second for the corona.

Before experiencing a 90° deflection the electron traverses a path

$$L = t_D u = \frac{\pi m_e^2 u^4}{32 n e^4 \ln \Lambda}. \tag{14}$$

The "mean free path," found by averaging over a Maxwellian distribution, is

$$\bar{L} = \frac{15\pi}{32} \frac{k^2 T^2}{n_e e^4 \ln \Lambda} = \frac{5.4 \times 10^5 \, T^2}{n \ln \Lambda}. \tag{15}$$

Thus the mean free path of electrons in the corona is several hundred kilometers. That of protons will be several times as great. Although the particle mass does not enter into the final expression that we have derived, the deflections of protons by protons will be only about half that of electrons by protons; and in addition, electrons will be significantly deflected by other electrons but protons will not be deflected by electrons.

Because of the very large mean free path of coronal particles, it is impossible for any marked temperature or density differences to exist along magnetic lines of force within a distance of a thousand kilometers or less. No such restriction applies normal to the magnetic field. Since radii of gyration are a few meters or less, extreme differences in temperature can coexist within a one-kilometer interval.

When conditions in the corona are changing slowly (i.e., over a period of hours) its thermodynamic state is described by statistical equilibrium— i.e., the rate of entry of atoms in a unit volume of coronal gas into a given state is put equal to the rate of removal of atoms from that state. The equations thus imply a steady state, but not thermodynamic equilibrium. In fact, there are few locations in the universe that depart more strongly from thermodynamic equilibrium than the corona. Its kinetic temperature is one to several million degrees, but it is so optically thin to practically all radiation that photons appropriate to its high temperature are very scarce indeed. Instead, the dominant radiation is that from the six-thousand degree solar photosphere, and even this is significantly diluted, since any point in the corona is more nearly surrounded by empty space than by glowing photosphere.

Steady-state equations are applicable to a portion of the corona only if its equilibrium has not been disturbed for several minutes. We have shown that coronal electrons undergo interactions producing significant changes in their velocity only about once each second. Similar changes in the more massive protons take place much more slowly. As a result, if some macroscopic disturbance imparts a higher temperature to one constituent in the corona than to another, considerable time must elapse before equipartition of energy is restored. During this time it is unlikely that statistical equilibrium obtains.

B. Chemical Composition of the Corona

The most direct evidence that hydrogen and helium are the principle chemical elements in the corona is that these elements constitute the greater part of the matter in prominences, and that prominences appear to form from coronal material. Until very recently about the only information we had concerning the helium content of the solar atmosphere was from the optical emission in prominences and chromosphere. The helium/hydrogen ratio indicated by such emission is fraught with rather large uncertainties, mostly because lines of sight through prominences or chromosphere probably do not lie along thermally homogeneous regions. Under these circumstances the ratio of hydrogen to helium emission will vary along a line of sight, and it is difficult to know what temperatures and densities to assign for computation of the relative abundance of the two elements from the observed emission. The situation is further complicated by the fact that both prominences and chromosphere are in a state rather far from thermodynamic equilibrium. Derived ratios of the number of helium to hydrogen atoms have varied from 5/100 to 20/100. Recently, Pottasch (1964b) has presented strong independent evidence for the larger ratio from a comparison of the intensities of helium ultraviolet lines to those of other elements.

The oldest method for determining the abundance of some of the heavier elements in the corona relative to hydrogen – or more precisely, relative to the abundance of free electrons—is the comparison of the white light scattered by the corona during an eclipse with the brightness of the optical emission lines. The electron density can be computed fairly well from the brightness of the K corona. The emission lines, in turn, give some evidence of the number of ions from which they arise along the line of sight—this information being weak because of uncertainties in the degree of excitation of the ions. The relative number of atoms of the emitting element in its various stages of ionization is an even greater source of uncertainty. When the degree of excitation and of ionization have been resolved by educated guesses, it appears that there are about enough electrons relative to the number of heavy atoms to have been supplied by ionization of the hydrogen and helium in a solar mixture. By similar arguments a rough correspondence is apparent between the relative numbers of several of the heavy elements in the corona to those in the photosphere. Thus a first approximation for the chemical composition of the corona, and a very plausible one, is that it is the same as that of the photosphere. This conclusion, formulated by Woolley and Allen (1948) and others was revolutionary to solar physics. Previously, the idea was generally accepted that gravitational settling brings about a chemical separation in the chromosphere, the observational basis for this idea being the dominance of metal lines in the lower part of the flash spectrum, with hydrogen and helium emission at greater heights above the photosphere.

In two recent studies, Pottasch (1963a, 1964a) has refined the use of optical emission lines for the determination of chemical abundance. In the first of these, for determining the abundance of iron, he compared line-intensity vs height data with white-light corona vs height. From this comparison he computed the ratio of the density of Fe X, XI, and XIV ions to the electron density as a function of height. He then assumed that the coronal temperature increased progressively from the solar limb outward, and that at the height in which the relative population of a given ion was greatest the temperature was most favorable for that ion. Under such circumstances he could expect about 40% of all of the iron ions to be of this particular species. The resulting iron abundances (relative to hydrogen)—$A \geq 1.7 \times 10^{-5}$ from Fe X, 3.4×10^{-5} from Fe XI, and 3.6×10^{-5} from Fe XIV—are reasonably consistent internally, but they are a factor of 10 higher than recently determined photospheric abundances. Unfortunately, the data did not yield an internally consistent justification for the temperature-gradient assumption that was made in the analysis. From the assumption, one would expect the Fe X abundance to maximize closest to the limb, the Fe XI higher up, and the Fe XIV even higher. Instead, all maximized at about the same height. Indeed, an assumption of *decreasing* temperature would have fit the observations just as well—and yielded the same abundances. The basic idea is an ingeneous one, however, and deserves to be repeated with better data than that used by Pottasch. His coronal green-line gradient is from the visual coronagraph estimates at Wendelstein during the years 1950 and 1951, normalized to fit the λ 5303 limb intensity at a particular limb position during the 1952 eclipse. Billings and Cooper (1957), however, have demonstrated the great variability of the emission gradients of the coronal lines. Only a detailed comparison of line emission to K-corona brightness might be expected to give correct information on ion abundance. Furthermore, even if such a comparison is carried out and the abundance of a particular ion maximizes at some location in the corona, one cannot be sure that the temperature is most favorable for that ion. Rather, at that point, the temperature could simply pass through a maximum or minimum that most closely approaches the temperature of maximum abundance for the ion. Furthermore, even the most detailed comparison of line to continuum emission could not take into account the possibility that several temperature regimes might be present along any line of sight.

In his 1964 study Pottasch provided, in a rough way, for the possibility of several temperature regimes (1964*a*). In this study, which included all coronal lines of measured intensity, he added the abundances of the various ions of each element, interpolating abundances of ions for which no lines were available. Thus for Fe he obtained an abundance of 7.5×10^{-5}—even further removed from the photospheric values than his 1963 abundance.

In a number of ways, the XUV emission lines are much more useful than any other part of the coronal spectrum for abundance determination. The oscillator strengths of these lines may be computed with a considerable degree of certainty, and their method of excitation can be demonstrated to be primarily collisional, from the ground state. Thus, given a temperature and density model for the corona and suitable atomic parameters for computation of the population of the excited level of each ion, it is possible to compute the abundances of the elements that emit the various lines with a precision comparable to the precision of the observations themselves. It is not even necessary to have a coronal model, as Pottasch demonstrated in 1963, if one makes use of the intensities of lines of several ions of the same element (1963*b*).

Pottasch's procedure was to express the emission at the sun in a given line as

$$E = 1.1 \times 10^{-15} \, Pf_{1u} \frac{N(\text{element})}{N(\text{hydrogen})} \int_0^\infty 10^{-5040W/T} \frac{N(\text{ion})}{N(\text{element})} N_e^2 \, dh,$$

(16)

where P is a correction factor of the order of unity, f the oscillator strength, and W the excitation energy in electron volts.

By averaging over the range of temperatures in the corona he reduced this equation, for intensity at the earth, to the form

$$E = 7.6 \times 10^{-21} \, Pf_{1u} \, \frac{N(\text{element})}{N(\text{hydrogen})}$$

$$\times \, \langle T^{-1/2} \cdot 10^{-5040W/T} \rangle \, \frac{N(\text{ion})}{N(\text{element})} \int_R N_e^2 \, dh. \quad (17)$$

Both the averaging and the integration are carried out over the temperature range in the corona for which the emitting ion exists in significant amounts. The average, in turn, was effected by the use of a single ion-concentration at a single appropriate temperature T.

The only factor in Eq. (17) related to the coronal structure, $\int_R N_e^2 \, dh$, is assumed to be the same for all ions existing in the same temperature range. Thus the quantity $N(\text{element})/N(\text{hydrogen}) \int_R N_e^2 \, dh$, computed by Eq. (17) from the observed line intensities for the various ions of one element, is a function of temperature that should have the same form as similarly computed functions for the various ions of other elements. Finally, the ratio of these functions for two elements should be equal to the ratio of their chemical abundance.

Pottasch determined the abundance of hydrogen relative to the line-emitting elements by comparing emission-line intensities with brightness temperatures at various radio frequencies. We shall not describe his procedure in detail, but note that by assuming an element/hydrogen ratio in Eq. (17), he could determine $\int_R N_e^2 T^{-3/2} \, dh$. Summing these integrals over the temperature ranges appropriate to various ions gave

$$\int_h^\infty N_e^2 T_e^{-3/2} \, dh,$$

a factor in the expression for the optical depth at a radio frequency. He computed this factor for various element/hydrogen ratios and determined which of these integrals best described the actual radio observations, hence which element/hydrogen ratio was consistent with radio data.

In 1964 Pottasch repeated these computations, using somewhat revised data (1964b). The most important change in his later work, however, was taking dielectronic recombination into account. The effect of the resulting increase in temperature lowered the computed abundance of the heavier elements relative to hydrogen by a factor of 2 or 3.

In Table I we compare the abundances found by Pottasch with recently published cosmic abundances by Aller (1963) and Allen (1963).

We note that except for iron, Pottasch's 1964 coronal abundances agree fairly well with the photospheric abundances of Aller and Allen, whereas the iron abundance is consistent with the optical coronal-line values.

The approximate agreement of photospheric and coronal abundances for calcium and the disagreement for iron are confirmed directly from coronagraph spectroscopic observations. The confirmation for calcium follows from a sequence of arguments beginning with observations of the two yellow lines of Ca XV, λ 5694 and λ 5445. Using principles that will be discussed later in this chapter, the density of a coronal condensation can be determined from the ratio of the intensity of these two lines (Zirin, 1964). From the density one computes the degree of excitation of the Ca XV ions

TABLE I

Log Chemical Abundance on Scale with Log N (Hydrogen) = 12.00

		H	C	N	O	Ne	Mg	Si	S	Ca	Fe
1963	Aller	12.00	8.60	8.04	8.95	8.70	7.43	7.50	7.30	6.05	6.95
1963	Allen	12.00	8.24	7.96	8.83	8.44	7.46	7.47	7.22	6.22	6.90
1963b	Pottasch	12.00	9.22	8.22	8.82	7.90	8.00	8.30	7.60	6.52	7.82
1964b	Pottasch	12.00	8.78	7.78	8.65	8.70	7.95	8.00	7.15	6.48	7.60

to the upper level for emission in each line. Also from the ratio of brightness in the line to that in the electron-scattered continuum one may determine the number of Ca XV atoms in each excited state relative to the number of electrons. The ratio of this number to the degree of excitation yields the number of Ca XV ions relative to the number of electrons, a quantity that should vary with temperature, but at most should be 30–50% of the abundance of calcium. Boardman and Billings (1966), using about twenty observations of these two yellow lines, are in essential agreement with the calcium abundance given by Allen.

If now, as Zirin has pointed out, we compare the ratio of the maximum brightness attained by the green coronal line to the continuum brightness with the corresponding ratio for λ 5694 of Ca XV, we can conclude that iron is a great deal more abundant than calcium. The lines of Ca XV never appear bright on spectrograms except when accompanied by a bright streak of continuum emission, whereas the coronal green line may intensify to a great brightness with a barely perceptible continuum intensification. Quantitatively, the brightest Ca XV lines are two or three times as bright as continuum from which they arise, whereas the coronal green line may be 20 times or more as bright. Furthermore, the electron density in the yellow-line region is typically an order of magnitude greater than that in the green-line region. Hence, if the cross sections for collisional excitation for the two lines are the same, the maximum abundance of Fe XIV must be 100 times or more that of Ca XV. Conversely, a much greater difference must be postulated between the excitation cross sections for the two ions if the relative abundance of the two elements is that given by Aller and Allen than if it is that given by Pottasch. Now although collisional cross sections for excitation are poorly known, and may well be in error by a factor of 10, there is no reason to expect that those for Fe XIV and for Ca XV will differ so widely. Hence we conclude that coronagraph observations confirm the larger difference between iron and calcium abundance as found by Pottasch.

Suzuki and Hirayama (1964), from a four-temperature model of a coronal condensation that had been studied by Aly *et al.* (1963), also concluded that the abundance of iron in the corona was about 10 times that found for the photosphere. Their approach was quite straightforward. They assumed that they had available suitable atomic parameters for computing states of ionization and excitation, and thus, using published chemical abundances, were able to compute the electron density in each of four shells in the condensation from the brightness of the emission line that distinguished the shell. The resulting number of electrons along the line of sight was found to exceed that indicated by electron scattering by a factor of about 10. Thus they concluded that the iron abundance they had used was much too low.

Either iron is more abundant in the corona than in the photosphere, or observations of one or the other region have been misinterpreted. The likelihood of the latter possibility appears to have been diminished in the case of the photosphere by a recent very careful determination of the log abundance of iron by Goldberg *et al.* (1964) as 6.64—even lower than that by Allen or Aller. Pottasch considered the possibility that the iron in the corona is enhanced by the influx of solid particles from the remainder of the solar system, but rejected the idea on the basis of computations of the drift velocity of iron atoms from such particles through the lower corona. Because of the observation of Trellis (1960) of an enhancement of the green coronal-line emission on the side of the sun facing the apex of its motion through the galaxy, however, the idea should perhaps be reconsidered. One might question any computed drift rate for heavy atoms through the solar atmosphere, since these computations would imply gravitational chemical separation of the solar constituents to the extent that the coronal chemical composition would not even approximate, as it does, that of the photosphere.

C. State of Ionization

The most important physical characteristic of the corona is its high temperature. The most important corollary of this characteristic is its state of extreme ionization. Most of its observational characteristics, including its white-light appearance, its emission spectrum, and its magnetically determined structure are direct consequences of its ionic properties.

The best description of the process of ionization in the corona, as we see it at the present moment, is a time-dependent one (House and Billings, 1964). Successive pulses of mechanical energy pass into the corona from the underlying chromosphere. These pulses impart gross motion to the gas, which deteriorates to thermal motion in a very short time. The new influx of thermal motion first resides primarily in the protons and α particles that make up most of the mass of the corona. Within about a minute, however, equipartition of energy takes place, and the electron temperature rises but never becomes quite equal to that of the protons. The electrons, in turn, interact with the heavy elements, bringing them to a state of ionization that approaches that appropriate to the electron temperature. Throughout the process the electrons are losing energy by radiation and conduction. Thus their temperature increases only so long as they are receiving more energy from the protons than they are dissipating; but when the temperature difference between protons and electrons has dropped to about 20,000°K both cool at the same rate, with the degree of ionization of the medium following the temperature change.

If the rate of dissipation of energy is low (a small fraction of an erg cm^{-2} sec^{-1} at the earth) or the pulse frequency one or more per minute, the temperature and the degree of ionization flutter only slightly about a steady-state value. If, however, we consider the impulses to have the frequency of photospheric oscillations, of about one every five minutes, and the energy radiated from the corona to be about 1 erg cm^{-2} sec^{-1} at the earth, the fluctuations in temperature and ionization are about as extreme as is possible if we are to speak meaningfully of a particular piece of coronal material having a specified temperature or a specified degree of ionization. Even though with longer periods or greater dissipation rates the fluctuations of these two quantities become more violent, the degree of ionization will follow rather closely the temperature change, keeping a relation that does not depart strongly from the relation that would exist in a corona of unchanging temperature. Consequently, it is meaningful to compute a steady-state relation between the degree of ionization and temperature for each of the various heavy ions that are of interest in the corona, even though we use the relationship in describing a fluctuating condition.

As we indicated earlier in the chapter, to postulate a steady state is not to postulate a condition of thermodynamic equilibrium. Instead, we simply set the rate at which atoms change from a lower to the next-higher degree of ionization equal to the rate at which they return from that state. We recognize two processes by which the ionization may take place—collisional and radiative—and two by which it may return—by radiative and by three-body collisional recombination. Thus we set

$$(\text{Collisional ionization rate}) + (\text{Radiative ionization rate})$$

$$= (\text{Three-body recombination rate}) + (\text{Radiative recombination rate}).$$

$$(18)$$

Now were the corona isothermal and so vast that from any point of interest within the corona a line of sight to the periphery would traverse infinite optical depth in any radiation produced in the corona, the gas at that point would be in a state of thermodynamic equilibrium and we could equate the rate of each process to that of the opposite process. Thus we could equate the rate of radiative ionization to the rate of radiative recombination. Similarly, since collisional ionization is a three-body process, we could equate the rate of collisional ionization to the rate of three-body recombination. The actual corona, as we shall show in the next chapter, is optically thin in all but radio wavelengths. Consequently, the energy-density in the radiation field in the actual corona is much lower than it would be for thermodynamic equilibrium—particularly in the extreme ultraviolet radiation that is necessary for further photoionization of the highly stripped coronal ions. The cool photosphere produces essentially no photons of these frequencies. Thus in the actual corona the radiative ionization rate falls far below the radiative recombination rate. The resulting decrease in the population of upper-state ions diminishes in turn the rate of three-body recombination. Collisional ionizations, however, are not diminished, since the kinetic state of the electrons is not affected by the low optical depth. Thus the three-body recombination rate is much less than the collisional ionization rate.

As a consequence of these two inequalities between rates of opposing ionizing and recombining processes, Eq. (18) reduces to

(Collisional ionization rate) = (Radiative recombination rate).   (19)

[Athay and Hyder (1963) showed that this relation does not hold if ionization can take place in two steps via a metastable state. Under these circumstances, radiative excitation to the metastable state may be important.] Now if N_i is the number density of ions of a given element in the ith state of ionization, N_{i+1} the number density in the next stage of ionization, and N_e the electron density, Eq. (19) may be written

$$N_i N_e C = N_{i+1} N_e R, \qquad (20)$$

where C and R are rate factors for collisional ionization and radiative recombination, respectively. Their precise evaluation is a long-standing problem that has not been completely solved as yet, but it has been recognized that both are strong functions of temperature, C an increasing and R a decreasing function. From (20) it follows that the ratio

$$N_{i+1}/N_i = C/R \qquad (21)$$

is independent of electron density as pointed out by Woolley and Allen (1948), but increases strongly with temperature. (The Athay-Hyder two-step ionization process renders this ratio density-dependent). If $C(T)$ and $R(T)$ are known, an observational determination of the relative number of ions in two successive states of an element provides a sharp evaluation of the electron temperature. Conversely, from a knowledge of the electron temperature, we can determine the distribution of the atoms of an element among its various stages of ionization. The most useful representation of a set of such computations is a plot against temperature of the fraction of the atoms of an element that are in each of several successive stages of ionization (Fig. 5.1).

It is apparent that the evaluation of collisional-ionization and radiative-recombination rates is of paramount importance in the interpretation of coronal spectra. Of the two, the collisional-ionization problem was considered for some time to be the more difficult, since it was essentially a three-body problem and could be solved either classically or quantum-mechanically only by successive approximations. Two early quantum-mechanical approaches were (1) to use the collisional excitation equation

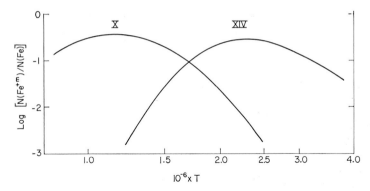

Fig. 5.1. A typical ionization-curve plot. These curves, by Burgess and Seaton (1964), show the logarithm of the fraction of iron in the forms Fe X and Fe XIV as a function of temperature. Dielectronic recombination is taken into account in the computation. Courtesy, Royal Astronomical Society.

derived by Hebb and Menzel (1940) for O III (Waldmeier, 1946); and (2) to use the Born approximation (Biermann, 1947). The first of these involved the assumption that parameters applicable to O III were also applicable to the very different coronal ions, as well as that the same functional form for the cross sections applied. The latter is strictly applicable only if the energy of the colliding electrons is much greater than the ionization energy, whereas in the corona the ionization energy of the heavy ions lies well beyond the maximum in the Maxwellian distribution of electron velocities. Furthermore, the cross section for collisional ionization, although its form is not known, almost certainly decreases with increasing electron velocity. Consequently, the ionization is effected primarily by electrons of kinetic energy just in excess of the ionization energy, in contradiction to the basic assumption of the Born approximation.

Elwert (1952), recognizing the difficulties with either of the above approaches, favored the classical ionization theory, which had already been used by Woolley and Allen (1948). The basic concepts of this theory are so unsophisticated that one may be somewhat surprised by the more recent conclusion of Seaton that the cross sections it yields cannot be very different from those one would get from a precise quantum-mechanical computation.

The classical theory of collisional ionization, which was developed by Thomson in 1912, predates the Bohr atom. The bound electron is visualized as so imbedded in the positive matrix of the atom that a certain definite amount of energy W is required to remove it. As the ionizing electron approaches the atom, it and the bound electron interact with a repulsive coulomb force—this being the only force considered. Its interaction with the positive part of the atom or with other electrons is ignored. The impulse experienced by the ionizing electron, resulting in its motion in a hyperbola rather than in a straight line, is set equal and opposite to the impulse experienced by the bound electron. If the bound electron acquires through this impulse kinetic energy equal to its ionization energy, it will leave the atom. The magnitude of the impulse can be expressed as a function of the velocity of the incident electron and the "impact parameter" d. Conversely, if d is the largest impact parameter that would produce ionization, it can be expressed as a function of the kinetic energy E of the incident electron, and of the binding energy, X_n of the nth shell. The resulting collision cross section for ionization is

$$\sigma_c = \pi d^2 = \frac{\pi \epsilon^4}{E} \left(\frac{1}{X_n} - \frac{1}{E} \right). \tag{22}$$

Elwert discussed corrections that had subsequently been introduced into this formula to care for the interaction of the incident electron and the remainder of the atom, and also to care for the orbital motion of the bound electron. Rather than use these corrections, however, he introduced empirical corrections of a similar but not identical form that would lead to a better fit of the scanty ionization data at his disposal. Finally, he integrated this corrected cross section over a Maxwellian distribution of energies of incident electrons, from the ionization energy to infinity, to obtain for the ionization rate coefficient

$$C = \int_{vI}^{\infty} v\sigma_c f(v)\, dv \propto \int_n \left(\frac{kT}{X_n} \right)^{1/2} \left(\frac{X_n}{X_{\mathrm{H}}} \right)^{-3/2} \exp\left(-X_n/kT \right). \tag{23}$$

Here X_{H} is the ionization energy of hydrogen from its ground state, and $\int_n$ the number of electrons in the nth shell of the atom.

Elwert derived a rate of recombination from Kramers' (1923) expression for the free–bound absorption coefficient per atom (see Chapter 6):

$$\alpha_n = \frac{64\pi^4}{3\sqrt{3}} \frac{Z^4 m e^{10}}{ch^6} \cdot \frac{1}{n^5} \cdot \frac{1}{\nu^3} g. \tag{24}$$

He proceeded from absorption coefficient to recombination cross section by noting that in the case of thermodynamic equilibrium the rate of radiation-absorbing transitions between bound and free energy levels must equal the rate of radiative recombinations between the same pair of levels—i.e.,

$$N_{i,n}\alpha_n I_\nu \frac{d\nu}{h\nu}(1 - e^{-h\nu/kT}) = N_{i+1,1}N_e\sigma_R f(v)\, v\, dv. \qquad (25)$$

[The factor $(1 - e^{-h\nu/kT})$ corrects for induced emission.] But in thermodynamic equilibrium, the ratio of the number of ions $N_{i,n}$ in the lower state of ionization but in excitation state n to the number in the next stage of ionization in the ground state $N_{i+1,1}$ is given by the Saha equation,

$$\frac{N_{i+1,1}N_e}{N_{i,n}} = \frac{(2\pi mkT)^{3/2}}{h^3}\cdot\frac{2g_{i+1,1}}{g_{i,n}}\exp\left(-X_n/kT\right). \qquad (26)$$

Combining (24), (25), and (26) and substituting $2n^2 = g_{i,n}/g_{i+1,1}$ for the ratio of the statistical weights leads to the radiative recombination cross section,

$$\sigma_R = \frac{2^7\pi^4}{3\sqrt{3}}\frac{Z^2 e^{10}}{mc^3 v^2 h^3}\cdot\frac{1}{n^3}\cdot\frac{1}{h\nu}f, \qquad (27)$$

where f is a correction factor near unity incorporating the Gaunt correction factor g.

Although Eq. (27) was derived on the assumption of thermodynamic equilibrium, it is applicable to the corona, since it does not depend on the radiation field. In other words, it defines an atomic parameter without reference to thermodynamic conditions.

Finally, again, the rate of radiative recombinations is determined by integrating over a Maxwellian distribution of recombining electrons:

$$R = \int_0^\infty v\sigma_R f(v)\, dv \propto \left(\frac{\chi_H}{kT}\right)^{1/2}\frac{\chi_n}{\chi_H}n. \qquad (28)$$

Substitution of Eqs. (23) and (28) into (21) and an approximate evaluation of various correcting terms leads to

$$\frac{N_{i+1}}{N_i} = 5\times 10^5\left(\frac{\chi_H}{\chi_i}\right)^2\frac{\exp\left(-\chi_i/kT\right)}{(\chi_i/kT)} \qquad (29)$$

for the ratio of the numbers of ions in two successive stages of ionization in the corona.

Although there are more direct and precise methods for demonstrating the point, we may use Eq. (29) to confirm our earlier statement that hydrogen and helium are essentially completely ionized in the corona.

Using it we find that ionized hydrogen is about 6,000,000 times as abundant as neutral hydrogen, doubly-ionized helium over 100,000 times as abundant as singly-ionized helium, and the latter about 1,000,000 times as abundant as neutral helium. Radiative ionizations due to chromospheric photons would increase the degree of both hydrogen and helium ionization.

When applied to the study of the spectra of the coronal ions for which it was derived, Eq. (29) indicated lower temperatures for the corona than were determined from most other methods of observation. The difficulty was resolved after many years when Burgess (1964) pointed out the inadequacy of Eq. (28). Equation (28) is derived on the assumption that recombination is a simple two-body process in which a free electron becomes a bound electron by giving up, in the form of radiation, energy equal to its kinetic energy plus the binding energy for the level to which it goes. If the incident electron happens to have a kinetic energy equal to the sum of the excitation energies of two bound states, however, it possesses an alternative method of recombination: it can excite a bound electron to one of the excited states, thereupon finding itself with energy appropriate to the other bound state. In other words, the free electron thus becomes a bound electron without emitting any radiation, its energy being manifest by the excited states of two electrons in a recombined atom. Of course, radiation will subsequently be emitted, but in line emission rather than in free–bound emission.

Burgess computed the dielectronic recombination rate from Fe XV to Fe XIV, demonstrating that it was about 20 times as great as the radiative recombination rate. Burgess and Seaton (1964) then discussed how similar considerations would apply to other ions of iron, and drew a new population-vs-temperature curve for Fe X and Fe XIV. When these are compared with earlier curves for the same quantity, we note that each ion achieves its maximum population at approximately twice the temperature that was found when radiative recombinations alone were considered.

A significant effect of introducing dielectronic recombination is that the temperature range over which a given stage of ionization is present is greatly broadened, thus increasing the number of stages of ionization that might be observed at a given temperature. The broadening is not adequate to explain the apparent near-equality of several successive stages of ionization in a single coronal feature (Firor and Zirin, 1962; Aly *et al.*, 1963), however, and it is still convenient to consider more than one temperature regime along a line of sight.

We have already mentioned the two-step ionization process pointed out by Athay and Hyder (1963). According to these authors, most coronal ions contain metastable levels of excitation, or at least levels of sufficient metastability that during their lifetime there is a significant chance of ionization taking place from them. The addition of an extra and lower energy-step path by which ionization may take place obviously lowers the temperature at which a given ion is most abundant, just as the addition of another recombination path increased that temperature. The effect is not nearly so strong, however, producing a temperature change of an order of magnitude less than that by the introduction of dielectronic recombination. Whereas the effect on the temperature of maximum abundance is opposite that of dielectronic recombination, the effect on the range of temperatures is in the same direction, increasing the range. From very general considerations one might expect that any increase in the number of paths by which ions would change from one charge to another would broaden the population-vs-temperature distribution of each species, although we know of no rigorous proof of such a theorem.

D. Excitation of Coronal Ions

The valence electrons of coronal ions move in a very strong Coulomb field. This has the effect that all atomic energy levels in coronal ions are much more separated than corresponding levels in neutral atoms. Thus ordinary dipole transitions are all in the extreme ultraviolet end of the spectrum, and the magnetic transitions from one spin configuration to another within a given angular-momentum state lie in or near the visible region.

With the notable exception of the 7059-Å transition of Fe XV, visible coronal lines result from magnetic transitions within the ground term of the atoms. Similarly, most extreme ultraviolet lines are transitions from the first excited states to the ground states of the ions. Thus we are generally interested in two types of excitation: excitation of a few electron volts within the ground term, and excitation above the ground state of one or two hundred electron volts. The former may be either radiative or collisional; the latter is almost entirely collisional. In either case, the number of excited ions is determined by statistical equilibrium—if equilibrium exists at all.

Radiative excitation would be one of the easiest phenomena in the corona to deal with in a quantitative fashion, except that its effect is difficult to separate observationally from collisional excitation. If the coronal ion is so located that the solid angle subtended at its position by the solar photosphere (of temperature T_p) is the fraction W of a sphere, the radiation energy density in the visible region is very nearly described by

$$u_\nu = \frac{8\pi h\nu^3}{c^3} W \cdot \frac{1}{\exp(h\nu/kT_p) - 1}. \tag{30}$$

Geometrical considerations give W, the dilution factor, as $W = \frac{1}{2}\{1 - [(r^2 - 1)^{1/2}/1]\}$ where r is the distance from the solar center in solar radii. The net rate of upward transitions is related to the energy density and the Einstein coefficients for induced upward and downward transitions, B_{12} and B_{21}, by

$$R_u = \frac{cu_\nu}{4\pi}(B_{12}N_1 - B_{21}N_2), \tag{31}$$

where N_1 and N_2 are the population densities in the lower and upper states for the transition, respectively. R_u is the net rate of radiative transitions upward.

It is convenient to express the Einstein coefficients in terms of the spontaneous emission probability, since the latter has been computed and tabulated (Appendix II) for many coronal lines. When we do this, the net upward transition rate becomes

$$R_u = W'A_{21}\left(\frac{g_2}{g_1}N_1 - N_2\right), \tag{32}$$

where $W' = \{W/[\exp(h\nu/kT_p) - 1]\}$.

Thus the effective rate of radiative excitation depends on the number of atoms in the upper as well as in the lower state. Unfortunately, N_2 depends on collisional as well as radiative processes. It also depends on radiative transitions downward from higher levels, as Pecker and Thomas (1962) have demonstrated. We shall ignore the effects of the higher levels for the moment, however, and write the equation of statistical equilibrium as

$$R_u + C_{12}N_1N_\epsilon = N_2A_{21} + C_{21}N_2N_\epsilon. \tag{33}$$

Here C_{12} is the coefficient for the rate of collisional excitations, and C_{21} the rate for collisional deexcitations. Hebb and Menzel (1940) derived formulas for these coefficients that are still in use, although the correct value for the quantity Ω to use in the case of coronal ions is uncertain

(Blaha, 1962; Dumont and Perche, 1964). The formulas are

$$C_{12} = 8.54 \times 10^{-6} \frac{\Omega g_2}{T^{1/2}} e^{-h\nu/kT}, \tag{34}$$

$$C_{21} = C_{12} \frac{g_1}{g_2} e^{h\nu/kT}. \tag{35}$$

Substituting (32), in (33) gives for the degree of excitation

$$\frac{N_2}{N_1} = \frac{g_2}{g_1} \cdot \frac{A_{21}W' + (g_1/g_2)\,C_{12}N_\epsilon}{A_{21}(W'+1) + (g_1/g_2)\,C_{12}N_\epsilon\, e^{h\nu/kT}}. \tag{36}$$

Woolley and Allen (1948), and Waldmeier (1955) have considered the possibility that emission of optical coronal lines should show a marked change in height gradient at some level in the corona, since at lower levels the excitation should be predominately collisional, hence the rate of emission proportional to the product of electron and ion density, whereas at greater heights radiative excitation should predominate and the rate of emission, being proportional to the ion density only, should not drop off so rapidly as at lower levels in the corona. We realize from the complexity of Eq. (36), however, that one can predict whether such a change should be observable or not only after carrying out a detailed computation—and, unfortunately, using atomic parameters that are not well determined.

In order to give an idea of the relative magnitude of the terms in Eq. (36) we have carried out the computations for λ 5303 at 2,000,000°. For this line $g_2/g_1 = 2$ and $A_{21} = 60/\text{sec}$. We have taken Ω as 0.05, following Dumont, as a compromise between the value found by Hebb and Menzel for O III and the later value found by Blaha, with a strong leaning toward Blaha. For a density model for the corona we have used that of van de Hulst (1953), multiplied by 2 as indicated by Newkirk (1961). The values of the various terms of Eq. (36) at several heights in the corona are given in Table II.

TABLE II

RELATIVE VALUES OF TERMS OF EQUATION (36)

r	N_ϵ	W	W'	$A_{21}W'$	$(g_1/g_2)C_{12}N_\epsilon$	$A_{21}(W'+1)$	$(g_1/g_2)C_{12}N_\epsilon$ $\times \exp(h\nu/kT)$
1.0	8.13×10^8	0.5	0.0056	0.338	0.732	60.3	0.744
1.1	3.16×10^8	0.29	0.0033	0.196	0.284	60.2	0.288
1.5	3.02×10^7	0.127	0.0014	0.086	0.027	60.1	0.027
2.0	4.47×10^6	0.067	0.00075	0.045	0.004	60.0	0.004

We note that the first term in the denominator of Eq. (36) is nearly constant, varying little from A_{21}, and always considerably greater than the second term. Thus, to as good an approximation as our knowledge of the parameter Ω justifies, we may write the excitation equation as

$$N_2/N_1 = \frac{g_2}{g_1} W' + \frac{C_{12}}{A_{21}} N_e . \tag{37}$$

As we have already indicated, Eq. (37) is considerably in error as a result of ignoring the enhancement of N_2 through radiative transitions from higher states of excitation. Since these higher states are populated almost entirely by collisional excitation from the ground state, the increase in N_2 is controlled primarily by the collision rate. It may be cared for to a good approximation for densities $<10^{10}$ by writing Eq. (37) in the form

$$N_2/N_1 = \frac{g_2}{g_1} W' + \left(\frac{C_{12}}{A_{21}} + 2.5 \times 10^{-11} \right) N_e . \tag{38}$$

The quantity 2.5×10^{-11} is chosen to be in agreement with the computations of Pecker and Thomas (1962). The first term on the right is clearly the contribution of radiative excitation, and the second, of collisional excitation. The values of these two terms at the heights in the corona considered in Table II are listed in Table III.

We see from Table III that the radiative excitations come into domination over the collisional between 1.1 and 1.5 solar radii from the solar center, but that there is no clean break from one type of excitation to the other. At 1.1 solar radii, radiative excitations are already important, and at 1.5 radii, collisional excitations are still comparable to radiative excitations. Consequently, we should not expect to find any extensive region in the corona in which the line emission is clearly proportional either to N_e or N_e^2. In principle, a study of emission-line polarization, as

TABLE III
RELATIVE VALUES OF TERMS OF EQUATION (38)

r	N_e	$(g_2/g_1)W'$	$(C_{12}/A_{21} + 2.5 \times 10^{-11})N_e$	N_2/N_1
1.0	8.13×10^8	0.0112	0.0447	0.0559
1.1	3.16×10^8	0.0066	0.0173	0.0239
1.5	3.02×10^7	0.0028	0.00166	0.0045
2.0	4.47×10^6	0.0015	0.00025	0.0018

carried out by Mogilevskii *et al.* (1960), would be a more decisive technique for separation of the two excitation effects than the use of the intensity gradient. The polarization of λ 5303 emission could be as high as 40%, and that of other lines considerably greater, given radiative excitation only. Collisional excitation, being isotropic, would not lead to polarized emission. Unfortunately, magnetic fields as small as 10^{-5} gauss will have a strong depolarizing effect (Hyder, 1966), which may invalidate the technique for the study of excitation. Theoretical considerations by Charvin (1964), Seaton (1964), and Hyder throw doubt on the validity of the Mogilevskii observations. Charvin, Seaton, and Hyder, for example, agree that λ 6374 should never be polarized, whereas Mogilevskii *et al.* reported it highly polarized.

In the cases in which the ground term of the coronal ion is split into three or more levels, an analysis of the excitation to the various levels is of particular interest, since it leads to an independent method of determination of coronal density. An excellent example of such a case is Ca XV. In this ion the ground term is represented in an energy-level diagram as follows:

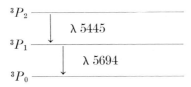

If the two upper states were populated by radiative excitations only, and were in turn depopulated only by radiative transitions downward, they would be in equilibrium with the radiation field—in this case the diluted photospheric radiation field—and their relative populations would be determined by a Boltzmann Distribution for the photospheric temperature. In this case the $^3P_1$ state would be about 40 times as populous as the $^3P_2$ state and λ 5694 a great deal more intense than λ 5445. On the other hand, the collisional excitation rate, as we have seen in Eq. (34), is proportional to $e^{-h\nu/kT}$, which is practically unity at coronal temperatures for all optical frequencies. Thus, were all excitations by collisions, the populations of the two upper levels would be approximately proportional to the ratio of their statistical weights, $\frac{5}{3}$. Now since the transition $^3P_2 \rightarrow {}^3P_0$ is more highly forbidden than $^3P_2 \rightarrow {}^3P_1$, all atoms in the $^5P_2$ state must return to the ground state via the $^3P_1$ state. Thus the number of λ 5694 photons would be equal to the number of λ 5445 photons plus the number of collisional excitations directly into the $^3P_1$ level. Correspondingly, the ratio of the number of the two species of photons would be $(\frac{5}{3} + 1)/\frac{5}{3} = 1.6$, a number that was first suggested by Shklovskii (1950). Thus we might expect the ratio of the intensity of the two lines to range from 1.6 upward with decreasing density, hence increasing importance of radiative excitation. Actually, the situation is somewhat more complex than we have pictured, since the $^3P_2$ level may be populated by transitions from higher levels, with the effect that the ratio of λ 5694 to λ 5445 is decreased at all densities. Zirin (1964) has computed the expected ratio of the intensities of the two lines for a range of densities. He obtains the values given in Table IV.

TABLE IV

CORONAL YELLOW-LINE RATIO VS DENSITY

N_e	5×10^8	2×10^9	8×10^9	3.2×10^{10}	1.28×10^{11}
$\dfrac{5694}{5445}$	3.18	1.92	1.53	1.22	1.22

He is displeased with the results of this computation because it leads to larger line/continuum ratios than those actually observed in several cases. For that reason he suggests that the collisional-excitation parameters used in the computations were not strictly correct, and that the densities pertinent to the ratios given in Table IV might better be each multiplied by a factor of 4. An alternative explanation is that the lines of sight containing enhanced yellow-line emission might generally also contain considerable material not at yellow-line temperature, so that the line/continuum ratios may generally be lower than would be the case were the line-emitting region the only region of enhanced density along the line of sight. Yellow-line emission generally occurs in the vicinity of very active prominences, and it is not unreasonable to expect that a significant amount of continuum emission is due to electrons in such prominence structures. Boardman and Billings (1966) favor the latter interpretation after a more detailed study than that carried out by Zirin.

In any event, if we can accept a table such as that given by Zirin, we have a unique tool for density determination in the corona, in that it can probe the density in the highly localized yellow-line regions rather than integrating along lines of sight. Although the same principle of determining density from the ratio of two lines from the same ground state can be applied to the two infrared lines from Fe XIII, λ 10798 and λ 10747, as was done by Dumont and Perche (1964), one cannot hope to achieve the spatial resolution that one has for the yellow lines, since the Fe XIII emissions are quite widely distributed throughout the lower solar corona. Thus the ratio of intensities of the two infrared lines is an average over a range of densities along a line of sight. There are advantages as well as disadvantages for these two lines, however. They come from an ion that is abundant at about the average temperature of the lower corona, and are therefore available on almost all occasions and in all parts of the limb, whereas yellow-line emission is rare and does not give us any information about the everyday corona.

We have dealt, now, in considerable detail, with excitations for optical emissions. From the standpoint of energy balance in the corona the excitations from the ground state to higher states, leading to X-ray emission, are of vastly greater importance. The more extensive discussion of the forbidden optical transitions reflects only the longer time that they have been a matter of concern to solar astronomers, and also their greater complexity, resulting from the combination of radiative with collisional excitation. There are few photons in the corona capable of producing XUV excitations. Thus we consider the process to be entirely collisional. Furthermore, the transition probabilities for radiation from the XUV states are high. Consequently, we may consider every collisional excitation to such states to be followed immediately by a radiative deexcitation. Thus the emission rate is completely determined by the rate of excitation. Woolley and Allen (1948) were among the first to consider the problem and adopted a collision cross-section for XUV excitation from Mott and Massey:

$$\sigma = 3\pi\epsilon^4 f \cdot \frac{1}{h\nu} \cdot \frac{2}{mv^2} \log \frac{2mv^2}{h\nu}, \tag{39}$$

where f is the oscillator strength for the downward transition. Using this cross-section, Bodenheimer *et al.* (1963) wrote for the emission rate for an X-ray transition in the corona:

$$[1.88 \times 10^{-15} N_e^2 / T^{1/2}] f p_i [\exp(-y) - y Ei(y)], \tag{40}$$

where $y = \chi/kT$, χ is the excitation potential of the upper level, p_i is the abundance of the ion relative to hydrogen in the corona, and $Ei(y)$ is the exponential integral. Varsavsky (1961), using a procedure from Mott and Massey based on the first Born approximation, computed excitation cross-sections for ultraviolet transitions for quite a number of coronal ions for electrons of 150- and 300-eV energies. The typical cross sections were a few hundredths to a few tenths of the area of a circle of one Bohr radius.

It is interesting to close this chapter with a rough computation of the implications of XUV excitation with regard to the state of the coronal gas. A plausible estimate of the rate of radiation in the X-ray region of the spectrum is 1 erg cm^{-2} sec^{-1} at the earth, which corresponds roughly to 10^{-5} ergs cm^{-3} from the lower corona. If we consider a typical wavelength of line emission as 200 Å, the typical photon energy is about 10^{-10} ergs. Hence the rate of radiation in the corona is about 10^5 photons cm^{-3} sec^{-1}. Since the transition probabilities are about 10^8 per second, it follows that on the average there will be one heavy ion excited above the ground level in each liter of coronal gas. Conversely, even though the excitation above the ground state of the heavy ions in the corona is one of the most important processes for the dissipation of coronal energy, only one out of every 10^{12} coronal atoms will be in the excited state at any one time.

REFERENCES

Allen, C. W. (1963). "Astrophysical Quantities," 2nd ed. Oxford Univ. Press (Athlone), London and New York.

Aller, L. H. (1963). "Astrophysics—The Atmospheres of the Sun and Stars," 2nd ed. Ronald Press, New York.

Aly M. K., Evans, J. W., and Orrall, F. Q. (1963). Emission line ratios in the solar corona. *Ap. J.* **137**, 1313.

Athay, R. G., and Hyder, C. L. (1963). Coronal ionization by two-step collision processes. *Ap. J.* **137**, 21.

Biermann, L. (1947). *Naturwissenschaften* **34**, 87.

Billings, D. E., and Cooper, R. H. (1957). Height gradient of the emission corona. *Z. Ap.* **43**, 218.

Blaha, M. (1962). Excitation of Fe XIV by electron collisions. *Bull. Astr. Inst. Czech.* **13**, 81.

Boardman, W. J., and Billings, D. E. (1966). Ionization and excitation of yellow-line coronal regions. *Ap. J.* In press.

Bodenheimer, P., Brandt, J. C., and Robbins, R. R. (1963). Interplanetary gas VIII on the importance of radiative losses. *Icarus* **2**, 411.

Burgess, A. (1964).Dielectronic recombination and the temperature of the solar corona. *Ap. J.* **139**, 776.

Burgess, A., and Seaton, M. (1964) The ionization equilibrium for iron in the solar corona. *M. N. R. A. S.* **127**, 355.

Charvin, P. (1964). On the intensity of the polarization of the forbidden lines of the solar corona. *Compt. rend.* **258**, 1155.

Dumont, J. P., and Perche, J. C. (1964). Study of the lines λ 3388, 10747, 10798 Å of Fe XIII in coronal conditions. *Mém. Roy. Soc. Sci., Liégé* **9**, 186.

Elwert, G. (1952). Concerning the ionization-recombination process in a plasma and the ionization formula for the solar corona. *Z. Naturforsch.* **7a**, 432.

Firor, J., and Zirin, H. (1962). Observations of five ionization stages of iron in the solar corona. *Ap. J.* **135**, 122.

Goldberg, L., Kopp, R. A., and Dupree, A. K. (1964). The abundance of iron in the solar photosphere. *Ap. J.* **140**, 707.

Hebb, M. H., and Menzel, D. H. (1940). Physical processes in gaseous nebulae. *Ap. J.* **92**, 408.

House, L. L., and Billings, D. E. (1964). Time-dependent coronal ionization. *Ap. J.* **140**, 1182.

Hyder, C. L. (1966). The polarization of emission lines in Astronomy. III. The polarization of coronal emission lines. *Ap. J.* (in press).

Kramers, H. A. (1923). On the theory of x-ray absorption and of the continuous x-ray spectrum. Phil. Mag. **44**, 836.

Mogilevskii, E. I., Nikolskii, G. M., and Nikol'skaya, K. I. (1960). The polarization of coronal emission lines, *Sov. Astr. A. J.* **4**, 225.

Newkirk, G. N., Jr. (1961). The solar corona in active regions and the thermal origin of the slowly varying component of solar radio radiation. *Ap. J.* **133**, 983.

Pecker C., and Thomas, R. N. (1962). Excitation of the red and green coronal lines. *Ann. d'Ap.* **25**, 100.

Pottasch, S. R. (1963a). The lower solar corona: The abundance of iron. *M. N. R. A. S.* **125**, 543.

Pottasch, S. R. (1963b). The lower solar corona: Interpretation of the ultraviolet spectrum. *Ap. J.* **127**, 945.

Pottasch, S. R. (1964a). On the chemical composition of the solar corona. *M. N. R. A. S.* **128**, 73.

Pottasch, S. R. (1964b). On the interpretation of the solar UV emission line spectrum. *Space Sci. Rev.* **3**, 816.

Seaton, M. J. (1964). The spectrum of the solar corona. *Planetary Space Sci.* **12**, 55.

Shklovskii, I. S. (1950). *Izv. Krymsk. Ap. Obs.* **4**, 80.

Spitzer, L., Jr. (1956) "Physics of Fully Ionized Gases." Wiley (Interscience), New York.

Suzuki, T., and Hirayama, T. (1964). A model of a coronal condensation and abundances of iron and nickel. *Publ. Astr. Soc. Japan* **16**, 58.

Trellis, M. (1960). East-West dissymetry of the monochromatic coronal intensity. *Compt. rend.* **250**, 58.

van de Hulst, H. C., (1953). Chicago, Illinois. The chromosphere and corona. *In* "The Sun" (G. P. Kuiper, ed.), p. 207. Univ. of Chicago Press,

Varsavsky, C. (1961). Some atomic parameters for UV lines. *Ap. J. Suppl.* **6**, 75.

Waldmeier, M. (1946). *Experientia* **2**, 1.

Waldmeier, M. (1955). How would the corona appear in front of the sun's disk? *Z. Ap.* **38**, 143.

Woolley, R. v.d. R., and Allen, C. W. (1948). The coronal emission spectrum. *M. N. R. A. S.* **108**, 292.

Zirin, H. (1964). The limb flare of November 20, 1960: A coronal phenomenon. *Ap. J.* **140**, 1216.

CHAPTER 6

RADIATIVE PROCESSES IN THE CORONA

A. Introduction

We can identify four processes by which coronal electrons are accelerated to emit radiation. The first and simplest is their acceleration by the electromagnetic field of photospheric radiation, resulting in the scattered radiation through which we see the white-light corona. A second is the interaction of the electrons in their thermal motion with the protons, α particles, and various heavy ions. In the case of electrons passing freely through the electrostatic field of the ions, the interaction yields bremsstrahlung, or as the astrophysicists prefer to call it, free–free emission. If the electrons are captured, free–bound emission results. Bound–bound or line emission does not fit quite as comfortably into this category, since the bound electrons may be excited to their upper states by interaction with the radiation field as well as with thermal electrons, but for lack of a better place we shall include it in this second class of emission processes. A third process that is of considerable importance in the production of longer wavelength radiation from the corona is the centripetal acceleration of electrons as they spiral around magnetic lines of force. Finally, we consider radiation arising from electrostatic and hydromagnetic waves in the coronal plasma. We call the electrostatic radiation "plasma radiation."

B. Scattering of Photospheric Radiation

The Thomson Cross Section

The corona is a gas in which the major constituents are completely ionized. Consequently, more than half of the particles present in the gas are free electrons. These electrons, being much more accelerated by an electromagnetic field passing through the corona than the more massive ions, are the primary scatterers of photospheric radiation.

To evaluate this scattering property of electrons we begin with an equation for the electric field E_α at time t at a considerable distance r from an accelerated point charge e:

$$E_\alpha = \frac{ea \sin \alpha}{rc^2},\tag{1}$$

where c is the velocity of light, and a is the acceleration of the charge e at time $(t - r/c)$. α is the angle between the direction of acceleration of the charge and the line joining the charge to the observer, and E_α is in the direction of increasing α. Equation (1) is basic to all of the radiation processes considered in this chapter.

Now if the accelerated charge resides on a particle of mass m, and is accelerated by an electric field E, the acceleration is

$$a = \frac{Ee}{m}.\tag{2}$$

Therefore,

$$E_\alpha = \frac{e^2 E}{mrc^2} \sin \alpha\tag{3}$$

and

$$\left(\frac{E_\alpha}{E}\right)^2 = \frac{e^4}{m^2 c^4 r^2} \sin^2 \alpha.\tag{4}$$

If E, and consequently E_α, are oscillatory, $(E_\alpha/E)^2$ represents the ratio of the power in the scattered to that in the incident radiation. Per steradian of scattered radiation, the scattering power of the electron is then

$$\frac{e^4}{m^2 c^4} \sin^2 \alpha.$$

The electron scattering cross section at $\alpha = \pi/2$, commonly known as the "Thomson cross section," is

$$\sigma = \frac{\epsilon^4}{m^2 c^4} = 7.95 \times 10^{-26} \text{ per steradian.}\tag{5}$$

where ϵ and m are the electronic charge and mass, respectively.

The scattered radiation per unit of incident radiation, integrated over an entire sphere,

$$2 \int_0^\pi (\sigma \sin^2 \theta) \cdot (2\pi \sin \theta \, d\theta) = \frac{8\pi}{3} \sigma = 0.6655 \times 10^{-24}, \tag{6}$$

is also sometimes referred to as the Thomson cross section.

Polarization of the K Corona

If the sun were a point source of light and the corona a small aggregate of scattering material lying at the vertex of a right angle between the sun and the observer, the scattered radiation would be 100% polarized, with its electric vector normal to the plane containing the incident and the scattered rays. This follows simply from the fact that the electric vector in any electromagnetic radiation is normal to the direction of propagation. We can resolve the electric vector of the incident radiation, hence the acceleration of scattering electrons, into components normal and parallel to the above-mentioned plane. Only the component of acceleration normal to the plane will result in scattered radiation along the line of sight. If the incident energy flux upon the scattering material is q ergs cm^{-2} sec^{-1} and the electron density of the scattering material is N_e, the scattered radiation in any direction normal to the incident radiation will be plane parallel and have an intensity of $\sigma (q/2) N_e$ ergs sec^{-1} steradian^{-1}.

Scattering in the Corona

In actual practice the sun is not a simple point source, but is extended. So is the corona. Consequently, it is necessary to consider the three-dimensional geometry of the process in detail, not only to separate the polarized and unpolarized components of coronal light, but also to compute the brightness of a single scattering condensation in the corona. It is essential for the discussion that the geometrical arrangement be very clearly understood by the reader.

Consider a point P in the corona, illuminated by the underlying photosphere, and scattering light in the direction of the observer, as indicated in Fig. 6.1. Let χ be the angle between the radius through P and the line of sight. We shall let this radius be vertical, as shown in the diagram.

It is useful to define two vertical planes intersecting at the radius through

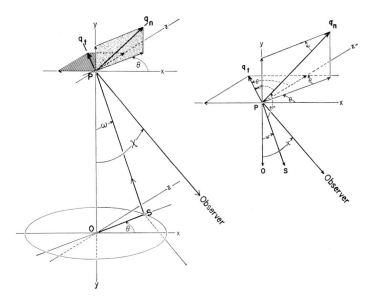

Fig. 6.1. Geometry of electron scattering in the corona. The ellipse is a circle about the y axis, on the solar photosphere, as seen in perspective. The plane of the paper, the x–y plane, also includes the line of sight to the observer. The source of radiation, S, on the photosphere, is represented as lying behind the plane of the paper in a plane OPS that makes an angle ν with the x–y plane. The radiation vector qn and its components also lie in this plane.

P. One of these, the "incident" plane, is defined by the radius and a ray of light passing from a point S on the solar surface to P. The other, the emergent plane, is defined by the radius and the observer. In our drawing the emergent plane is the plane of the paper. By the "horizontal" plane we mean the plane through P normal to both the incident and emergent planes. The point S is located on the solar surface by two angles, ω, between the radius and SP, and θ, the angle between the incident and the emergent planes.

The ray of light SP, being unpolarized, may be considered to be made up of any pair of orthogonally polarized, equal-intensity components. It is convenient to consider one of these components q_t to have its electric vector normal to the incident plane (i.e., tangential to the solar surface) and the other, q_n to have its electric vector in the incident plane. Electric vectors of both q_t and q_n are, of course, normal to SP. Note that q_t will lie in the horizontal plane.

Let us resolve q_n into two components in the incident plane, one component along and another normal to the radius. The magnitudes of these two components are, respectively, $(q_n \sin^2 \omega)_y$ and $q_n \cos^2 \omega$.

The former of these two components already lies in the emergent plane. The latter lies in the horizontal plane but not in the emergent plane. Thus we resolve it, in turn, into two components, one with the electric vector normal to, and the other with the electric vector in the emergent plane. These are $(q_n \cos^2 \omega \sin^2 \theta)_z$, and $(q_n \cos^2 \omega \cos^2 \theta)_x$.

Since q_t already lies in the horizontal plane, its components normal to and in the emergent plane are $(q_t \cos^2 \theta)_z$ and $(q_t \sin^2 \theta)_x$.

The subscripts indicate the directions of the electric vectors of the various components in a coordinate system in which the intersection of the horizontal and the emergent plane is the x axis, the intersection of the incident and emergent plane is the y axis, and the z axis is normal to the x and y axes.

Now if I is the radiation per unit area per steradian from the solar surface, the flux at P from the element of surface at S will be $I \sin \omega \, d\omega \, d\theta$ ergs cm^{-2} sec^{-1}, or, in another form,

$$q = -I \, d\theta \, d(\cos \omega). \tag{7}$$

q_n and q_t of the preceding discussion are each equal to one-half of this flux.

Of the various components of q_n and q_t, only the z components will contribute to the scattered radiation with a tangential electric vector. and this contribution is independent of χ. Hence, the tangential electric-vector component of the scattered radiation is

$$I_t = \frac{N_e \sigma}{2} \int_{\cos \Omega}^{1} \int_{0}^{2\pi} I(\cos^2 \theta + \cos^2 \omega \sin^2 \theta) \, d(\cos \omega) \, d\theta. \tag{8}$$

where Ω is the angle between $\overline{OP}$ and a tangent from P to the photosphere. The z components will not contribute to the scattered radiation with radial electric vector. The contributions of the y components will be proportional to $\sin^2 \chi$ and those of the x components, to $\cos^2 \chi$. Hence the intensity of the radially-electric vector-scattered radiation is

$$I_r = \frac{N_e \sigma}{2} \int_{\cos \Omega}^{1} \int_{0}^{2\pi} I(\sin^2 \omega \sin^2 \chi + \cos^2 \omega \cos^2 \theta \cos^2 \chi + \sin^2 \theta \cos^2 \chi)$$

$$\times d(\cos \omega) \, d\theta. \tag{9}$$

If we integrate each expression over θ we get

$$I_t = \frac{N_e \pi \sigma}{2} \int_{\cos \Omega}^{1} I(1 + \cos^2 \omega) \, d(\cos \omega) \qquad (10)$$

and

$$I_r = \frac{N_e \pi \sigma}{2} \int_{\cos \Omega}^{1} I[(1 + \sin^2 \chi) + \cos^2 \omega(1 - 3 \sin^2 \chi)] \, d(\cos \omega). \qquad (11)$$

A straightforward procedure from this point would be to evaluate I in Eqs. (10) and (11) as a function of ω to take limb darkening into account, then to integrate the equations.

It is easier, however, to deal with I_t and $I_r - I_t$, since in the latter expression $\sin^2 \chi$ can be factored out—i.e.,

$$I_r - I_t = \frac{N_e \pi \sigma}{2} \int_{\cos \Omega}^{1} I \sin^2 \chi (1 - 3 \cos^2 \omega) \, d(\cos \omega). \qquad (12)$$

If ψ is the angle between the outgoing ray SP and the solar radius, we may write

$$I = I_0(1 - u + u \cos \psi), \qquad (13)$$

where u is an empirical function of wavelength. Furthermore, if O is the center of the sun and a is the length of a solar radius (see Fig. 6.2),

$$\frac{\sin \psi}{\sin \omega} = \frac{\overline{OP}}{a}. \qquad (14)$$

Also we may write

$$a = \overline{OP} \sin \Omega. \qquad (15)$$

The combination of (14) and (15) gives

$$\sin \psi = \frac{\sin \omega}{\sin \Omega}. \qquad (16)$$

Thus (13) may be written

$$I = I_0 \left[1 - u + \frac{u(\cos^2 \omega - \cos^2 \Omega)^{1/2}}{\sin \Omega} \right] \qquad (17)$$

for substitution into Eqs. (10) and (12).

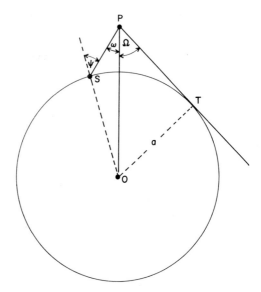

Fig. 6.2. An auxiliary diagram for the electron-scattering theory.

The resulting integrals can be evaluated directly:

$$I_t = I_0 \frac{N_e \pi \sigma}{2} \big[(1 - u)\,C + uD\big] \qquad (18)$$

and

$$I_t - I_r = I_0 \frac{N_e \pi \sigma}{2} \sin^2 \chi \big[(1 - u)\,A + uB\big], \qquad (19)$$

where A, B, C, and D are functions of Ω only:

$$A = \cos \Omega \sin^2 \Omega, \qquad (20)$$

$$B = -\frac{1}{8}\left[1 - 3\sin^2 \Omega - \frac{\cos^2 \Omega}{\sin \Omega}\,(1 + 3\sin^2 \Omega)\ln \frac{1 + \sin \Omega}{\cos \Omega}\right], \qquad (21)$$

$$C = \tfrac{4}{3} - \cos \Omega - \frac{\cos^3 \Omega}{3}, \qquad (22)$$

$$D = \frac{1}{8}\left[5 + \sin^2 \Omega - \frac{\cos^2 \Omega}{\sin \Omega}\,(5 - \sin^2 \Omega)\ln \frac{1 + \sin \Omega}{\cos \Omega}\right]. \qquad (23)$$

A, B, C, and D, as computed for various Ω's (i.e., for various heights of P above the limb) by Minneart (1930), are listed in Appendix V. Van de Hulst (1950), by a regrouping of terms, reduced the number of tabulated functions of Ω from four to two, one of which described the isotropic and the other the polarized radiation field at P.

As an application of Eqs. (18) and (19), consider a condensation very close to the limb. $\Omega = \chi = \pi/2$. From (20)–(23), $A = 0$; $B = \frac{1}{4}$; $C = \frac{4}{3}$ and $D = \frac{3}{4}$. Then

$$I_t = \frac{I_0 N_e \pi \sigma}{24} (16 - 7u) \tag{24}$$

and

$$I_r = \frac{I_0 N_e \pi \sigma}{24} (13 - 7u). \tag{25}$$

Thus the total intensity is

$$I_t + I_r = \frac{I_0 N_e \pi \sigma}{24} (29 - 14u) \tag{26}$$

and the polarization is

$$\frac{I_t - I_r}{I_t + I_r} = \frac{6}{29 - 14u}. \tag{27}$$

Two questions of interest can be investigated by the use of Eq. (26): the effect of limb darkening and the effect of anisotropic scattering on the total brightness of condensations near the limb. Were there no limb darkening, u would equal zero, whereas a typical value for u is 0.56. Hence the effect of limb darkening is to reduce the brightness of the scattered radiation to 73% of what it would be were the disk uniformly as bright as its center. To investigate the effect of anisotropic scattering we shall consider only the simple case of $u = 0$. Were the scattering isotropic we could use Eq. (6). The incident flux upon a point near the limb would be $2\pi I$, and the scattered, $16\pi^2 I_0 \sigma N_e/3$. This is 10% greater than the value found from Eq. (26) for $u = 0$.

A third question of interest is the color of the scattered radiation. Let ρ be the ratio of the scattered light intensities at two wavelengths, ρ_t being the ratio for the component with electrical vector tangential, and ρ_r, for that with radial electric vector. Then we find, from Eq. (24), that for points near the limb,

$$\rho_t = \rho_0 \left(\frac{16 - 7u_1}{16 - 7u_2} \right), \tag{28}$$

where $\rho_0 = I_0(\lambda_1)/I_0(\lambda_2)$, the ratio of center-of-disk intensities at the two wavelengths.

Similarly, from Eq. 25),

$$\rho_r = \rho_0 \left(\frac{13 - 7u_1}{13 - 7u_2}\right). \tag{29}$$

From Allen (1963), for $\lambda_1 = 6000$ Å and $\lambda_2 = 4500$ Å, $u_1 = 0.55$ and $u_2 = 0.73$.

Thus $\rho_t = 1.12\rho_0$ and $\rho_r = 1.16\rho_0$. Both components are thus significantly redder than the center of the disk, as one might expect since short waves are more strongly limb-darkened than longer waves. Somewhat less obvious, though, is the measurable reddening of the radial compared to the tangential electric vector.

Both polarized components of radiation scattered by a condensation near the limb are redder than the integral solar radiation (averaged over the disk) as seen from the earth. We can evaluate the latter radiation directly for a bundle of parallel rays leaving the solar hemisphere. If ψ, as before, is the angle between a ray from an element of surface ds and a solar radius,

$$Q = \int_{\text{hemisphere}} I \cos \psi \, ds. \tag{30}$$

If we substitute (13), and $2\pi r^2 \sin \psi \, d\psi$ for ds, and integrate from $\psi = 0$ to $\psi = \pi 2$, we get

$$Q = \frac{\pi I_0 \sin^2 \Omega}{2}\left(1 - \frac{u}{?}\right), \tag{31}$$

or, for the radiation scattered by a condensation very far from the sun,

$$I_t = \frac{\pi I_0 \sigma N_e \sin^2 r}{2}\left(1 - \frac{u}{3}\right)$$

$$I_r = 0. \tag{32}$$

(Equation [32] may also be obtained by evaluating Eqs. [18] and [19] for very small Ω.)

Thus from Eq. (32) we have $\rho_t = \rho_0[(3 - u_1)/(3 - u_2)] = 1.08\rho_0$, confirming that the integrated solar radiation is less red than either component of the K corona.

The phenomenon of reddening of the radial electric vector compared to the tangential near the sun might be used as a supplement to the method used by Saito and Billings (1964) for determining the position of a coronal feature with respect to the limb along a line of sight. Saito and Billings used the degree of polarization, which can be shown from Eqs. (18) and (19) to increase with distance in front of or behind the limb for lines of sight close to the limb, and to decrease for more distant lines of sight. Their method is of little value in the vicinity of $1.1R_\odot$, however, and since the reddening of the radial electric vector decreases monotonically with distance from the limb one might use it in the three-dimensional location of a coronal feature.

Equations (18) and (19) are suitable for computing the two polarization components of coronal light from a condensation in which some special distribution of density in space is postulated. In the special case in which one assumes a spherically symmetrical model for the electron-density distribution, $N_e = N_e(r)$. In this case we note that for a line of sight passing at distance h from the solar limb, Ω and χ are both functions of r; $\sin \chi = (h + R_\odot)/r$ and $\sin \Omega = R_\odot/r$, hence we can express $(A, B, C, D) = f(\Omega)$ as $(A, B, C, D) = g(r)$. Furthermore, an element of path dx containing $N_e \, dx$ electrons per square centimeter of cross section, when expressed in terms r is,

$$dx = \frac{r \, dr}{[r^2 + (h + R_\odot)^2]^{1/2}}.$$

When we substitute into Eqs. (18) and (19), and integrate over the optical path along a line of sight, we have

$$\int I_t \, dx = I_0 \pi \sigma \int_h^\infty \frac{N_e(r) r}{[r^2 + (h + R_\odot)^2]^{1/2}} [(1 - u) \, C(r) + uD(r)] \, dr, \quad (33)$$

and

$$\int (I_t - I_r) \, dx = I_0 \pi \sigma \int_h^\infty \frac{(h + R_\odot)^2 N_e(r)}{r[r^2 + (h + R_\odot)^2]^{1/2}}$$

$$\times [(1 - u) \, A(r) + uB(r)] \, dr. \quad (34)$$

The problem with which we are usually confronted is not the evaluation of the integral in Eqs. (33) and (34), but, given I_t and I_r as functions of h, to determine $N_e(r)$. The process is obviously very laborious and worth carrying out only if the assumption of spherical symmetry can first be justified. The assumption is certainly not valid at or near the solar poles. In these regions lines of sight cross various polar plumes and may or may not intersect the protruding edges of fans. At times of high activity it cannot be valid near the limb in the equatorial regions, for the concentration of electron density over very active regions is much greater than elsewhere. If the active regions are so numerous in the active zones that they may be considered to form a uniform belt around the sun there might be some justification in an assumption of spherical symmetry—except that at times of such high activity some coronal condensations are almost certainly present with densities an order of magnitude or more greater than densities over the remaining active regions. Probably the safest situation for the assumption of spherical symmetry is in the equatorial extensions of the corona at times of sunspot minimum—and even in this case care must be taken not to choose lines of sight that depart very much from parallelism with the solar equator.

If, on the other hand, the assumption of spherical symmetry is not made there is generally no unique electron-density distribution to fit an eclipse observation. The situation is simplified if one is dealing with a condensation of such brightness that it can be considered to be highly localized along any line of sight. Thus, if the feature at a given apparent height above the limb displays a certain polarization, there are a unique pair of points, in front and behind the plane of the limb, at which the feature may be located. These points, in turn, specify the distance of the feature from the limb and its absolute brightness in either component of its radiation indicates its electron density—or at least the number of electrons along the line of sight.

In certain instances—as in the case of the polar corona at sunspot minimum, or streamers or condensations on the limb—it may be reasonable to assume that the distribution of density has cylindrical symmetry. In such cases one can determine the density as a function of distance (v) from the axis of symmetry (assumed to be in the plane of the sky), at a given height above the limb, by an inversion of the Abelian integral (van de Hulst, 1950). In order to proceed, however, it is necessary to assume that the scattering is isotropic. In this case, if $J(v)$ is the scattered radiation per unit solid angle from a cm³ at distance (v) from the axis of symmetry, then the observed brightness of the K corona at the projected distance x from the axis, as measured on the sky normal to the axis, is

$$K(x) = 2 \int_x^\infty J(v) \frac{v \, dv}{(v^2 - x^2)^{1/2}}. \tag{35}$$

The inversion of the integral is given in terms of $P(x) = -(1/x)\,dK/dx$ as

$$J(v) = \frac{1}{\pi} \int_{v}^{\infty} P(x)\, \frac{x\,dx}{(x^2 - v^2)^{1/2}}. \tag{36}$$

Thus, since $P(x)$ can be determined by measuring brightness along a line that crosses the cylindrical structure normal to its axis, then for each v a value $J(v)$ can be computed, either by analytical or numerical integration. In turn, v is $(R_{\odot} + h)\tan\theta$, where θ is the angle between the solar radius containing the scattering element and the axis of symmetry, and h is the height above the limb at which the line containing the various observations intersects the axis. Thus one may express $J(v)$ as $J(r, \theta)$.

If one assumes isotropic scattering, he finds that J is related to N_e, according to Eq. (6), by

$$J = \tfrac{2}{3}\sigma N_e\, I(\Omega). \tag{37}$$

This assumption introduces an error of the order of about 10%, as we have seen from a consideration of Eqs. (6) and (26). This error, in most cases, is no greater than errors introduced by the assumption of cylindrical symmetry in the first place.

C. Thermal Emission

Free–Free Emission

When a moving electron passes in the vicinity of a positive ion, it is accelerated by Coulomb attraction. Thus, from the classical point of view, it emits a pulse of electromagnetic energy in which the electric field at some distance from the electron is described by Eq. (1). The resulting component of the electric field along any coordinate is a peaked function of time. The function can be represented as a Fourier integral—that is, as the superposition of an infinite number of harmonic oscillations with properly chosen amplitudes. If a large number of electrons are sending out a sequence of identical pulses, an observer who is equipped to receive electromagnetic waves of various frequencies instead of separate pulses will detect a continuous spectrum of such waves. Other electrons passing the positive ions at other distances and with other velocities will emit pulses of different shapes, corresponding to a different distribution of frequencies. The observed free–free spectrum from the entire plasma might thus be obtained by integrating over various impact parameters and velocities, then summing over the different species of positive ions present.

In one of the early attacks on the problem by Kramers (1923) the procedure was somewhat different from that outlined above, in that the components of acceleration rather than electric field were represented by Fourier integrals. Other investigators have chosen other parameters of the electron–ion encounter, such as the electron velocity or the dipole moment, for the Fourier-integral representation (see Oster, 1961a). These various approaches are essentially equivalent. In any of them the frequencies that characterize an encounter are clustered about the reciprocal of the time spent by the electron in the vicinity of the ion—i.e., $\nu \sim v/p$ where p is the impact parameter and v the speed of the electron prior to the encounter. Thus low-frequency emission arises from distant encounters or low-speed electrons. Higher frequencies require closer encounters or faster electrons. Also, if the energy of a quantum of radiation emitted in the encounter is significant compared with the initial kinetic energy of the electrons, one cannot consider the emerging electron to be following the same Keplerian path as that with which it approached the ion. Consequently, the short-wavelength end of the free–free emission spectrum must be studied by the methods of quantum mechanics rather than by classical electrodynamics. Instead of Eq. (1) for relating acceleration to electromagnetic field, Kramers used the more familiar expression for radiation rate as a function of acceleration of the electron. We can derive this expression from Eq. (1) by noting that the energy density in an electric field is $E^2/8\pi$, and that in the electromagnetic field an equal magnetic-energy density is present. Thus the energy flux density is

$$I = \frac{cE^2}{4\pi} = \frac{c}{4\pi} \frac{\epsilon^2 a^2 \sin^2 \theta}{r^2 c^4} \tag{38}$$

at an angle θ from the direction of acceleration. The rate of emission is

$$R = \int_{4\pi r^2} I \, dS = \frac{\epsilon^2 a^2}{4\pi c^3} \int_0^{2\pi} \int_0^{\pi} \sin^3 \theta \, d\theta \, d\phi = \frac{2}{3} \frac{\epsilon^2 a^2}{c^3}. \tag{39}$$

Kramers did not evaluate the acceleration for a general hyperbolic orbit of the electron, but considered two special cases: (1) the case in which the orbit is very nearly parabolic and (2) the case in which it is very nearly a straight line. Oster (1961a), in a very thorough reconsideration of the entire problem of free–free emission at radio frequencies, kept the expression for the orbit in its general form. Both investigators arrived at expressions for the distribution of energy with frequency for an encounter in terms of Hankel functions of the frequency, collision parameter, and initial electron speed. (Hankel functions are defined as functions of ordinary Bessel functions.)

In integrating over collision parameters, Oster expanded the Hankel functions to a higher order of precision than in the expansion used by Kramers. Also, because he had maintained a general expression for the orbits, he was not forced, as Kramers had been, to an approximation in which the larger collision parameters were assumed to give straight-line orbits and the closer, parabolic orbits.

In spite of their differences, both procedures lead to an expression for the emission per unit volume in the frequency interval $d\nu$:

$$dE_{\mathrm{ff}}\,d\nu = \frac{32\pi^2 Z^2 \epsilon^6 N_i}{3\sqrt{3}c^3 m^2 v}\,g\,dN_e\,d\nu, \tag{40}$$

where N_i is the number of ions of charge Ze per unit volume, and dN_e is the number of electrons per unit volume with speed v in the range $d\nu$. m is the electron mass. Kramers introduced the factor g to correct for the fact that not all of the orbits are parabolic, and by a method of crude numerical evaluation concluded that the factor was close to unity. Oster evaluated g analytically, obtaining

$$g = \frac{3}{\pi}\ln\left[\frac{4\pi m}{Ze^2\nu}\left(\frac{2kT}{\gamma m}\right)^{3/2}\right], \tag{41}$$

where $\gamma = 1.78\ldots$ (Euler's Constant).

Integration of (40) over a Maxwellian distribution of initial velocities leads to an equation for the emission per unit volume per unit frequency in the form

$$E_{\mathrm{ff}} = \frac{64\pi^2 Z^2 \epsilon^6 N_i N_e}{3\sqrt{3}\,(2\pi kT)^{1/2} m^{3/2} C^3}\,g = \frac{6.83\times 10^{-38}\,Z^2 N_i N_e}{T^{1/2}}\,g = Kg, \tag{42}$$

sometimes referred to as Kramers' equation. From Eq. (42), Kramers inferred that to a first approximation the energy distribution was independent of frequency. Indeed, from Eq. (41) we see that the frequency dependence of the free–free emission, being logarithmic, is not strong except for very low frequencies.

The factor g plays an important role in radiation theory. As we have used it here, it may be regarded as the frequency-dependent part of the expression for free–free emission. Or it may alternatively be considered to be a correcting factor to apply to the parabolic-orbit approximation $E_{ff} = K$ of the Kramers' equation. Through evolution in the latter role it came to be considered by a number of investigators, including Gaunt, as a correction to apply to the Kramers equation, or any equations derived from this equation, to care for differences between quantum-mechanical and classical theory. As such a correction factor it is known as the Gaunt factor.

The conceptual basis of the quantum-mechanical approach is quite different from that of the classical approach. Each electron, instead of radiating throughout its passage through the field of an ion, emits a photon as it changes from one orbit to another. The probability of such an emission is governed by the dipole moment matrix element,

$$M = \int_{\tau} \psi_i r \psi_o^* \, d\tau, \tag{43}$$

where ψ_i is the wave function of the incident electron and ψ_o^* the complex conjugate of that of the outgoing electron. Oster (1961a) summarizes the work of Sommerfeld and others in evaluating these matrix elements and integrating over all directions of the outgoing waves (a process analogous to the classical process of integrating over all collision parameters), then over Maxwellian velocity distributions to obtain photon energy distributions. The general relationship derived by Sommerfeld is very complex. It is simplified by introducing approximations that are different for high-velocity than for low-velocity electrons. The result for low-velocity electrons goes over, in the limit of very long wavelengths, to Eq. (41), as should be the case if the Bohr correspondence principle holds. For high-velocity electrons, in the limit of long wavelengths,

$$g = \ln \frac{4kT}{h\nu}. \tag{44}$$

One is thus faced with the decision as to whether to use (41) or (44) for the Gaunt factor when dealing with the radio-frequency portion of the coronal spectrum. Oster considers this question in some detail (1961a,b) and concludes that for temperatures lower than 550,000°K the classical form (Eq. [41]) should be used. For higher temperatures one should use Eq. (44). At 550,000° the two give identical results.

The radio-frequency range constitutes one part of the coronal spectrum in which free–free emission is of interest. The other part is the far ultra-violet or X-ray range. Throughout the infrared, visible, and near ultraviolet spectrum the scattered photospheric light is much more intense than the free–free emission. It is obvious that the quantum-mechanical approach is essential for analysis of the XUV emission. By far the greatest part of the theoretical study of such emission has been carried out by Elwert, whose publications on the subject extend over a period of more than two decades. Among his conclusions, which are summarized in 1961, one is that the emission rate is given by

$$E_{ff} = Ke^{-h\nu/kT}g_{XUV}, \tag{45}$$

but that g_{XUV} must be determined numerically, as has been done by Greene (1959). The exponential factor does not really differentiate Eq. (45) from Eq. (42), since it is unity in the corona, to a high order of approximation, except in the XUV region. In the short-wavelength part of the XUV region, on the other hand, the factor plays a dominant role.

Free–Bound Emission

Using the quantum interpretation of Eq. (40) we can pass from free–free to free–bound emission, as Kramers did, by a simple algebraic manipulation. The logic behind the manipulation has difficulties that are by no means trivial, however. Let us consider the velocity range of the incident electrons in free–free emission to be so narrow that the entire frequency range $d\nu$ in Eq. (40) defines the width of a band of energies from among the emergent electrons—i.e.,

$$d(h\nu) = d(\tfrac{1}{2}mv^2 - \tfrac{1}{2}mv_f^2) = -mv_f \, dv_f, \tag{46}$$

where v_f is the velocity of the emergent electrons.

We can alternatively express Eq. (46) in a form resembling the Balmer equation:

$$d(h\nu) = d\left(\frac{hRZ^2}{\kappa^2} - \frac{hRZ^2}{\kappa_f^2}\right) = \frac{2hRZ^2}{\kappa_f^3} \, d\kappa_f. \tag{47}$$

Here we have used the elegant notation devised by Menzel and Pekeris (1935) to bring out the continuity between discrete and continuous processes. According to this notation the quantum number n, which designates the energy levels in the Balmer formula

$$\nu = RZ^2\left(\frac{1}{n^2} - \frac{1}{n_2^2}\right) \qquad R = \frac{2\pi^2\epsilon^4 m}{h^3}, \tag{48}$$

changes from the real integer n to the continuous imaginary number $i\kappa$ as

n passes through its infinite limit and the energy levels change from negative to positive. Thus the continuum of levels of the free electron is defined by the positive real number κ, which can assume fractional as well as integral values. At the base of the continuum, $n = \kappa = \infty$, and higher levels in the continuum are identified by decreasing values of κ. A free–free emission, according to this notation, is a transition from a state designated by a smaller to that designated by a larger continuous quantum number. In Eq. (47) $d\kappa_f$ designates an interval in the continuous sequence of numbers in which the quantum number designating the final state is located.

If the final state is a bound state, we have for our Balmer formula

$$\nu = RZ^2 \left(\frac{1}{\kappa^2} + \frac{1}{n^2} \right). \tag{49}$$

Now if we deal with (49) in the same manner as we have (47), we obtain

$$|\, d\nu \,| = \frac{2RZ^2}{n^3} \, dn. \tag{50}$$

We would like to interpret dn as *the integral number of discrete states lying in an infinitesimal interval of bound-electron energies.* Such an interpretation is approximately correct for large n, for which the energy levels lie very close together. Indeed we can justify our violation of the concepts of elementary calculus, our differentiation of a discontinuous function, by pointing out that since spectral lines always have a certain amount of natural and instrumental broadening the higher bound levels of an atom are not operationally different in nature from the continuum. Rigorous arguments for extending the interpretation of dn to lower bound levels become difficult to muster. Perhaps we should simply regard the application of the formula that we shall derive from this interpretation to all bound levels as an act of faith in the uniformity of nature, and let the Gaunt factor take care of any discrepancy that may be present.

We proceed by substituting Eq. (50) into Eq. (40) and dividing through by dn to obtain the free–bound emission per bound state:

$$E_{\text{fb}} \, d\nu' = \frac{2^6 \pi^2 Z^4 \epsilon^6 N_i \, dN_e \, gR}{3\sqrt{3}\, C^3 m^2 n^3 \nu}. \tag{51}$$

Here the frequency range $d\nu'$ arises from the distribution of velocities among the group of incident electrons, dN_e. Although we have assumed this range of energies of the free particles to be very narrow compared to that described by the band of quantum numbers dn, we consider it broad compared to the width of a single bound level. Correspondingly,

$$dv' = \frac{mv\,dv}{h}. \tag{52}$$

Also, since the velocity of the free electrons obeys a Maxwellian distribution,

$$dN_\epsilon = 4\pi N_e \left(\frac{m}{2\pi kT}\right)^{3/2} \exp\,(-mv^2/2kT)v^2\,dv. \tag{53}$$

When we substitute (52) and (53) into (51), we have

$$E_{\rm fb} = \frac{2^9 \pi^5 Z^4 \epsilon^{10} m \exp\,(-mv^2/2kT)N_i N_e}{3\sqrt{3}\,C^3(2\pi mkT)^{3/2}h^2 n^3}. \tag{54}$$

The velocity of the electron appears only in the exponential term of Eq. (54). Aller (1963) has removed it explicitly by introducing $v_n = RZ^2/n^2$, the lowest free–bound frequency associated with level n. Then, since

$$h\nu = h\nu_n + \tfrac{1}{2}mv^2, \tag{55}$$

$$E_{\rm fb} = \frac{2^9 \pi^5 Z^4 \epsilon^{10} mg N_i N_e}{3\sqrt{3}\,C^3(2\pi mkT)^{3/2}h^2 n^3} \exp\left[-\frac{h(\nu - \nu_n)}{kT}\right]$$

$$= 2.16 \times 10^{-32} \frac{Z^4 g N_i N_e}{n^3 T^{3/2}} \exp\left[-\frac{h(\nu - \nu_n)}{kT}\right]. \tag{56}$$

Equation (56) applies only to hydrogen and hydrogen-like atoms. In the corona such atoms are in the great majority, since helium as well as hydrogen is totally ionized. Also, to a free electron, the electric field of a highly ionized metal atom is nearly hydrogenic. Because of the Z^4 factor the metal ions play a strong role in producing free–bound emission. In recombination to a certain level in O VIII, for example, the resulting free–bound emission is 2.7 times as great (using Allen's 1963 chemical abundances) as recombination from the same continuum energy to a corresponding level in hydrogen. The O VIII frequencies are, of course, a great deal higher than the hydrogen frequencies to which they are being compared. The wavelength of the Lyman series limit for O VIII is about 14 Å, $1/Z^2$ that of the hydrogen Lyman series. At 14 Å and coronal temperatures the hydrogen Lyman continuum has dropped, in accordance with the exponential factor of Eq. (56), to about one-fifth of its value at the series limit. Thus we see that at wavelengths sufficiently short to fall within the continua arising from recombinations to the ground state of coronal ions the free–bound emissions for the more populous heavy ions are each an order of magnitude greater than that for hydrogen. At wavelengths short of its Lyman limit, 228 Å, the helium free–bound emission is also greater than the hydrogen free–bound, by about a factor of 2. Throughout this range it is very nearly equal to the hydrogen free–free emission.

In terms of percentage of the total thermal continuum emission in the corona, we can say that at wavelengths longer than ultraviolet free–free interaction of electrons with hydrogen nuclei contributes about 70% of the emission, interactions with heavy ions 1 or 2%, and interactions with helium nuclei the remainder. At the Lyman limit of hydrogen, hydrogen free–bound interactions begin to contribute about 10% of the emission, but this percentage drops off with decreasing wavelength. Helium free–bound emission comes in at its Lyman limit, about twice as strong percentagewise as the free-bound limit of hydrogen, but also drops off rapidly with higher frequencies. In the meantime, free–bound recombinations to higher states in the metals begin to be significant, and as ground-state series limits begin to appear, the free–bound metal contribution increases enormously. Finally, at about 10 Å, free–bound transitions to metals are contributing about 80% of the thermal continuum emission, hydrogen free–free transitions about 15%, and the helium free–free transitions about 5%. Remaining processes are relatively insignificant. These results must be regarded as rather crude approximations. They are in line with those found by Acton (1964) but disagree considerably with the conclusions of Fetisov (1963) for the 2–10 Å region. Part of the discrepancy is due to the choice of H/He ratio for the corona. Another is that the abundance of the various ions, as a function of temperature, was computed by Fetisov without recourse to the concept of dielectronic recombination.

In a more precise computation than ours, one should use the best available value for the Gaunt factor. The results of recent computations of this factor are given by Greene (1959), Kazachevskaya and Ivanov-Kholodnyi (1960), Karzas and Latter (1961), and Brussaard and van de Hulst (1962).

Continuum Opacity in the Corona

The coefficients for either free–free or bound–free absorption at a given frequency can be determined by dividing the emission coefficient for the corresponding process at that frequency by the Planck black-body emission function—i.e.,

$$k_\nu = \frac{E_\nu}{B_\nu}. \tag{57}$$

The use of Eq. (57) in this context deserves justification, since it is generally applicable only in the case of thermodynamic equilibrium. Let us consider first the case of free–free emission and absorption by hydrogen and helium ions in the corona. If the corona were sufficiently vast that it was optically deep at all wavelengths, and all parts of it were at the same kinetic temperature, any volume deep within such a huge aggregate of gas would be strictly in thermodynamic equilibrium, and Eq. (57) could be applied without question. If now we compare the actual with the hypothetical case, we see that the primary difference is that the radiation field is much more intense in the hypothetical equilibrium corona than in the actual corona. The state of the electrons and the hydrogen and helium ions is precisely the same in both cases. Consequently, the interactions between electrons and protons or α particles to produce radiation will take place in exactly the same manner in the two cases. The absorption coefficient in any case describes only the manner in which an atomic system will interact with a passing photon. It depends only on the condition of the atomic system and not on the radiation field in which it is immersed. Thus, since in both cases the hydrogen and helium atoms are completely ionized and the kinetic state of electrons and ions is the same in the two cases, the fraction of photons absorbed by free–free transitions will also be the same.

When we examine free–bound transitions with hydrogen or helium, or either free–free or free–bound interactions of the electrons with heavy ions, the situation appears to be complicated by the fact that the degree of ionization and the states of excitation are considerably different in the corona than in an equilibrium corona. Again, however, the nature of the interaction of the electrons with a given ion in a given state is identical to what it would be in the equilibrium case. We need only to include the actual rather than the equilibrium density of ions in each state in computing the emission for substitution in Eq. (57).

We can obtain a general idea of the continuum opacities in the corona by applying (57) to free–free emission in the radio wavelength range, and to free–bound emission by one of the heavy ions in the XUV range In the former case we can use the Rayleigh-Jeans approximation for the Planck law, and for wavelengths of 30 Å or less in the second case, the Wien approximation. The radio optical depth so determined can be expressed as

$$\tau_{ff} = 2.47 \times 10^{-22} \lambda^2 Z^2 \frac{N_i}{N_e} \int_0^\infty \frac{N_e^2}{T^{3/2}} \, dh, \tag{58}$$

and the X-ray,

$$\tau_{fb} = 1.47 \times 10^{15} \frac{Z^4 g}{\nu^3} \frac{N_{i,n}}{N_e} \int_0^\infty \frac{\exp{(h\nu_n/kT)}}{T^{3/2}} \, N_e^2 \, dh. \tag{59}$$

The van de Hulst (1953) model for the equatorial corona during sunspot maximum gives

$$\int_0^\infty N_e^2 \, dh$$

to be approximately 10^{27}. The Newkirk model (1961) gives about four times this amount outside of coronal enhancements and 16 times as much in coronal enhancements. If we assume that the temperature throughout the corona is a constant 2,000,000°, we conclude that the optical depth is nearly unity for meter-wavelength radiation, using the van de Hulst model. Using the Newkirk model outside and inside regions of coronal enhancement, the same optical depth is attained for wavelengths of 50 and 25 cm, respectively. In radiation longer than 3 or 4 m the corona can be regarded as a black body, whereas for wavelengths of a few centimeters and shorter it is optically thin and the total radiation can be computed by integrating the emission along a line of sight.

The latter conclusion can be confirmed by applying Eq. (59) to free–bound emission leading to the formation of ground-state Fe XIV. We assume that at a temperature of 2,000,000° this ion in its ground state constitutes about one-fourth of all iron ions, and conclude that the optical depth is about 10^{-19}. Thus it follows that all of the heavy ions in the corona combined cannot introduce significant opacity in the X-ray region of the spectrum.

Line Emission

Most of the information necessary for analysis of line emission is found in Chapter 5. For computing the emission rate in optical lines we simply multiply the number of ions in the excited state per unit volume by the product of the spontaneous-emission coefficient and the energy per photon, $h\nu$.

Considerable interest has been aroused by Mogilevskii *et al.* (1960) in recent years concerning the possibility of polarization in these optical lines. The coronal ions are subjected to the same anisotropic radiation field as the free electrons, and if they were without electron spin and initially in an s state, the degree of polarization of the radiationally excited emission would be identical with that of the K corona (Seaton, 1964). In actual coronal ions, however, the effect of spin–orbit interaction is to produce a precession that tends to destroy the orientation of the atom before the emission takes place As a result, the polarization expected in the red line is zero, as pointed out by Seaton (1964), Charvin (1964), and Hyder (1966). The polarization expected in the green line is reduced for the same reason by a factor somewhat less than 0.5. Charvin and Hyder have pointed out, further, that even a small magnetic field would reduce the polarization much more, an effect that we shall discuss further in Chapter 10, "Magnetic Fields in the Corona."

Expected emission rates for various XUV lines have been computed by Ivanov-Kholodnyi and Nikolskii (1962), Bodenheimer *et al.* (1963), and Fetisov (1963, 1964) by equating rate of emission to rate of collisional excitation from the ground state. The justification for this procedure is that the lifetimes of the excited states are very short, so no opportunity exists for the atom to be de-excited by any process other than radiation. The procedure overlooks the important phenomenon of population of the excited states from higher levels. Pottasch (1964) took this additional effect into account by assuming it to be 25% as effective as collisional excitation to the first excited level from the ground state. Bodenheimer, Brandt, and Robbins similarly assumed a 50% correction in computing the total XUV line emission. Both corrections are probably somewhat too low. If we accept the conclusion by Burgess and Seaton (1964) that dielectronic recombination increases the recombination rate by a factor of about 20, it follows that for each ion the line emission resulting from dielectronic recombination alone is about 20 times as energetic as the free–bound emission. Bodenheimer, Brandt, and Robbins, however, have concluded from their computations that emission resulting from collisional excitation from the ground state to the first excited level is only about 20 times as energetic as free–bound emission from the heavy ions. Thus, if dielectronic emission were the only cascade process involved, the correction should be 100%; and since other processes are almost certainly involved, the correction should be even higher.

In summary, whereas line emission in the XUV spectrum is by far the most important radiative mechanism for the discharge of energy from the corona, the theory is in a much less satisfactory state than that of free–free and free–bound emission. Many lines have been predicted that have not been identified, and many other lines have been found in the spectrum that had not been predicted. The intensities of many lines, particularly from ions in high states of ionization, have been quite unexpected, and the theory for the intensity of all lines is still beset with many uncertainties.

D. Magnetic Emission

Thermal Magnetic Emission

A coronal electron experiencing centripetal acceleration in its spiral orbit about magnetic lines of force emits radiation in accordance with the laws of classical electrodynamics. If the velocity of the electron is small compared to that of light we may express the electric intensity in such radiation by Eq. (1). It is convenient to write Eq. (1) in vector form for substitution of the Lorentz acceleration $\epsilon \mathbf{v} \times \mathbf{B}/mc$. We obtain

$$\mathbf{E} = \epsilon^2 \frac{\mathbf{r} \times [\mathbf{r} \times (\mathbf{v} \times \mathbf{H})]}{r^3 mc^3}. \tag{60}$$

Here $\mathbf{r}$ is the vector from the observer to the center of the circle described by the electron.

The radiation described by (60) is elliptically polarized, the ratio of the major to the minor axis of the ellipse being the cosine of the angle between $\mathbf{r}$ and $\mathbf{H}$. The frequency is found by equating Lorentz to centripetal force:

$$\frac{\epsilon v_\perp H}{c} = \frac{m v_\perp^2}{r}, \tag{61}$$

from which the angular frequency,

$$\omega_L = \frac{v_\perp}{r} = \frac{\epsilon H}{mc} = 1.76 \times 10^7 H \tag{62}$$

is seen to be independent of the velocity of the electron, depending only on the intensity of the magnetic field. For fields of 10 gauss or more the frequencies of such radiation are accessible to ground-based receivers of sufficient sensitivity.

The power radiated per electron is given by the substitution of the Lorentz acceleration into Eq. (39). In the substitution, since v includes two degrees of freedom, $v^2 = \frac{2}{3}v^2 = 2kT/m$. Hence,

$$P = \frac{4}{3}\,\frac{\epsilon^4 kTH^2}{m^3c^5}\ \text{ergs/sec.} \tag{63}$$

If we substitute a plausible active region magnetic field—100 gauss, for example—into Eq. (63), we come to the remarkable conclusion that only a few centimeters of corona are necessary to provide black-body emission at the gyrofrequency. Since active regions in the corona could contain magnetic fields of various intensities, one might expect the gyroemission from such regions to completely dominate the free–free emission over a wide range of wavelengths. The reason it does not is that at the gyro-frequency the velocity of the extraordinary electromagnetic wave emitted by the electrons in the coronal plasma is essentially zero. The magnetic plasma does not permit such waves to escape, but, like a hot piece of burnished metal, reflects the thermal conditions of its environment rather than emitting according to its own temperature. The radiation that we receive from the corona has not been reflected from this $\omega = \omega_L$ level, however, but from a higher level that results from the coupling of gyrations and plasma oscillations (see Section E). This second reflecting layer is so located that

$$\frac{\omega_L}{\omega} = 1 - \frac{\omega_P{}^2}{\omega^2}. \tag{64}$$

When we substitute the Larmour and plasma frequencies we get

$$\frac{\epsilon H}{mc\omega} = 1 - \frac{4\pi N_\epsilon \epsilon^2}{m\omega^2}. \tag{65}$$

Since the right-hand side of Eq. (65) is obviously less than unity, the reflection must occur for a smaller magnetic field than that which makes $\omega_L = \omega$. Now since magnetic fields generally decrease with height in the corona, we conclude that the reflecting layer described by Eqs. (64) and (65) lies above that described by Eq. (62). Thus the fundamental frequency in the thermal gyroradiation is well obscured from our view.

The modification of optical paths is only one of several ways in which the presence of magnetic fields affects radiation from the corona. Any radiation, no matter what its origin, becomes circularly polarized in passing along a magnetic field in a plasma. Thus an unpolarized radiation at the gyrofrequency, resulting from free–free emission, would be broken into an ordinary and an extraordinary component. The latter would be suppressed and the former transmitted, causing the outgoing radiation to be circularly polarized. Optical depths for radiation at all frequencies are increased by the presence of the magnetic field, the greatest effect being at the gyrofrequency.

It is important that harmonics of the gyrofrequency can escape, even though the fundamental cannot. That they are emitted can be demonstrated from a more precise expression than Eq. (60):

$$\mathbf{E} = \epsilon^2 \frac{\mathbf{r} \times [\mathbf{r} \times (\mathbf{v} \times \mathbf{B})]}{r^3 m c^3} \left(1 + \frac{\mathbf{v} \cdot \mathbf{r}}{cr} \right)^{-3} \tag{66}$$

(Griem, 1964). The correction term, which is negligible only for very small electron velocities, results from the varying spatial relationship of the electron and the observer during the course of a gyration. According to Kakinuma and Swarup (1962) these harmonics are necessary in explaining simultaneously the relative intensity and the polarization of 10- and 3-cm radiation from active regions in the corona.

Synchrotron Radiation

If the velocities of electrons in a magnetic field approach the speed of light, the equations that we have developed for gyroradiation no longer hold. Schwinger (1949) based his thorough analysis of the resulting problem on the modifications necessary to keep the scalar quantity, the power generated, invariant to a Lorentz transformation from the framework of the observer to that of the moving electron.

The modification of the power equation is relatively simple, giving

$$P = \frac{2}{3} \frac{\epsilon^4 H^2 v^2}{m^2 c^5 (1 - \beta^2)^2}, \qquad \beta = \frac{v}{c}. \tag{67}$$

The more remarkable change appears in the manner in which the radiation is emitted. With increasing electron speed, the radiation becomes confined to an increasingly narrow cone of angle $\theta = 1 - \beta^2$ with axis in the direction of the moving electron. Thus only an observer in or near the orbital plane of an electron will see the radiation from that electron, and then only as a sequence of short pulses that repeat with the gyrofrequency. The Fourier analysis of the pulsed spectrum gives a continuous spectrum in which the intensity increases gradually with frequency to the vicinity of

$$\omega_c = \tfrac{3}{2} \omega_L (1 - \beta^2)^{-3/2}, \tag{68}$$

then decreases rather abruptly for higher frequencies. The radiation is highly polarized.

We see from Eq. (68) that the continuous synchrotron spectrum of sufficiently energetic electrons may extend into the visible range, even in magnetic fields for which the gyrofrequencies are in the radio range. Thus, if such electrons are present in the corona, the visible portion of their radiation would be included in the white-light corona and might be detected through a nonradial orientation of the magnetic vector in the polarized radiation.

Attempts to detect any anomaly in the polarization of the white-light corona have generally yielded negative results (Ney *et al.*, 1961; Saito and Yamashita, 1962). These observations can be construed to indicate only that relativistic electrons are not present in the everyday corona. If a violent solar event should be in progress during K-coronameter observations or an eclipse at which careful polarigraphic measurements were being made, the results might be quite different.

Although synchrotron emission in the visible range requires electron velocities that are a significant fraction of the speed of light, the electron energy may be two or three orders of magnitude below that for radio-frequency synchrotron radiation. Thus we are not surprised to find types of solar radio noise that are readily explained by the synchrotron mechanism—the Type-IV and Type-V bursts. The continuum emission in these bursts, the circular polarization, the occurrence in association with solar events in which we would expect magnetic fields to play an important role, and their high association with the incidence of high-energy solar protons on the earth all support this explanation of the phenomena.

E. Plasma Emission

It has long been realized that coherent oscillations due to internal electrostatic forces might be set up in a plasma. One of the easiest ways to see that this is so is to visualize a thin slab of the plasma. If the negative charge in the plasma is displaced a small distance x centimeters in the direction of the thickness of the slab there will result a thin layer of negative charge of $N\epsilon x$ electrostatic units per square centimeter on one face of the slab, and an equal positive charge on the opposite face. Thus we will have a situation similar to that of a charged parallel-plate condenser. $4\pi N_e \epsilon x$ lines of force will leave the positive face, cross the neutral portion of the slab, and terminate on the negative charges. The force on each square centimeter of negative charge will be $4\pi(N_e \epsilon x)^2$ acting on a mass of $N_e m x$ grams. The acceleration of this mass is thus $4\pi N_e \epsilon^2 x/m$, directed toward the equilibrium position. The motion so described is simple harmonic, damped only by an occasional collision of electrons with positive ions. The period, $\omega_P = (4\pi N_e \epsilon^2/m)^{1/2}$, is known as the *plasma frequency*.

Since they were first distinguished as separate types of solar radio noise, the narrow-band Type-II and Type-III bursts have been identified with the oscillation of the coronal plasma through which some kind of disturbance was passing. The observed radio frequency has generally been considered to be equal to the plasma frequency at the disturbed level in the corona, and the decreasing frequency with time, to indicate the upward motion of the disturbance through the corona. This concept has proved to be extremely useful in the interpretation of Type-II and Type-III bursts. Wild *et al.* (1954) and others have used it to conclude that Type-II bursts travel at a speed comparable to that of higher velocity flare surges, but that Type-III bursts progress with a few tenths of the speed of light. Although difficulties have been encountered in the precise equating of velocities computed from Type-II bursts with those observed in simultaneously occurring optical surges, and the question has arisen whether the observed frequency is the plasma frequency or its second harmonic, and although the great velocity suggested by the frequency drifts in Type-III bursts remains a source of constant amazement, the role of plasma oscillations in such phenomena has come to be a well-established part of our thinking.

In spite of its general acceptance, the idea that plasma oscillations are the source of Type-II and Type-III bursts has left many questions unanswered. What, for example, is the nature of the disturbance that excites the oscillations? Also, just what kind of interaction takes place between the disturbance and the corona to set the latter into oscillation? Perhaps the most difficult question of all has been: What is the coupling between the plasma and the electromagnetic field? In other words: If the plasma oscillates, why does it follow that electromagnetic radiation of the plasma frequency must be emitted? Finally, how is it possible that energies so much in excess of those emitted by black-body radiation may appear at the emitted frequencies in these and other radio bursts?

The most recent answer to these questions to date has come from Altschuler and Oster (Oster and Altschuler, 1964; Altschuler, 1964). These investigators have analyzed in detail the electric and magnetic field and the distribution of matter in a plasma as a positive ion (test particle) of various velocities passes through it. They concluded that if the velocity of the test particle is less than the thermal velocity of the electrons, the cloud of electrons surrounding the ion—the Debye shield—will be flattened in the direction of motion of the ion. If its velocity is greater than the electron thermal velocity, the Debye shield cannot surround it, but will extend backward in the form of a Mach cone. Along the axis of the cone— i.e., along the path just traversed by the test particle—the electric potential will go through a sequence of maxima and minima, the minima being spaced behind the test particle at intervals of $2\pi(u^2 - v^2)^{1/2}/\omega_P$, where u = speed of test particle and v = electron thermal velocity kT/m.

The electric and magnetic fields consistent with the perturbed density distribution in the plasma and the velocities of the test and perturbed particles do not constitute a radiation field. The Poynting flux corresponding to these fields, integrated over an infinite sphere, is zero. It is the interaction of these fields with the unperturbed electrons that gives rise to the observed radiation. If the velocity of the test particle is less than the electron thermal velocity, the spectrum of the resulting radiation maximizes at zero frequency. There is no resonant frequency. Consequently, if the frequency-drift rate of Type-II bursts is given its usual interpretation, leading to subsonic velocities, the narrow-band spectrum cannot be explained by the Altschuler mechanism. It appears necessary to attribute a supersonic substructure to Type-II bursts in spite of their subsonic general motion—a concept that Smerd *et al.* (1960) expressed some time ago.

Type-III bursts fit more simply into the theory. The radiation resulting from the passage of a supersonic ion through a plasma maximizes strongly at $\omega_r = \omega_P/[1 - (v^2/u^2)]^{1/2}$. The higher the test-particle velocity, the sharper the resonance, and of course, the closer the resonant frequency to the plasma frequency.

If other ions follow the test ion they will tend to collect in the potential minima mentioned above. When so located, their fields combine with the leading electron or electrons to enhance the even harmonics in the radio noise. The intensity of the emitted radiation is proportional to the sums of the squares of the charges in various charge aggregates. The power radiated by a "Mach-6" test particle (speed 6 times the electron thermal velocity) is 10^{-22} ergs/sec. Since the power depends on the square of the number of test particles in each aggregate, an important consideration with regard to the energy requirements for the mechanism is the stability of an aggregate against disruption due to Coulomb repulsion. This stability depends on the depth of the potential minima. Oster and Altschuler have not reported any detailed considerations of this problem. The theory now appears to be developed to the point that a detailed description of the geometric distribution of charge in a stream of test particles, to fit some actual observed Type-III bursts, is in order.

Malville (1961) had already considered the generation of Type-III bursts in the wake of fast-moving particles, but had rejected the idea on the grounds of efficiency in favor of the generation of plasma oscillations in the shock front preceding the particles.

REFERENCES

Acton, L. W. (1964). X-radiation from the sun. Ph.D. Thesis, University of Colorado.

Allen, C. W. (1963). "Astrophysical Quantities," 2nd Ed. Oxford University Press (Athlone).

Aller, L. H. (1963). "Astrophysics—The Atmospheres of the Sun and Stars," 2nd Ed. Ronald Press, New York.

Altschuler, M. D. (1964). Interaction of fast charged particles with the coronal plasma. Ph.D. Thesis, Yale University.

Bodenheimer, P., Brandt, J. C., and Robbins, R. R. (1963). Interplanetary gas VIII on the importance of radiative losses. Icarus 2, 411.

Brussaard, P. J., and van de Hulst, H. C. (1962). Approximation formulas for nonrelativistic Bremsstrahlung and average gaunt factors for a Maxwellian gas. Rev. Mod. Phys. 34, 507.

Burgess, A. and Seaton, M. (1964). The ionization equilibrium for iron in the solar corona. M. N. R. A. S. 127, 355.

Charvin, P. (1964). On the intensity and polarization of forbidden lines of the solar corona. Compt. rend. 258, 1155.

Elwert, G. (1961). Theory of X-ray emission of the sun. J. G. R. 66, 391.

Fetisov, E. P., (1963). Solar coronal emission in the soft X-ray region. Cosmic Res. 1, 171.

Fetisov, E. P. (1964). Coronal radiation shortward of 10 Å. Soviet Astronomy A. J. 8, 251.

Greene, J. (1959). Bremsstrahlung from a Maxwellian gas. Ap. J. 130, 693.

Griem, H. R. (1964). "Plasma Spectroscopy." Mc-Graw-Hill, New York.

Hyder, C. L. (1966). The polarization of emission lines in astronomy. III. The polarization of coronal emission lines. Ap. J. 141, 78.

Ivanov-Kholodnyi, G. S., and Nikolskii, G. M. (1962). A prediction of solar line emission in the extreme UV. Sov. Astr.-A. J. 5, 632.

Kakinuma, T., and Swarup, G. (1962). A model for the sources of the slowly-varying component of microwave solar radiation. Ap. J. 136, 975.

Karzas, W. J., and Latter, R. (1961). Electron radiative transitions in a Coulomb field. Ap. J. Suppl. 6, 167.

Kazachevskaya, T. V., and Ivanov-Kholodnyi, G. S. (1960). Continuous solar emission in the X-ray region. Sov. Astr.-A. J. 3, 937.

Kramers, H. A. (1923). On the theory of X-ray absorption and of the continuous X-ray spectrum. Phil. Mag. [6] 44, 836.

Malville, J. M. (1961). Studies of fast-drift radio bursts and related phenomena. Thesis, University of Colorado.

Menzel, D. H., and Pekeris, C. L. (1935). Absorption coefficients and hydrogen line intensities. *M. N. R. A. S.* **96,** 77.

Minnaert, M. (1930). On the continuous spectrum of the corona and its interpretation. *Z. Ap.* **1,** 209.

Mogilevskii, E. I., Nikolskii, G. M., and Nikol'skaya, K. I. (1960). The polarization of coronal emission lines. *Sov. Astr.-A. J.* **4,** 225.

Newkirk, G., Jr. (1961). The solar corona in active regions and the thermal origin of the slowly varying component of solar radio radiation. *Ap. J.* **133,** 983.

Ney, E. P., Huch, W. F., Kellogg, P. J., Stein, W., and Gillett, F. (1961). Polarization and intensity studies of the eclipse of October 2, 1959. *Ap. J.* **133,** 616.

Oster, L. (1961a). Emission, absorption and conductivity of a fully ionized gas at radio frequencies. *Rev. Mod. Phys.* **33,** 525.

Oster, L. (1961b). Emission and absorption of thermal radio radiation. *Ap. J.* **134,** 1010.

Oster, L., and Altschuler, M. (1964). Electromagnetic radiation from plasma oscillations. "AAS-NASA Symposium on the Physics of Solar Flares, 1963." N. A. S. A., Washington, D. C.

Pottasch, S. R. (1964). On the interpretation of the solar UV emission line spectrum. *Space Sci. Rev.* **3,** 816.

Saito, K., and Yamashita, Y. (1962). Polarigraphic observations of the solar corona at the total eclipse on October 12, 1958 in the Southern Pacific. *Ann. Tokyo Astr. Obs.* **7,** 163.

Saito, K., and Billings, D. E. (1964). Polarimetric observations of a coronal condensation. *Ap. J.* **140,** 760. (1964).

Schwinger, J. (1949). On the classical radiation of accelerated electrons. *Phys. Rev.* **75,** 1912.

Seaton, M. J. (1964). The spectrum of the solar corona. *Planetary and Space Sci.* **12,** 55.

Smerd, S. F., Wild, J. P., and Sheridan, K. V. (1960). On the relative position and origin of harmonics in the spectra of solar radio bursts of spectral Types II and III. *Aust. J. Phys.* **15,** 180.

van de Hulst, H. C. (1950). Electron density of the solar corona. *B. A. N.* **11,** 135.

van de Hulst, H. C. (1953). The chromosphere and corona. *In* "The Sun" (G. P. Kuiper, ed.), p. 207. Univ. of Chicago Press, Chicago, Illinois.

Wild, J. P., Murray, J. D., and Rowe, W. C. (1954). Harmonics in the spectra of solar radio disturbances. *Aust. J. Phys.* **7,** 439.

CHAPTER 7

THE MECHANICS OF THE CORONA

A. Introduction

The general problem of the mechanics of the corona is difficult because of great uncertainty concerning the framework in which it should be formulated. We expect, for example, that in much of the lower corona the motions of the coronal plasma are dominated by magnetic fields of photospheric origin—i.e., the current systems that determine the configuration of the magnetic fields are thought to lie primarily in or below the photosphere. We are uncertain, however, as to whether 1 gauss or 100 gauss is the better quantity for describing such fields. We expect that at some height above the limb the fields cease to dominate the mechanical state of the gas, but in our uncertainty concerning these fields we cannot specify that height. Finally, we are confronted with a host of hypotheses concerning shock waves that heat the corona or solar winds that carry it out into space, but have succeeded in gathering only crumbs of observational evidence to compare with these hypotheses. In the face of these uncertainties we shall attempt only to point out some of the basic dynamical principles that must hold, note some of the conclusions concerning the dynamical state of the corona that have been derived from these principles, and point out the observations that may have bearing on these conclusions.

B. Hydromagnetic Considerations

Frozen-In Magnetic Fields

The most positive statement that we can make concerning the hydromagnetic behavior of the corona is that the magnetic field is frozen into

174

the coronal gas. Any motion of the gas carries the magnetic field with it—or conversely, any change in the magnetic field carries the coronal gas into a new position. The two statements are not equivalent. The first implies a mechanical force within the corona—either pressure or impact by fast-moving material—that is sufficiently great to overcome and distort the magnetic field. We often make the rough statement that this can happen if the mechanical energy per unit volume in the corona, $\frac{1}{2} nmV^2$, is greater than the magnetic energy, $H^2/8\pi$. It would be more precise to say that the material can move the field if more mechanical energy is available, either in the form of gross kinetic energy or a differential in gravitational or pressure energy, than the gain in magnetic energy that results from the distortion of a magnetic field. On the other hand, motions in the photosphere may produce sufficient distortions of the magnetic field threading the corona to cause major disturbance of the coronal gas.

The frozen-in magnetic fields are a consequence of the high electrical conductivity of the coronal gas. In computing this conductivity, we begin with the concept of the conduction per electron (Spitzer, 1956). Let us suppose i_e = the current carried by a single electron that moves with speed u at an angle θ to the direction of net electron flow. Then

$$i_e = \frac{\epsilon u \cos \theta}{c} \text{ emu.} \tag{1}$$

The electron is retarded in its motion by interaction with the protons in the plasma. Only the component of the retarding force F opposite the direction of the net electron flow will be involved in power dissipation, however. The power dissipation by this force will be $Fu \cos \theta$. The conduction per electron, s, is defined to conform with the concept of ohmic power loss:

$$\frac{i^2}{s} = Fu \cos \theta. \tag{2}$$

But if t_D = time for the electron to lose its forward momentum, the mean force acting on the electron is

$$F = \frac{mu \cos \theta}{t_D}. \tag{3}$$

When we substitute for i and F in the power equation, we have

$$s = \frac{\epsilon^2 t_D}{m_e c^2}. \tag{4}$$

The conductivity of the medium will then be

$$\sigma = \frac{ne^2 \bar{t}_D}{m_e c^2},$$ (5)

where $\bar{t}_D$ is an average of t_D over a Maxwellian distribution. If we substitute for $\bar{t}_D$, from Eq. (13) Chapter 5, we have

$$\sigma = \frac{1}{c^2 \epsilon^2 \ln \Lambda} \left(\frac{\pi}{m}\right)^{1/2} \left(\frac{kT}{2}\right)^{3/2} \text{emu.}$$ (6)

In the corona this gives $\sigma = 8 \times 10^{-15} \, T^{3/2}$. Spitzer (1956) points out that the assumption of a stationary field of protons introduces an error of about a factor of 2. However, the value we have derived is entirely adequate for deducing the hydromagnetic behavior of the corona.

The rate of change of magnetic field in a conductive medium is

$$\frac{\partial \mathbf{H}}{\partial t} = \nabla \times (\mathbf{v} \times \mathbf{H}) + \frac{\nabla^2 \mathbf{H}}{4\pi\sigma}$$ (7)

(Cowling, 1957, p. 4).

Since $\partial \mathbf{H}/\partial t = \nabla \times (\mathbf{v} \times \mathbf{H})$ expresses the complete "freezing" of magnetic fields into the matter, whereas $\partial H/\partial t = n\nabla^2 \mathbf{H}$ describes the diffusion of a magnetic field through matter, the relative magnitudes of the first to the second term in Eq. (2) determines the extent to which the coronal matter will move with the lines of force.

If L is a distance through which H changes appreciably,

$$|\nabla \times (\mathbf{v} \times \mathbf{H})| \sim \frac{vH}{L}$$

and

$$\left|\frac{\nabla^2 \mathbf{H}}{\sigma}\right| \sim \frac{H}{\sigma L^2}.$$

Thus the condition that the magnetic field be frozen into the plasma is that $VL\sigma \gg 1$.

In the corona $\sigma \sim 10^{-5}$ emu. Speeds as small as 1 km/sec are of interest, and structural features as small as 10^4 km are readily observed. For such structures and speeds, $VL\sigma \sim 10^9$. Therefore, any magnetic fields that exist in such structures are definitely "frozen in."

The Hydromagnetic Equations

Equation (7) relates electromotive forces and may therefore be considered as a generalization of Ohm's law. It is frequently referred to as one of the two hydromagnetic equations. The other equation, relating forces in the hydromagnetic medium, is

$$\rho \frac{d\mathbf{v}}{dt} = -\nabla p + \rho \mathbf{g} + \rho \nu \, \nabla^2 \mathbf{v} + \frac{1}{4\pi} \, (\nabla \times \mathbf{H}) \times \mathbf{H}. \tag{8}$$

If we are dealing with rapidly moving aggregates of gas in the inner corona, or with the solar wind in the outer corona, viscous forces can be important. For the present we shall ignore them, however. Then the hydromagnetic equations reduce to

$$\rho \frac{d\mathbf{v}}{dt} = -\nabla p + \rho \mathbf{g} + \frac{1}{4\pi} \, (\nabla \times \mathbf{H}) \times \mathbf{H} \tag{9}$$

and

$$\frac{\partial H}{\partial t} = \nabla \times (\mathbf{v} \times \mathbf{H}). \tag{10}$$

Static Considerations

Let us consider now a static coronal feature. Equation (9) gives

$$\frac{1}{4\pi} \, (\nabla \times \mathbf{H}) \times \mathbf{H} = \nabla p - \rho \mathbf{g}. \tag{11}$$

Suppose a typical dimension of the feature is L, and the electron density $\sim 10^9$. Thus, $\nabla p \sim nkT/L \sim 10^{-1}/L$, whereas in general $(\nabla \times \mathbf{H}) \times \mathbf{H} \sim H^2/L$. Thus a magnetic field of a fraction of a gauss is adequate to maintain the most extreme density irregularities that we see in the corona. If the field is much stronger than 1 gauss, we may consider it to consist of two components, a small component obeying Eq. (11) and a larger component obeying

$$(\nabla \times \mathbf{H}) \times \mathbf{H} = 0. \tag{12}$$

A field described by Eq. (12) is called a "force-free field."

The magnetic configurations specified by Eq. (12) have been studied quite extensively. In general they must satisfy the condition

$$\nabla \times \mathbf{H} = c\mathbf{H} \tag{13}$$

(Ferraro and Plumpton, 1961), where α is a scalar function of space and time. If the configuration is stable, α is constant. In such a case the field is a solution of

$$\nabla^2\mathbf{H} + \alpha^2\mathbf{H} = 0. \tag{14}$$

Equation (14) has three independent solutions:

$$\mathbf{L} = \nabla\psi, \qquad \mathbf{T} = \nabla \times (\mathbf{a}\psi), \qquad \mathbf{S} = (1/\alpha)(\nabla \times \mathbf{T}), \tag{15}$$

where $\mathbf{a}$ is a constant unit vector and ψ is a scalar solution of $\nabla^2\psi + \alpha^2\psi = 0$. $\mathbf{L}$ vanishes because $\nabla\cdot\mathbf{H} = 0$, leaving the toroidal field $\mathbf{T}$ and a poloidal field $\mathbf{S}$. The general force-free field is

$$\mathbf{H} = \mathbf{T} + \mathbf{S}. \tag{16}$$

Thus, given a toroidal field $\mathbf{T}$, one can determine the poloidal field $\mathbf{S} = (1/\alpha)(\nabla \times \mathbf{T})$ such that their sum will be a force-free field.

One might expect a force-free configuration in the corona to be axially symmetric. In one such configuration a line of force threads the axis of symmetry. Other lines are circular helices around the axis of symmetry, with pitch decreasing with distance from the axis. In another configuration, lines of force spiral around ring surfaces.

Since force-free fields do not affect the density distribution in the corona, we can only speculate on their existence and form, except when such spectroscopic data as Zeeman splitting or emission line polarization gives some direct evidence of their presence. In the meantime, we note that coronal forms, particularly as revealed by monochromatic photographs, show configurations highly suggestive of magnetic fields. As a matter of fact, their shape and stability can be explained only by the presence of magnetic fields. Since these forms mark the presence of density irregularities, we must conclude that the coronal magnetic fields have a small non–force-free component.

A remarkable aspect of the density distribution in the corona is that densities are greatest in the active regions where magnetic fields would also be expected to be greatest. Furthermore, spectroscopic observations generally suggest high temperatures in portions, at least, of those active regions. Now although force-free magnetic fields, no matter how intense, do not affect the density distribution, non-force-free magnetic fields add a magnetic pressure $H^2/8\pi$ to the thermal pressure in the gas. We see this if for the case of equilibrium in the absence of a gravitational field we write Eq. (11) as

$$\nabla p = \frac{1}{4\pi} (\nabla \times \mathbf{H}) \times \mathbf{H} \tag{17}$$

and expand the triple-vector product to get

$$\nabla p = \frac{1}{4\pi} \mathbf{H} \cdot \nabla \mathbf{H} - \frac{1}{8\pi} \nabla H^2. \tag{18}$$

If the lines of force are straight and parallel,

$$\mathbf{H} \cdot \nabla \mathbf{H} = 0,$$

and (18) integrates to give

$$p + \frac{H^2}{8\pi} = \text{const.} \tag{19}$$

Thus we conclude that force-free fields dominate the center of active regions in the corona, but that small non–force-free fields lying outside provide adequate magnetic pressure to balance the greater density in the active regions.

We can obtain some idea of the configuration of the non–force-free fields in the corona from an observation of the distribution of matter—either from white-light or monochromatic observations. If we could assume (a) a uniform density distribution and magnetic field configuration along each line of sight (z axis), (b) the gravitational field to be directed along the y axis only, and (c) the corona to be isothermal, Eq. (11) would have two rectangular components,

$$\frac{\partial p}{\partial x} = \frac{Hy}{4\pi} \left(\frac{\partial Hx}{\partial y} - \frac{\partial Hy}{\partial x} \right) \tag{20}$$

and

$$\frac{\partial p}{\partial y} = \frac{Hx}{4\pi} \left(\frac{\partial Hy}{\partial x} - \frac{\partial Hx}{\partial y} \right) - \rho g. \tag{21}$$

Assumption (b) is quite well approximated by the monochromatic corona, since most of the emission along any line of sight comes from the lower-lying portions of the corona. Assumption (c) is probably in error, but will be maintained in this discussion for simplicity. Assumption (a) is probably also in error, but it can be demonstrated that less stringent assumptions will lead to the same conclusion.

From Eqs. (20) and (21) we can write

$$\frac{Hy}{Hx} = \frac{-(\partial p/\partial x)}{\rho g + (\partial p/\partial y)} \tag{22}$$

which for an isothermal gas becomes

$$\frac{Hy}{Hx} = \frac{-(1/\rho)(\partial p/\partial x)}{(mg/kT) + (1/\rho)(\partial p/\partial y)} \tag{23}$$

In white-light observations we can take $(1/\rho)(\partial\rho/\partial x)$ and $(1/\rho)(\partial\rho/\partial y)$ as approximately equal to $(1/I)(\partial I/\partial x)$ and $(1/I)(\partial I/\partial y)$. For monochromatic observations, in which the intensity is proportional to the square of the electron density, the equation for an isothermal corona becomes

$$\frac{Hy}{Hx} = \frac{-(1/I)(\partial I/\partial x)}{(2mg/kT) + (1/I)(\partial I/\partial y)} \tag{24}$$

Thus we can map point by point the direction of the magnetic field, from a measurement of brightness gradients in our coronal observations.

Magnetohydrodynamic Waves in the Corona

The corona is a compressible fluid in which magnetic fields are generally present. In such a fluid disturbances are propagated through the combined effects of the pressure gradients and the magnetic field distortions that the disturbances impose. Let us suppose that a small disturbance changes the equilibrium pressure from p_0 to $p_0 + \delta p$ and the equilibrium magnetic field from $\mathbf{H}_0$ to $\mathbf{H}_0 + \mathbf{h}$, but that the displacement of material does not result in a significant change in the gravitational field. Suppose, further, that viscous forces are negligible. Then, from Eq. (9),

$$0 = -\nabla p_0 + \rho\mathbf{g} + \frac{1}{4\pi}(\nabla \times \mathbf{H}_0) \times \mathbf{H}_0 \tag{25}$$

and

$$\rho\frac{\partial \mathbf{v}}{\partial t} = -\nabla(p_0 + \delta p) + (\rho + \delta\rho)\mathbf{g} + \frac{1}{4\pi}[\nabla \times (\mathbf{H}_0 + \mathbf{h})] \times [\mathbf{H}_0 + \mathbf{h}]. \tag{26}$$

Hence, since $\delta\rho = \delta p/w^2$, where $w = (\gamma p/\rho)^{1/2}$ = velocity of sound,

$$\rho \frac{\partial \mathbf{v}}{\partial t} = -w^2 \nabla(\delta\rho) + (\delta\rho)\mathbf{g} + \frac{1}{4\pi} \left[(\nabla \times \mathbf{h}) \times \mathbf{H}_0 + (\nabla \times \mathbf{H}_0) \times \mathbf{h} \right].$$

$$(27)$$

In the corona $w^2/L \sim 10^{10}\, g$. Hence, if the characteristic dimension $L \ll 10^{10}$ cm, the second term on the right-hand side of Eq. (27) is insignificant compared to the first and the equation reduces to

$$\rho \frac{\partial \mathbf{v}}{\partial t} = -w^2 \nabla(\delta\rho) + \frac{1}{4\pi} (\nabla \times \mathbf{h}) \times \mathbf{H}_0 + \frac{1}{4\pi} (\nabla \times \mathbf{H}_0) \times \mathbf{h}. \quad (28)$$

In addition, we have the equation of continuity,

$$\frac{\partial \rho}{\partial t} + \nabla \cdot (\rho \mathbf{v}) = 0, \quad (29)$$

and Faraday's law, which reduces to

$$\frac{\partial \mathbf{h}}{\partial t} = \nabla \times (\mathbf{v} \times \mathbf{H}_0) + \nabla \times (\mathbf{v} \times \mathbf{h}). \quad (30)$$

Let us now impose two simplifying conditions on the motion described by Eqs. (28)–(30).

(a) The state of motion is propagated in the z direction (upward) only. Fields and velocities are identical at all points in any plane parallel to the x–y plane. Thus $\partial H/\partial x = 0$ and $\partial h/\partial y = 0$. Therefore, since $\nabla \cdot h = 0$, $h_z = 0$. Also, for this condition to hold, H_0 is uniform throughout the space involved. For convenience we take H_0 parallel to the y–z plane, making an angle θ with the z axis. Because H_0 is constant in space and time, the last term in Eq. (28) is zero.

(b) The second condition is that

$$\nabla \times (\mathbf{v} \times \mathbf{H}_0) \gg \nabla \times (\mathbf{v} \times \mathbf{h}). \quad (31)$$

This condition does not follow necessarily from $H_0 \gg h$. For example, the angle between $\mathbf{v}$ and $\mathbf{H}_0$ may be very small compared to the angle between $\mathbf{v}$ and $\mathbf{h}$.

It is justified *a posteriori* by the conclusion that $\mathbf{h}$ oscillates about its zero value. Hence $\partial h/\partial t$ is a maximum when $\mathbf{h} = 0$, indicating that $\nabla \times (\mathbf{v} \times \mathbf{H}_0)$ is the dominant term in $\partial h/\partial t$.

From a combination of the x components of Eqs. (28)–(30) as simplified by assumptions (a) and (b), we can obtain two wave equations:

$$\frac{\partial^2 v_x}{\partial t^2} = \frac{H_0^2 \cos^2 \theta}{4\pi\rho} \frac{\partial^2 v_x}{\partial z^2} \tag{32}$$

and

$$\frac{\partial^2 h_x}{\partial t^2} = \frac{H_0^2 \cos^2 \theta}{4\pi\rho} \frac{\partial^2 h_x}{\partial z^2}. \tag{33}$$

These two equations tell us that the component of the disturbance normal to both the magnetic field and the direction of propagation is propagated with a velocity

$$V_{zx} = \frac{H_0 \cos \theta}{(4\pi\rho)^{1/2}}. \tag{34}$$

If $\theta = 0$, the phase velocity is $H_0/(4\pi\rho)^{1/2}$, a conclusion of historic interest, since the first magnetohydrodynamic waves to be investigated were of such velocity, now called the Alfvén velocity (see Alfvén, 1950).

On the other hand, if δp and y and z components of $\mathbf{h}$ and $\mathbf{v}$ are assumed to vary sinusoidally with the same frequency and phase velocity, Eqs. (28)–(30) can be combined to give

$$U^4 - (V^2 + W^2)U^2 + V^2W^2 \cos^2 \theta = 0, \tag{35}$$

where U is the phase velocity, and V the Alfvén velocity. When $\cos^2 \neq 1$ the roots of Eq. (35) are

$$U_1^2 = \frac{(V^2 + W^2) + [(V^2 + W^2)^2 - 4V^2W^2 \cos^2 \theta]^{1/2}}{2} \tag{36}$$

and

$$U_2 = \frac{(V^2 + W^2) - [(V^2 + W^2)^2 - 4V^2W^2 \cos^2 \theta]^{1/2}}{2}. \tag{37}$$

It follows from Eqs. (36) and (37) that $U_1 >$ either V or W, and $U_2 <$ either V or W.

In general, then, the components of the velocity and the magnetic field distortion lying in the plane of the fixed magnetic field and direction of propagation, as well as the density perturbation, are transmitted by two independent modes—a fast mode with phase velocity in excess of either the Alfvén velocity or the sound velocity, and a slow mode with phase velocity less than either the Alfvén or sound velocity.

For large field intensities, $V \gg W$, $U_1 = V$ and $U_2 = W \cos \theta$. In this case the velocity of the fast mode, U_1, is independent of the direction of propagation of the wave. In the corona $V \sim W$ for H_0 of 1 gauss—a field intensity that we might expect outside of active centers. Under these circumstances both modes are direction dependent, so we would not in general expect to find magnetohydrodynamic waves being transmitted through the corona with spherical wave fronts. For very weak fields, $W \gg V$, $U_1 = W$ and $U_2 = V \cos \theta$. It is doubtful that these conditions exist anywhere in the corona.

If $\cos \theta = 1$—i.e., if the direction of propagation is along the magnetic field—

$$U_1 = V \text{ or } W, \text{ whichever is larger, and}$$

$$U_2 = V \text{ or } W, \text{ whichever is smaller.}$$

Thus we conclude that for waves traveling in the direction of the magnetic field, one mode has sound and one, Alfvén velocity. Velocities and displacements normal to the field are propagated as Alfvén waves, whereas velocities in the direction of the magnetic field and density perturbations are propagated along the magnetic field as sound waves.

When $\theta = \pi/2$, Eqs. (36) and (37) give $U_1{}^2 = V^2 + W^2$ and $U_2 = 0$. Only one mode of propagation is present. The material motion is entirely in the direction of propagation, whereas the increment of magnetic field is entirely in the y direction. The wave is a compressional wave, propagated by compressing both the gas and the magnetic field. The increments in density and magnetic field intensity are related by

$$h_y = H_0 \frac{\delta \rho}{\rho}. \tag{38}$$

Finally we ask whether magnetohydrodynamic waves are likely to exist in the corona. The conditions necessary for their existence are that a mechanism or mechanisms be present for generation of disturbances, that such disturbances reach the corona, and that they be propagated significant distances through the corona. Osterbrock (1961) considered in detail the question of origin of disturbances in the solar atmosphere and their propagation to the corona. He concluded that a broad spectrum of hydromagnetic noise of considerable amplitude will be generated by the interaction of convective cells of the hydrogen convective zone with the overlying photosphere. Slow-mode, fast-mode and Alfvén waves will leave the point of generation. In general slow-mode waves will be much more strongly dissipated than fast-mode because of their shorter wavelengths, hence higher field gradients.

From the hydrogen convective zone into the photosphere the fast-mode waves will be acoustic in nature, since $W \gg V$. Disturbances of frequencies $\sim 5 \times 10^{-4}/\text{sec}$ will resonate in the photosphere and are recognized as the periodic motions that have been studied in detail by Evans and Michard (1962). Studies by Jensen and Orrall (1963) indicate that the velocities in such disturbances increase with height in the photosphere and lower chromosphere. Higher frequencies will be transmitted through the photosphere. In the chromosphere the fast-mode waves become more hydromagnetic than acoustic in character, acquire sharp fronts, and dissipate as shocks. They are also strongly refracted due to the increasing wave velocity. Thus Osterbrock concludes that very little energy reaches the corona through fast-mode disturbances. The slow-mode and Alfvén disturbances from the hydrogen convective zone are already dissipated before reaching the photosphere. Therefore, no significant disturbance ever reaches the corona directly from the hydrogen convective layer.

To explain the heating in the corona, Osterbrock postulates collisions between fast-mode shocks in the chromosphere, which generate slow-mode and Alfvén disturbances. The slow-mode disturbances, being primarily acoustic in nature, are manifest by the upward motion of matter in spicules. The Alfvén disturbances are readily propagated into the corona, where they steepen into shocks, heating the corona.

The serious difficulty with Osterbrock's picture is that such Alfvén shocks would be rather infrequent, hence very violent, in order to heat the corona. However, such observations as repeated spectroscopic observations of the same part of the corona (see Chapter 3), which we might expect to show such shocks, do not reveal their presence. The same difficulty is probably present in the idea of Whitaker (1963) that waves of lower frequency than the resonant frequency of the photosphere—i.e., gravity waves—penetrate the photosphere and are amplified to heat the corona.

We are thus confronted with the situation that although turbulence in the hydrogen convection zone could generate adequate disturbance to explain the physical state of the chromosphere and corona, and although photospheric phenomena present direct evidence of such disturbances, it is difficult to explain the transmission of the disturbances into the corona or to find direct observational evidence that they are so transmitted. One possibility that has been considered (Kuperus, 1963) is that the energy is carried through the photosphere and chromosphere along the strong sunspot magnetic fields. We shall discuss this question in more detail later in the chapter.

Shocks

Before proceeding further into the problem of heating of the corona, we shall consider the manner in which waves develop into shocks and review some of the basic concepts of shock phenomena. For the moment we shall ignore magnetic fields and deal with the hydrodynamic equations

$$\frac{d\mathbf{v}}{dt} + \frac{1}{\rho} \nabla p = 0 \tag{39}$$

and

$$\frac{\partial \rho}{\partial t} + \nabla(\rho \mathbf{v}) = 0. \tag{40}$$

Equations (39) and (40) combine to give a wave equation in ρ only if the total derivative $d\mathbf{v}/dt = \partial \mathbf{v}/\partial t + \mathbf{v} \cdot \nabla \mathbf{v}$ is replaced by the partial derivative $\partial \mathbf{v}/\partial t$—i.e., only if the displacement of a particle along the direction of propagation during an oscillation is very small compared to one wavelength. If the quadratic term $\mathbf{v} \cdot \nabla \mathbf{v}$ in the force equation is maintained, the progression in one dimension through the medium of a given state of motion is no longer with the constant speed $W = (dp/d\rho)_0^{1/2}$, but with speed $u + W$, where $W = (dp/d\rho)^{1/2}$ and $u =$ material velocity in the direction of the wave propagation. Thus the portion of the wave with greater material velocity overtakes the portion with slower moving material, and the wave ultimately acquires a velocity discontinuity known as a shock front. If the physical circumstances are such that u increases as the wave progresses, the shock front develops rapidly. Such circumstances are present if the wave propagates through an atmosphere of rapidly decreasing density. In this case, if there is no dissipation of kinetic energy in the wave and the wave-front is plane, the kinetic energy flux $\frac{1}{2}\rho u^2 U$ must be constant along the path of the wave. Here U is the wave velocity. The material velocity in the waves we are considering, at the entrance of the wave into the corona at least, is small compared to the acoustic velocity. Under these circumstances $U \sim W = $ const at constant temperature. Hence the material velocity u increases inversely as the square root of the density.

We first investigate the circumstances under which the increase in u is a significant factor in shock formation.

If u remained unchanged in a crest as the wave advanced, the crest of the wave, moving with speed $(W + u)$, would overtake the trough moving with speed $(W - u)$ in time t when

$$(W + u)t - (W - u)t = \lambda/2$$

i.e., when

$$t = \lambda/4u, \qquad (41)$$

or when the wave has progressed a distance $(\lambda/4)(U/u)$.

Now if the wave is progressing through a decreasing density with constant speed U and without dissipation of energy, u will increase by a factor $e^{1/2}$ in one scale height, $\mathfrak{K}$. Since the high temperature in the corona appears at heights above the base much less than one scale height, a wave could not be an effective mechanism for coronal heating if it did not develop into a shock before one scale height.

We can compute a mean value of u over one scale height by writing

$$\rho = \rho_0\, e^{-h/\mathfrak{K}}$$

and then

$$\tfrac{1}{2}\rho_0\, e^{-h/\mathfrak{K}}\, u^2 U = \tfrac{1}{2}\rho_0 u_0^2\, U \qquad (42)$$

$$u = u_0\, e^{h/2\mathfrak{K}} \qquad (43)$$

$$\bar{u} = \frac{1}{\mathfrak{K}} \int_0^{\mathfrak{K}} u\, dh = \frac{u_0}{\mathfrak{K}} \int_0^{\mathfrak{K}} e^{h/2\mathfrak{K}}\, dh = 2u_0[e^{1/2} - 1]. \qquad (44)$$

Whereas for a wave that would become a well-developed shock in distance $\mathfrak{K}$ in a medium of constant density

$$\frac{\lambda}{4}\frac{U}{u_0} = \mathfrak{K},$$

a wave in decreasing density will become a well-developed shock in distance $\mathfrak{K}'$, where

$$\frac{\lambda}{4}\frac{U}{2u_0(e^{1/2} - 1)} = \mathfrak{K}'$$

or

$$\frac{\mathfrak{K}'}{\mathfrak{K}} = \frac{1}{2(e^{1/2} - 1)} = \frac{1}{2(0.6486)} = 0.773. \qquad (45)$$

Thus, even if there is no dissipation, the accelerating effect on the material in a wave as the wave passes upward through the lower corona does not hasten shock formation very much. When we consider radiation loss, the effect of the acceleration by density gradient is even less. Suppose we assume that the dissipation per cm^3 is $\delta = K n_e^2$ and that the total dissipation in a cm^2 vertical column of corona is ϕ. Then

$$\int_0^\infty K n_e^2\, dh = \phi. \tag{46}$$

If $n_e = n_0 e^{-h/\mathcal{H}}$,

$$K n_0^2 \int_0^\infty e^{-2h/\mathcal{H}}\, dh = \frac{\mathcal{H} K n_0^2}{2} = \phi, \tag{47}$$

and

$$\delta = \frac{2\phi}{\mathcal{H}}\, e^{-2h/\mathcal{H}}. \tag{48}$$

Now since

$$\frac{d}{dh}\left(\tfrac{1}{2} n_e m u^2 U\right) = -\frac{2\phi}{\mathcal{H}}\, e^{-2h/\mathcal{H}}, \tag{49}$$

$$\frac{du}{dh} = \frac{u}{2\mathcal{H}} - \frac{2\phi\, e^{-h/\mathcal{H}}}{U u \mathcal{H} m n_0}. \tag{50}$$

Consequently, the material velocity does not increase with height unless

$$u^2 > \frac{4\phi\, e^{-h/\mathcal{H}}}{U m n_0}. \tag{51}$$

At the present moment it is difficult to estimate the value of ϕ, but 10^6 ergs cm^{-2} sec^{-1} is not unreasonable (Billings, 1963). Thus if we take $U \sim 10^7$ cm/sec, $n_0 = 10^9$, and the mean particle mass, m, as 10^{-24} gm, we find that the material velocity will not increase unless

$$u > 200\, e^{-h/2\mathcal{H}} \text{ km/sec}. \tag{52}$$

In order words, for a wave to be amplified in so heavily dissipating a medium, it would have to enter the corona with supersonic velocity and would develop into a shock very rapidly.

Incidentally, Eq. (50) integrates directly to give

$$u^2 = u_0^2 e^{h/\mathcal{H}} - \frac{4\phi}{W m n_0}\, \sinh\frac{h}{\mathcal{H}}. \tag{53}$$

We see from the above discussion that a wave will not be amplified in the corona unless it enters the base of the corona with sonic or near sonic material velocities. If the propagation through a medium of decreasing density is to be the accelerating mechanism, it is necessary that the acceleration take place in the photosphere and chromosphere.

Let us now consider the effect of a magnetic field on shock phenomena in the corona. We will deal with two cases only: a vertical field and a horizontal field. If the field is vertical and the impulses radial, all waves will be propagated simply as acoustic waves, guided by the field, and the entire discussion given above for acoustic waves is applicable.

If the field is horizontal and the material motion vertical, the wave velocity becomes $U = (V^2 + W^2)^{1/2}$ from Eq. (36).

In case $V \gg W$, so that $U \simeq V$, the nondissipative energy relation becomes

$$\rho^{1/2}u^2H = \text{const.} \tag{54}$$

Thus in a constant horizontal magnetic field an upward-propagating impulse would be accelerated only as $\rho^{-1/4}$, or by a factor of $e^{1/4}$ in one scale height. If H and ρ both decrease, the acceleration may be comparable to the acoustic case.

Besides inhibiting the acceleration of material velocity in a wave, as just discussed, the presence of a magnetic field also retards shock development by increasing the length of waves formed by a sequence of impulses. If the frequency of the impulses is ν and the acoustic velocity W, $\lambda = W/\nu$, and an acoustic wave must progress a distance $W^2/4u\nu$ before a shock develops. If the wave is being propagated normal to the magnetic field, the required distance becomes $(W^2 + V^2)/4u\nu$. In the corona the latter distance may be much greater than the former. Thus, if it is necessary for shocks to have sonic material velocity upon reaching the corona in the case of no magnetic fields, it is even more necessary when magnetic fields are present.

If the heating of the corona is to be explained by the passage of shocks, one not only must show that shocks will be present in the corona but must describe the detailed process by which shocks dissipate into thermal energy. We shall not reproduce the theory relating the conditions on opposite sides of a shock discontinuity, since it is given in many hydrodynamics and hydromagnetics texts. [We have found the treatment by Ferraro and Plumpton (1961) to be particularly helpful.] It is useful however, to write down some of the conclusions from this theory, and to note the assumptions that are made in deriving them.

The basic equations in shock theory, the Rankin-Hugoniot equations, are generally expressed in a frame of reference fixed in the shock front. In such a system material is seen to be flowing across the front in the opposite direction to the actual motion of the front. The three equations express the continuity of matter, the continuity of momentum and the continuity of energy across the front.

The energy equation requires that no significant amount of energy be lost by radiation during the passage of the shock front—i.e., between conditions I (p_1, U_1, ρ_1, T_1, B_1) and II (P_2, U_2, ρ_2, T_2, B_2). In order for the state properties to be meaningful, I and II must be sufficiently separated in time that the random velocities become Maxwellian following the passage of the shock. This requires several collisions between massive particles or several hundred collisions with electrons. The particular problem at hand will determine whether the shock should be considered as having passed when the electrons have achieved kinetic equilibrium, or whether kinetic equilibrium should be required of all the particles. If we are concerned with radiation phenomena only, for example, the former is adequate. In the corona the electrons will have undergone several collisions in a small fraction of a second, and the protons in one to a few seconds. We do not yet know a precise decay time for coronal energy by radiation, but the times observed for decay following small sudden enhancements of solar X rays, as observed by the Orbiting Solar Observatory, are of the order of 80 min. Thus, if we assume that the source of the enhancements is impulsive, it appears that the energy loss by radiation during the passage of the shock does not invalidate the energy equation. There are obvious uncertainties in this assumption, however.

In the corona the combination of the three equations, for no magnetic fields, gives

$$\frac{p^2}{p_1} = \frac{5\sigma^2 - 1}{4}, \tag{55}$$

$$\frac{\rho_2}{\rho_1} = \frac{8\sigma^2}{2\sigma^2 + 6}, \tag{56}$$

and

$$\frac{T_2}{T_1} = \sigma^2 \left[\frac{5\sigma^2 - 1}{4} \right]. \tag{57}$$

Here the Mach number $\sigma = U_1/W_1$, the ratio of the speed of the shock to the speed of sound in front of the shock. It is distinguished by the under bar from the symbol used for electrical conductivity.

We note that whereas the ratios of temperature and pressure behind the shock increase indefinitely with increasing Mach number, the ratio of densities cannot exceed 4. Hence, the emission in the corona, which depends primarily on n_e^2, could not be increased more than 16-fold by any disturbance, however strong.

In case a magnetic field is present, the Rankin-Huginoit equations are modified by the inclusion of magnetic-pressure and magnetic-energy terms. Two useful equations that emerge are

$$B_1^2 = \frac{8\pi p_1 (4 - X)(XZ - 1)}{(X - 1)^3} \tag{58}$$

and

$$S^2 = \frac{3(XZ - 1)(X + 5)}{(X - 1)^3[6(4 - X)(XZ - 1) + 5]} \tag{59}$$

Here S, the hydromagnetic equivalent of the Mach number σ, is defined as $S = U_1/V$. $V =$ Alfvén velocity. $X = \rho_2/\rho_1$; $Z = T_2/T_1$.

The Rankin-Hugoniot equations and their consequences apply only to the conditions on opposite sides of the shock interface and do not deal with the subsequent behavior during the remainder of the interval between successive shocks. They do not describe in any way the relaxation of the conditions produced by one shock into the initial conditions for a later shock. If shocks were merely the steepened fronts of successive sine waves, the remainder of the cycle would be strictly sinusoidal. There is no reason, however, to expect that a gas that has undergone a sudden increase in pressure will return to its original condition in the same manner in which it would have returned had it undergone a sinusoidal increase in pressure. The concept of a sinusoidal return can give us a rough approximation for describing a shock, however. From the shock interface to the succeeding null point is one-fourth cycle. If we replace this quarter-cycle by a rectangle having the same "power," the width of the rectangle is one-eighth cycle. Thus we may very crudely represent a succession of shocks as a series of pulses such that for one-eighth the interval between pulses the conditions immediately behind the shock prevail.

The passage of the shock imparts energy to the gas, both through compression and through an increase in temperature. Following the shock a certain amount of this energy is utilized by the gas in its return to its initial condition. The remainder goes into radiation or gross motion such as production of a solar wind. In principle, if the atomic properties of a gas are known, it should be possible to compute the thermodynamic path followed by the gas in the return cycle. In practice, the cycle has been approximated by simple thermodynamic paths that have been justified by plausibility arguments. For example, Weymann (1960) assumed that most of the radiation takes place immediately behind the shock front—a very plausible assumption for the corona in which the radiation varies as n_e^2. Thus he assumed that the gas behind the shock radiates at constant volume until it had reached its original entropy, then expands adiabatically to its original condition. He showed, however, that the energy going into radiation in such a cycle was, to the first approximation, the same as that computed by Schatzman (1949) by assuming that the gas first expands adiabatically to its original pressure, then decrease in volume, while radiating, to its original volume. The approximate expression arrived at by both is

$$Q = \frac{p_0\lambda_0(\gamma + 1)\Sigma^3}{12\gamma^2} \text{ ergs cycle}^{-1} \text{ cm}^{-3}, \tag{60}$$

where p_0 and λ_0 are the time average values of pressure and specific volume and Σ, the shock strength as defined by Weymann, is $\Sigma = (p_2 - p_1)/p_0$. The relation of Σ and $\underline{\sigma}$ depends on the form of the cycle. For a sawtooth variation of pressure with time, Σ is related to the difference in speeds on the two sides of the shock by

$$u_2 - u_1 = 0.45\Sigma V_T, \tag{61}$$

where V_T = proton thermal velocity.

If the shock is moving across a magnetic field, Σ would be defined in terms of total pressures—thermal plus magnetic. As we have already noted, the presence of the magnetic field has the effect of requiring greater particle velocities to cause a given shock strength, but given such a shock, the energy dissipation will depend only on the thermodynamic cycle subsequently followed—where, however, the pressure in the p, λ cycle is again the total pressure, thermal plus magnetic.

C. The Problem of Coronal Heating

Energy Requirements

Having discussed some of the pertinent aspects of waves and shocks, let us consider the status of the problem of coronal heating. Although we have become so familiar with the concept of the high temperature of the corona that we are inclined to accept it as a matter of course, the phenomenon remains one of the most remarkable aspects of the sun. In order that this high temperature be maintained, some source of energy must be present to continually replenish that which is lost by radiation, outward flux of high-energy particles, and thermal conduction into and out of the sun. We have noted in earlier chapters that the XUV solar radiation incident on the earth is several ergs sec^{-1} cm^{-2}, although this amount may vary by a factor of 10 or more during a solar cycle. Such energies correspond to a flux from the corona of 10^5 to 10^6 ergs cm^{-2} sec^{-1}. The kinetic energy flux at one A.U. is about one order of magnitude less than the XUV flux.

The amount of energy lost by thermal conduction is extremely difficult to evaluate. The thermal conductivity is well known: about 10^{-6} $T^{5/2}$. This result can be derived to various degrees of sophistication (Chapman, 1957). It is adequate for our purposes to note that the thermal and electrical conduction processes in the corona are both similar to those in a metal, and that we can therefore relate one to the other by the Wiedemann-Franz law:

$$K_{\text{(thermal)}} = 3\sigma \left(\frac{kc}{\epsilon}\right)^2 T = 1.8 \times 10^{-6} T^{5/2} \text{ ergs cm}^{-1} \text{ degree}^{-1}. \quad (62)$$

Our difficulty is our almost total ignorance of temperature gradients in the corona. We know that the temperature rises quite rapidly between the chromosphere and corona (Athay and Roberts, 1955), reaches a maximum somewhere in the inner corona (Billings and Lilliequist, 1963), and declines thereafter. The temperature decline is certainly not more than a few degrees per kilometer, or the gas would be unstable to convection. The sketchy evidence to be discussed in a later chapter indicates about $3°/\text{km}$. Thus the energy conducted outward thermally is an order of magnitude less than that radiated outward.

The temperature gradient between the chromosphere and corona is unknown to within one or two orders of magnitude. A number of observations suggest that the change from chromospheric to coronal temperatures is very abrupt, taking place over a distance of about 1000 km. The temperature varies so strongly over this range that it would be inappropriate to take any single value for computation of the thermal conductivity. It is better to ignore the energy sources and sinks over the corona–chromosphere interface, or make the equivalent but less stringent assumption that they are equal, so that we may write for the energy conducted into the chromosphere

$$10^{-6} T^{5/2} \frac{dT}{dx} = Q \text{ (a constant)}. \tag{63}$$

Equation (63) integrates to give

$$\tfrac{2}{7} \times 10^{-6} (T^{7/2} - T_0^{7/2}) = Qx. \tag{64}$$

If we put $T = 10^6$ and $T_0 = 10^4$ °K, we conclude that for $x = 1000$ km the heat conducted inward is an order of magnitude greater than any other energy loss from the corona; if $x = 10{,}000$ km, the conducted heat is comparable to that lost by radiation; and if $x = 100{,}000$ km, inward conduction may be ignored. It is only through our ignorance that we prefer the intermediate value, using it to augment the energy lost by radiation to the extent that we set the total mean energy requirement in the corona equal to 10^6 ergs cm^{-2} sec^{-1}.

XUV photographs and spectroheliograms of the sun during the decline of the last solar cycle indicate that most of the radiation comes from active regions covering 0.1 to 0.01 of the solar surface. Consequently, it might be more realistic to estimate the energy requirement for the active regions to be 10^7 to 10^8 ergs cm^{-2} sec^{-1}, and that of the remainder, considerably less.

We have very little information concerning the distribution of the energy input with height in the corona. It may be deposited just above the chromosphere, producing a temperature maximum very low in the corona, then distributed upward by conduction; or it may be distributed throughout the lower corona. If we consider the energy to be distributed uniformly over one scale height of 10^5 km, the input into active regions is 10^{-3} to 10^{-2} ergs cm^{-3} sec^{-1}. If the distribution is more localized, the energy input per unit volume may be a great deal higher. Solar wind computations carried out by Anderson (1965) suggest that considerable energy input may be required out to several solar radii.

In spite of our uncertainties, we can say that the energy requirements for the corona are considerable, and that we cannot consider ourselves to have any thorough understanding of the corona until we know the source of this energy. The source must be neither thermal nor radiative, for the corona lies between the much cooler, opaque photosphere and the low temperatures of outer space. We are thus left with two general types of sources to consider: mechanical and magnetic. The magnetic fields that have generally been considered in theories of heating the corona have been the perturbations on existing fields in the form of hydromagnetic waves or shocks. These disturbances are attributed to interaction with the hydrogen convective zone; hence the ultimate nonthermal source of such heating is the convective zone, the source also postulated for mechanical waves and shocks. A rather different theory might be developed in which the heating arises from the direct conversion of magnetic fields into energy. A catastrophic process of this type has been invoked to explain flares. A much slower process might apply heat steadily to the coronal regions, as suggested by Hoyle and Wickramasinghe (1961). In such a theory the ultimate mechanical source of the energy would be the differential rotation of the sun. A third source of mechanical energy that has been postulated for heating the corona is the potential energy of galactic material gathered up by the sun in its motion through the galaxy. We shall discuss this last hypothesis, called the "accretion hypothesis," before returning to the various ramifications of the shock-heating hypothesis. The accretion hypothesis has remained essentially as formulated by Hoyle and associates, and summarized by Hoyle (1949), whereas many hypotheses by many authors have been formulated for coronal heating by energy from the solar interior.

Heating of the Corona by Accretion

A major advantage of the accretion hypothesis is that it suggests a very simple process by which a temperature of the order of 1,000,000° may be achieved in the corona while the lower lying gas remains cooler. Moreover, the energy influx predicted more than a decade ago by the hypothesis agrees fairly well with the energy efflux currently being observed in coronal X rays. The key quantitative relation on which the hypothesis is based is that the thermal velocities of protons in the corona is about the same as that of particles falling freely from infinity to the surface of the sun. According to the hypothesis, the sun captures interstellar particles in its passage through space. Not only are those particles captured that lie directly in the path of the sun, but many that would independently describe parabolic orbits and return to space lose their angular momentum in interaction with other particles behind the sun. Thus the capture cross-section of the sun is greatly enhanced. The kinetic energy associated with the lost angular momentum becomes thermal energy, and heated aggregates of gas fall into the solar atmosphere.

Hoyle (1949) computed, from simple proton–proton interaction theory, that the falling material will descend to about 130,000 km above the photosphere before all of its free-fall energy is converted into thermal energy. Thus, he predicted the maximum temperature to be at this height.

In order to explain heating below the 130,000-km level, Hoyle introduces the idea of a remarkable convective process that would drive heat downward rather than upward. The picture of the lower corona that emerges is one consisting of streams of upward and downward flowing material, the two kinds of streams differing in temperature by a factor of 2 or 3. By a proper choice of the rate of incident flux, Hoyle was able to deduce temperature and density distributions that agreed reasonably well with observations available at the time.

A number of developments during the past fifteen years have bearing on the status of the accretion hypothesis. Two already-mentioned discoveries have been in its favor: the observation by Trellis (1960) that the green-line emission is enhanced on the side of the sun in the direction of the motion of our solar system through the galaxy, and the various indications pointed out by Pottasch (1963a,b, 1964, 1965) and others during the past two or three years that the chemical composition of the corona is closer to that of extrasolar material than of the photosphere. We should point out, however, that the enhanced emission noted by Trellis is on the opposite side of the sun from where it would have been predicted by Hoyle.

In opposition to the hypothesis, Blackwell and Dewhirst (1956) reviewed data on coronal densities and pointed out discrepencies that they considered fatal to the theory. Both the inverted convective process and the particle-trapping process are very difficult, and stronger arguments are needed than have been presented to date to demonstrate that either would actually work. The height of maximum coronal temperature predicted by the hypothesis is considerably greater than emission-line data might indicate, although the evidence is still contradictory. Certainly the theory could not explain the very-high–temperature low-lying yellow-line regions. Finally, the accretion hypothesis was formulated before the conception or discovery of solar wind, and as a consequence makes no provision for simultaneous inward and outward flowing material in interplanetary space.

In summary, the accretion hypothesis must be reexamined and reformulated before it can be considered to be the basis of a current theory for the heating of the corona. On the other hand, since some new evidence has appeared in its support and no completely adequate theory has taken its place, it should not be deemed entirely dead.

General Comments on Heating from the Interior

All existing theories of coronal heating from the solar interior consider the hydrogen convection zone to be the origin of the energy. The various theories differ in the type of nonthermal motion that is postulated to carry energy from the convective zone to the corona and the manner in which this energy is dissipated after it reaches the corona.

The nonthermal energy-transport mechanisms fall into three general classes: acoustic waves throughout, hydromagnetic waves throughout, and combinations of acoustic and hydromagnetic waves—i.e., acoustic waves part way and hydromagnetic waves part way. Gravity waves have also been suggested. A major problem has been to postulate a transport mechanism that will carry enough energy through the photosphere and chromosphere to heat the corona and still dissipate its energy in the corona. Various mechanisms that have been suggested for dissipating acoustic and hydromagnetic energy in the corona are development of acoustic shocks, development of hydromagnetic shocks, viscous heating, and Joule heating. We shall consider each mode of transportation and dissipation in more detail.

Heating by Acoustic Energy Flux

Cells of hot gas moving upward through the hydrogen convective zone generate acoustic waves in the overlying photosphere. The oscillatory motion observed in photospheric features by Evans and Michard (1962) and others may be the material motion in such waves. If so, we may compute the mechanical power being transported through each square centimeter of the photosphere by

$$P = \rho u^2 W, \tag{65}$$

where ρ is the density of the photospheric material, u is the material velocity, and W the velocity of sound in the photosphere. Using $u = 0.8$ km/sec, from Evans and Michard, we compute a power transport of 5×10^7 ergs cm^{-2} sec^{-1}, which may be adequate to meet the radiation losses from the chromosphere and corona.

The velocity fluctuation in such waves is amplified as the waves pass from the photosphere through the chromosphere into the corona, in the manner that we have already discussed. In the photosphere the velocity amplitudes are small compared to the thermal velocity; hence the dissipation is small. In the chromosphere and corona, however, velocity amplitudes become comparable to thermal velocities, and the waves become shocks and dissipate rapidly. This process was first described in 1946 by Biermann to explain the evidences of enhanced temperature in the chromosphere.

Schwarzschild (1948) explained the high temperature of the corona by the same simple energy argument and, assuming the temperature at each point in the chromosphere and the corona to be determined by the material velocity in the shock at that point ($T \sim mu^2/k$), concluded that the temperature of the corona would reach a value of 1,000,000° at 35,000 km above the photosphere.

Schatzman (1949) extended the ideas of Schwarzschild. He evaluated rates of energy transport, dissipation, emission, and conduction, and formulated a transfer equation in which these elements entered. From it, he concluded that above about 40,000 km the transport would be entirely by thermal conduction, whereas below that level it would be primarily mechanical.

An important aspect of the work of both Schwarzschild and Schatzman is the tacit assumption that adequate mechanical energy will pass, without significant attenuation, through the chromosphere to heat the corona. We have already noted earlier in this chapter the difficulties in amplification of a wave or shock after it enters the corona. Biermann (1948) followed the acoustic waves from their formation through the photosphere and chromosphere, and concluded that dissipation in the chromosphere would heat the chromosphere but make coronal heating by acoustic waves impossible. He concludes that we must look for some entirely different mechanism for heating the corona and hints at a preference for accretion.

Uchida (1963) has suggested a way out of the chromospheric-dissipation difficulty. He points out that earlier formulations of the energy-balance equations have left out the effect of thermal conductivity. When this term is introduced, sufficient energy is conducted backward from the corona into the chromosphere to provide for a considerable part of the chromospheric radiation. Thus the energy demands on the shock wave are relatively small, and the impulse reaches the corona with high material velocity—a condition that we have shown to be necessary if further amplification in the corona is to take place. With the thermal conductivity introduced into his equations, Uchida showed that acoustic shocks could heat the corona quite effectively, but that if a 10-gauss magnetic field is introduced the results agree even more closely with observations. Uchida's work may be criticized both on the basis of the rather large number of simplifying assumptions that he made to keep the equations tractable and because the velocity amplitude of the waves introduced at the base of the chromosphere may be larger than those observed by perhaps an order of magnitude.

Between the work of Biermann and that of Uchida, two other contributions to the concept of acoustic heating should be noted. Weymann, in 1960, introduced some very convenient approximate methods for evaluation of the dissipation in weak shocks, then applied his theory to the heating of a stellar atmosphere. He concluded that in many stellar atmospheres a discontinuity in the quantity $(d \log T)/(d \log p)$ would appear, and

identified this discontinuity with the corona-chromosphere interface. De
Jager and Kuperus (1961) have also invoked the mechanism, using it as
a means of computing the coronal temperature. Their approach was to
assume that the temperatures at the He-I–He-II and He-II–corona inter-
faces were known, then assuming heating by acoustic shocks, to find the
coronal temperature (650,000 ± 50,000°).

Coronal Heating by Hydromagnetic Waves

If a magnetic field is present in an agitated solar atmosphere, the nature
of the resulting waves is greatly modified. This was pointed out by Alfvén
in 1947, but it was not until a decade later, as a result of the work of
Simon (1958), Weymann and Howard (1958), and Plumpton (1959) that
the extreme complexity of the resulting wave pattern was appreciated.

Working under the assumption that the general magnetic field of the
sun was about 40 gauss, Alfvén (1947) concluded that the motion of the
granulations in the photosphere would produce large perturbations in the
magnetic field (of about 500 gauss), which would be transmitted as Alfvén
waves. These waves would be amplified in the chromosphere and corona
because of decreasing density, and would ultimately be dissipated through
Joule heating from the currents accompanying the oscillating magnetic
field. In providing sufficient electrical resistivity to yield the required
amount of Joule heating, Alfvén invoked the Cowling "transverse resistivity," since the matter in an Alfvén wave moves normal to the magnetic
field. Cowling (1953) confirmed Alfvén's conclusion that hydromagnetic
waves transport adequate energy into the corona, but pointed out that
Joule heating would be inadequate to dissipate these waves. He showed
that Alfvén's use of transverse conductivity was not appropriate, since the
matter moves with the fluctuating magnetic field and the presence of the
magnetic field in no ways increases the number of particle collisions, hence
the resistivity.

Joule heating is only one of a number of mechanisms that have been
suggested for accomplishing the difficult task of dissipating a hydromagnetic wave in the corona. Cowling (1953) suggested two other processes.
One was the stirring up of the material in the solar atmosphere, against
gravity, by the passage of hydromagnetic waves; the other was the interference of the various hydromagnetic modes, which would make the wave
very irregular, thereby increasing the energy in high-frequency, rapidly
dissipating components.

Two kinds of dissipation of hydromagnetic waves in the corona by
viscosity effects have also been considered. Van de Hulst (1949) considered

ordinary viscosity effects and concluded that they were quite inadequate. Landseer-Jones (1961) reopened the question and concluded that for waves making a significant angle with the magnetic field, viscous heating was important. We note, however, that Landseer-Jones used a much higher coefficient of viscosity than that used by Osterbrock (1961) or given by Linhart (1960), and that if one uses the latter coefficients in Landseer-Jones' equations, he will find only a small fraction of the wave to be dissipating.

Piddington (1956) suggested a special kind of viscous effect—acting under circumstances in which the gas is partially ionized. The ionic constituents of the gas are impelled by the hydromagnetic waves to move independently of the neutral constituents. Thus the neutral constituents are driven into forced oscillations, but in some cases the phase lag, and hence the relative velocity and the increase in collision frequency between ions and neutral particles, becomes quite significant. Piddington computed that as a result of this interaction most of the energy in hydromagnetic waves would be dissipated, the greatest dissipation occurring in the 7000–9000 km level. Obviously, such heating would be effective only in the presence of neutral atoms, namely, in the chromosphere. Piddington extended it to heating the corona by noting that at the very top of the chromosphere the interaction velocity could exceed 200 km/sec. Some of the protons from such collisions would be thrown upward into the corona with coronal thermal energy.

Piddington's mechanism has one appealing feature: it requires that the maximum temperature in the corona be very close to the top of the chromosphere—within one mean free path, as a matter of fact. The persistence of coronal line emission very close to the chromosphere, as Athay and Roberts (1955) have demonstrated, suggests that coronal temperatures do extend to the top of the chromosphere. The principal difficulty with Piddington's mechanism is that the energy it places into the corona is inadequate by one or two orders of magnitude.

The most hopeful mechanism for dissipation of hydromagnetic wave energy in the corona is the hydromagnetic equivalent of the acoustic process considered by Schwarzschild, Schatzman and Biermann—the dissipation of hydromagnetic shocks. The basic theory for this process was presented by Bazer and Ericson (1959) and discussed by Parker (1959, 1960). The most comprehensive discussion of the process to date is that given by Osterbrock, whose arguments we have outlined earlier in the chapter. Uchida (1963), as we have already noted, has applied it quite successfully to the corona.

In comparing the conclusion of Osterbrock with those of Uchida we note the following points:

(1)   The velocities at the base of the chromosphere assumed by Oster-brock are much closer to those observed by Evans and Michard than those assumed by Uchida.

(2)   Uchida carries impulses directly through the chromosphere into the corona, whereas the impulses that Osterbrock brings into the corona are generated by interaction of the fast-mode waves in the chromosphere. As a consequence, we would expect the impulses discussed by Uchida to be of higher frequency and lower amplitude than those by Osterbrock.

(3)   Since Osterbrock does not work out the details of fast-mode inter-action in the upper chromosphere, he makes no estimate of the amount of energy that the resulting secondary waves carry into the corona. Uchida shows that his mechanism provides adequate energy to maintain the corona at its observed temperature.

Spectroscopic and Radar Observations Pertinent to Coronal Heating

Any direct observations in the corona that would suggest the passage of shocks or waves through it are disturbingly rare. No regular pulses of brightening are observed to pass upward through the monochromatic corona. Neither can any regular movement even as large as that observed in the photosphere be detected by Doppler shifts of the coronal lines. This latter consideration is especially noteworthy, since the entire concept of shock heating is based on the idea of a large amplification of the material velocity as the impulses pass upward from the photosphere through the solar atmosphere. A few years ago, Lüst *et al.* (1962) took the great widths of the emission lines to be evidence of superposition of heating pulses along the line of sight, but with the introduction of dielectronic recombi-nation, most of the line broadening is explained by thermal motion. When we have held the coronagraph spectrograph slit on the same coronal feature for many successive spectrograms, then made very detailed com-parison of the microphotometer tracings of different spectrograms, we have been able to detect small wavelength variations in the emission lines corresponding to velocities of a few tenths of a kilometer per second, and have noted suggestions of periodicity in these velocities of about 300 seconds which may or may not be real.

The most significant observation of motion to date has been made by radar by Chisholm and James (1964). Their observed random velocity of 35 km/sec at about 1.5 $R_\odot$ agrees nicely with the velocities computed by Uchida for heating the corona. If, furthermore, we consider these velocities to be radial to the sun and constant in the corona (as Uchida computed to be the case when a magnetic field was assumed), the effective root-mean-square velocity along a line of sight,

$$\langle V^2 \rangle = \frac{\int V^2 \sin^2 \theta \, dQ}{\int dQ}, \qquad (66)$$

is 8 or 9 km/sec. The effect of such a velocity would be to broaden an iron coronal line by an amount equivalent to about 250,000°K (Billings, 1965). This is in good agreement with the current differences between line width and ionization temperatures for Fe XIV. Small departures from radial motion would produce considerable increase in the line widths.

We can combine the computed effective rms velocity along a line of sight, computed above, with the observed Doppler velocities of about 0.2 km/sec to estimate the cross-sectional dimension of a shock front (Billings, 1963). If there are n cells along a line of sight, their net effect should be to introduce an observed Doppler velocity of about $1/\sqrt{n}$ of the rms velocity of the cells. From the data that we have just given, we conclude that there are about 1800 cells along a line of sight. Since we are dealing with effective rms velocity—i.e., we are taking the change in brightness with height into account—we should also introduce an effective line of sight for computing a typical dimension per cell. We do not feel that the spherically symmetrical assumption that was used for computing the effective rms velocity is good enough to justify any computation of an effective line of sight, however. Instead, we simply note that since most of the emission along a line of sight comes from close to the sun, one solar radius should be an ample effective line of sight. With such an estimate, we conclude that the cell dimension is about 400 km. We suspect that we may have grossly overestimated the effective line of sight. Coronal structures of dimensions of $\frac{1}{10} R_\odot$ show as small Doppler shifts as larger features. If we use $\frac{1}{10} R_\odot$ for the effective line of sight, the resulting cell dimensions become so small compared to any observed coronal features as to lend discredit to the entire concept of shock heating. The small cells certainly favor the concepts of Uchida over those of Osterbrock, since the former would have at least as many disturbances in the corona as at the base of the chromosphere, whereas the latter would predict only a fraction as many disturbances.

Summary of the Status of the Theory of Coronal Heating

The heating of the corona remains one of the outstanding problems of astrophysics. The accretion hypothesis, though not dead, is obsolete in its present form. Hydromagnetic shocks, though highly favored, have little observational evidence to support them. None of the several other hypotheses that have been advanced have gained any widespread support. Although all hypotheses in which magnetic fields have been involved have led to a greater heating in the active regions than outside, none stresses the orders-of-magnitude difference between the two heating requirements. A theory of heating the corona that begins with the heating of the active regions and includes the rest of the corona as incidental may be more successful than any of the existing theories.

A Hypothesis for Heating Active Regions

The hypothesis that we shall now consider in a general way is that there is an intimate relationship between the heating mechanism and the structural features in the corona. Before giving our formulation of the hypothesis in more detail, let us review some of the observational characteristics of these features:

(1)   The corona contains a great deal of filamentary structure. We cannot, under present observing conditions, determine whether it can be described as entirely filamentary, or as filaments imbedded in a more homogeneous gas. On coronal spectrograms features in $H\alpha$ frequently appear that are clearly smaller than anything observed in coronal emission. We must regard this piece of evidence suggestive rather than conclusive, however, since the ability to see smaller features in $H\alpha$ may be purely a consequence of the stronger contrast in the prominence lines.

(2)   Over active regions the coronal features generally show a loop structure. When prominences are observed in the same localities, they are similarly looped but more sharply defined than the loops in the corona.

(3)   The same features frequently appear bright in emission from ions of quite different ionization potential. In this observation emissions from Fe X and Fe XIV have been most widely studied. The details of features in these two lines frequently show small differences, but the general form is often the same. Billings and Lehman (1962) studied the profiles of a number of features that are bright in both lines, and found that the λ 6374 profiles generally corresponded to a lower temperature than the λ 5303 profiles (by about 800,000°) (Fig. 7.1). Thus they concluded that the emission in the two lines came from different parts of the same feature. They also found that in the locations where λ 5303 was enhanced but λ 6374 diminished, the λ 5303 profiles were exceptionally wide.

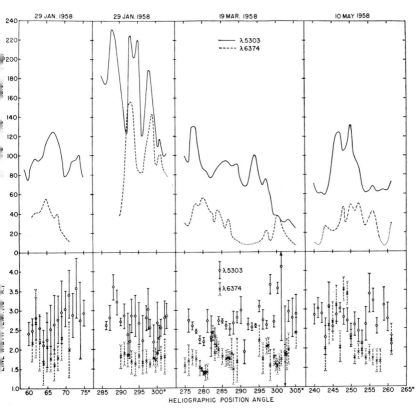

Fig. 7.1. A comparison of the widths of the green and red coronal lines in the same well-identified coronal features, from Billings and Lehman (1962). The persistently lower temperature to which the red line corresponds than that to which the green line corresponds is conclusive evidence that the two radiations originate from different temperature sources along the line of sight. Courtesy, *Astrophysical Journal.*

In order to examine the heating processes within a filament of coronal gas, we need to postulate, first, a model for the coronal filament. For the moment we need assume only that in the filament both density and magnetic field are enhanced. A plausible model is one in which the magnetic field is proportional to the excess density in the filament, each having a Gaussian distribution across the filament. A distribution of this sort would result if a flux tube from beneath the solar surface erupted as a loop into the corona, as Babcock (1961) has suggested, then expanded in the direction normal to the magnetic field until the density at the boundary joined continuously with the density in the coronal medium into which the tube was injected.

Let us consider a plane hydromagnetic wave, incident from below entering the filament with the plane of the wave front normal to the axis of the filament. Within a very short time the wave front will be elongated strongly along the axis of the filament, since the wave velocity will be greatest there. Thereafter, further progression of the wave may be described as advance along the axis of the filament and spreading out from the axis. Since the magnetic field does not vary along the axis of the filament, there will be no tendency for the wave front in and near the axis to develop into a shock front, for the wave velocity would increase as the square root of the density decreases, whereas the material velocity would increase at a lesser rate, since kinetic energy would spread out from the axis of the filament. The spreading component of the wave, however, will pass through a decreasing density and a decreasing magnetic field. The former will enhance the material velocity; the latter will diminish the wave velocity. Thus conditions are favorable for the development of shock fronts progressing radially outward from the axis of the filament.

The thermal structure in the filament, resulting from the shock front, will be as follows: a cool core along the axis of the filament, with the temperature increasing radially outward to a maximum as the material velocity in the shock builds up, then decreasing under the combined effect of a decreasing density gradient and dissipation of energy. In many active regions, the cool, dense core is manifest by an $H\alpha$ loop; in others, the temperature of the core may be too high to be visible in hydrogen radiation. The bright, highly localized λ 6374 emission features frequently appearing in active regions can, according to this model, lie between the core and the high-temperature portions of the filament. Outside the λ 6374 emitting region, λ 5303 and perhaps λ 5694 of Ca XV will appear.

Two attractive features of the hypothesis are that it yields maximum heating at the top of prominence loops—the common location of yellow-line emission—and that it provides an easy way for transmission of energy from the convective zone through the photosphere and chromosphere into the corona. The density in a prominence loop (for reasons unknown) does not vary greatly along the loop. The corona outside the loop, however, is more or less in hydrostatic equilibrium. Consequently, the greatest density gradient between the inside and the outside of the loop occurs at the top of the loop. At this position an outward-moving shock may be most strongly amplified, yielding the yellow-line regions.

Concerning the transmission of energy through the photosphere, Osterbrock shows that hydromagnetic waves originating in the convective layer are so strongly damped in the photosphere that they never reach the chromosphere—if the magnetic fields are assumed to be 1–20 gauss. However, it is not at all unreasonable that a strongly looped sunspot prominence indicates a flux tube extending from below the photosphere with a magnetic field of several hundred to several thousand gauss. Under such circumstances the damping length is increased to millions of kilometers. Thus mechanical energy received by the flux tube from the convective layer—where a great deal of mechanical energy is present—would be readily carried into the corona without a change of mode.

D. Gross Dynamics of the Corona

Considerations for a Static Corona

Chapman, in 1957, brought to light an interesting aspect of the corona. If we assume that the corona is in hydrostatic equilibrium and that the temperature is maintained by thermal conduction outward from a million-degree base, the solar atmosphere extends to infinity, and at infinity still exerts significant pressure. We can see this if we write for the condition of hydrostatic equilibrium:

$$d(nkT) = -Mg_0 \frac{r_0^2}{r^2} N \, dr, \qquad (67)$$

where N is the total number of particles per unit volume, M the mean molecular weight, g_0 the acceleration of gravity at the base of the corona, r_0 and dr the distance from the center of the sun, and for the heat conducted thermally outward, from Eq. (62),

$$Q = -4\pi r^2 A T^{5/2} \frac{dT}{dr} = \text{const, where } A \sim 10^{-6}. \qquad (68)$$

Equation (68), when integrated from r_0 to r, gives

$$\frac{Q}{4\pi A} \left(\frac{1}{r_0} - \frac{1}{r} \right) = \tfrac{2}{7} (T_0^{7/2} - T^{7/2}). \qquad (69)$$

We can evaluate Q at $r = \infty$, whereupon Eq. (69) becomes

$$T^{7/2} = T_\infty^{7/2} + \frac{r_0}{r} (T_0^{7/2} - T_\infty^{7/2}). \qquad (70)$$

Substitution of (70) into (67) gives

$$\frac{1}{NT} d(NT) = -\frac{Mg_0r_0^2}{k} \cdot \frac{dr}{r^2[T_\infty^{7/2} + (r_0/r)(T_0^{7/2} - T_\infty^{7/2})]^{2/7}}, \quad (71)$$

which integrates to

$$\ln \frac{NT}{N_0T_0} = -\frac{7}{5} \frac{Mg_0r_0}{k} \left(\frac{T_0^{5/2} - T^{5/2}}{T_0^{7/2} - T_\infty^{7/2}} \right). \quad (72)$$

An alternate form of (72) is

$$p = p_0 \exp \left\{ -\frac{19.2 \times 10^6}{T_0} \frac{[1 - (T/T_0)]^{5/2}}{[1 - (T/T_0)]^{7/2}} \right\}. \quad (73)$$

From (73) we see that if T is vanishingly small compared to T_0 but still finite at great distances from the sun, the pressure does not vanish but approaches a constant value $\sim 10^{-8}$ that at the base of the corona for $T_0 = 10^6$ °K. Now the density of interstellar gas is about one particle cm^{-3} and the temperature, 125°K (Allen, 1963). Thus the pressure in interstellar space is about 10^{-12} that at the base of the corona, or considerably less than the pressure at infinity just computed for the coronal gas. The phenomenon is very sensitive to T_0, the temperature at the base of the corona, however. If T_0 is 7×10^5 °K, the coronal pressure at infinity is equal to the pressure of interstellar gas.

Chapman interpreted the excess pressure at infinity simply to indicate that the equations could not be used at too great a distance from the sun—perhaps not much beyond 1 A.U. Parker, on the other hand, considered it to mean that a corona would require external pressure at infinity equal to that computed for the coronal gas at infinity in order for the total system to remain in static equilibrium.

The Expanding Corona

Parker (1960) concluded that since the pressure of interstellar gas was not adequate to maintain the corona in a state of hydrostatic equilibrium, the entire atmosphere must be in a state of continual expansion. Consequently, he replaced the equation of static equilibrium by an equation of motion:

$$\frac{d}{dr}(NkT) = -NMg_0 \frac{r_0^2}{r^2} - NMv \frac{dv}{dr}. \quad (74)$$

He coupled Eq. (74) with an equation of continuity, which for a spherically-symmetrical corona is

$$r^2 v N = r_0^2 v_0 N_0 . \tag{75}$$

A third relation is needed in which the temperature variation with distance from the sun is involved. Such a relation has been difficult to write with certainty, since we know very little about either the temperature variation of the corona with distance from the sun or of the manner in which energy is deposited in the corona by its unknown heating mechanism. During the several years that Parker has worked on this subject, and in the many articles and the book (1963) that he has written, he has obtained the third relation in various ways. In some instances he has considered the energy input above a certain level to be entirely from thermal conduction On other occasions he has assumed it to be of such a nature that the temperature distribution is polytropic

$$T = T_0 (N/N_0)^{\alpha-1} \tag{76}$$

then considered the behavior of the corona with various polytropic indices α. He has generalized this by considering a series of shells in which each shell is described by a polytropic index—a sufficiently versatile procedure to include almost any temperature variation. He has also investigated a generalization of the conduction corona temperature function,

$$T = T_0/r^b. \tag{77}$$

The three relationships (force, continuity, temperature) lead to four families of solutions, and much controversy during recent years has been centered in the question of the proper choice of a solution to fit the boundary conditions. The general arrangement of these four families of solutions, about a critical point, C, is shown in Fig. 7.2. Parker has demonstrated that only one solution can be taken from this system that meets the two requirements (a) zero velocity at the base of the corona and (b) zero pressure at infinity.

This solution passes through the critical point, C, as indicated by the dotted line. Thus the lower part of the solution follows the envelope of one family of solutions; the upper part, of another family. At point C, the velocity changes from subsonic to supersonic, and at 1 A.U. is about 300 km/sec, in agreement with space-probe observations.

Parker has found that in using (77) for the temperature relationship: (a) For all $0 \le b < 1$ there is a supersonic solar wind at large distances from the sun. (b) The particle flux is determined completely by the

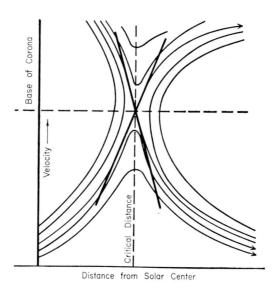

Fig. 7.2. The families of solutions of the hydrodynamic equations of an expanding corona. From Parker, *Ap. J.* **132**, 175 (1960).   Courtesy, *Astrophysical Journal*.

temperature conditions between the base of the corona and the critical distance—the steeper the temperature gradient in this region the lower the particle flux.   (c) The particle flux is strongly dependent on the temperature at the base of the corona (as exp $[-A/T_0]$), whereas the velocity at infinity is roughly proportional to the square root of the base temperature only.

As the corona expands, a part of the thermal energy conducted into each volume element is converted into kinetic and potential energy of the expanding gas. Thus the temperature gradient in an expanding conduction corona is steeper than in a static conduction corona. Were the expanding corona very dense there would be an intermediate set of values of r for which the temperature would vary as $1/r$, and in the case of extremely high densities this intermediate region would extend to infinity and there would be no solar wind. On the other hand, were the density very low, the reciprocal two-sevenths power law would hold as in the case of the static corona (see Eq. 70) in spite of the expansion. The actual density of the corona lies somewhere between the low-density and the high-density case.

The plasma relation for thermal conductivity, $K = A T^{5/2}$, cannot be expected to apply throughout the entire corona. If, in the outer reaches of the corona, the temperature drops to the point that the gas is no longer completely ionized, the conductivity becomes proportional to a lower power of temperature. The relation also breaks down if the density is so low that the maximum energy that could possibly be transferred by thermal conductivity: $(3NkT/2)(2kT/3m)^{1/2}$ is less than $A T^{5/2} dT/dr$. Either of these breakdowns would occur only far out from the sun, having the effect of increasing the distant temperature gradient, thus decreasing the gradient between the sun and the critical distance—thereby increasing the particle flux.

A third effect that decreases the conductivity is the presence of a non-radial magnetic field. If such magnetic fields exist far out in the corona as a result of turbulent effects in the supersonic wind, they enhance the particle flux. On the other hand, they almost certainly are present in the inner corona in the form of loop structures. In the inner corona they have the effect of increasing the temperature gradient, thereby inhibiting or blocking the particle flux—unless the source of coronal heating extends beyond the loop structures (Billings and Roberts, 1964). Evidence of such inhibition of particle flux has been noted by Allen (1944), Bell and Glazer (1954), and Pecker and Roberts (1955), in the anticorrelation between geomagnetic activity and the central-meridian passage of active coronal regions during sunspot-cycle decline.

The solar wind remains a very active topic for coronal research. Chamberlain (1965) since 1961 has repeatedly expressed doubts that Parker's supersonic solution is the only one giving zero pressure at infinity. Parker (1965) has apparently resolved the problem very recently by discovering that large densities at the base of the corona lead to subsonic expansion and lower densities to supersonic expansion. In the meantime various investigators (Noble and Scarf, 1962, 1963; Brandt *et al.*, 1964; Scarf and Noble, 1965; Anderson, 1965) along with Parker have been utilizing space-probe, coronal-density and radar data in the solar-wind theory to determine a coronal model extending from the earth to the sun. As a result of their work, we who observe the inner corona find ourselves in the embarrassing position of learning its characteristics from probe observations made at 1 A.U.

The Rotation of the Corona

Coronal emission lines are so broad that the Doppler displacements from solar rotation give only a rough indication of the rotation rate. The question of the variation of rotation rate with height has not been answered in any way, and the variation with latitude had been studied until recently only from the observation of successive limb passages of bright emission regions. Hansen (1966) has been carrying out a detailed analysis of the coronal rotation rate based on K-coronameter white-light observations.

The most extensive study from monochromatic observations was carried out by Trellis (1957), using successive east and west limb passages of bright λ 5303 regions. The technique was to determine the Carrington meridian of the brightest portion of a region as seen at one limb, then designating the time of arrival of that meridian at the next limb as zero time to plot the brightness at the latitude being studied as a function of time. He repeated this process for a number of regions at the same latitude, and summed the resulting curves of brightness as a function of time to get a bell-shaped curve with a maximum generally displaced somewhat from zero time. From the amount of such displacement he determined the difference between the coronal rotation rate and the Carrington rate, hence the coronal rotation rate for each latitude, from zero to 70°. He concluded that the corona rotated a little more slowly than the photosphere at latitudes below 35°, and more rapidly at latitudes above 35°, the difference becoming quite marked at high latitudes. The precision of the measurements became less at high latitudes, primarily because of less available data.

Two other determinations of rotation rate at high latitudes have been made, each from observations of a single long-lived region. Waldmeier (1950) noted an emission region at 55° that maintained its identity for almost seven rotations, and determined its rotation rate from the successive observations. The rate that he found was significantly higher than the 55° rate on the curve determined by Trellis, but lay almost on the curve found by d'Azambuja and d'Azambuja (1948) from the rotation of filaments. Cooper and Billings (1962), from 29 successive rotations of an emission region at 65°, determined a rotation rate that was in excess of either that found by Waldmeier or by Trellis. Thus it appears that high-latitude phenomena at coronal heights in the solar atmosphere rotate significantly faster than the photosphere. Also, since the difference between the rate found by Billings and Cooper and that found by Trellis is greater than the observational uncertainty of either measurement, there is a suggestion that the rate may not be a consistent function of latitude.

There are several observations that may be related to the rather remarkable difference between coronal and photospheric differential rotation. One of these is an observation by Trellis (1957) that the bright regions at latitudes less than 35° tend to move toward higher latitudes, whereas those at latitudes greater than 35° tend to move toward lower latitudes. Trellis has also noted an asymmetry between the east and west wings of emitting regions, which also depends on latitude and can be interpreted as indicating that the tops of the regions at latitudes less than 35° are bent toward the east, those at higher latitudes toward the west. Finally, both Waldmeier (1955) and Nagasawa (1961) have found that bright coronal emission regions in the polar zones are generally accompanied by bright regions in the active zones at the same longitude. The polar region studied by Cooper and Billings fell into this category. Waldmeier has explained this correspondence in terms of the phenomena, often observed during an eclipse, of coronal material arching over quiescent prominences, the suggestion being that coronal material in the two bright regions is joined by magnetic lines of force arching over the prominence zone, and that interchange of matter between the active zone and the polar coronal regions takes place along these lines of force.

By putting these various observations and ideas together, we arrive at the concept that the tension in the lines of force joining the active zone and polar coronal regions has the effect of causing each to move slowly toward the major zone of quiescent prominences, which at the time of maximum solar activity is about 35° latitude, and also tends to bring the two coronal regions to more nearly the same angular velocity than is the case for the underlying photospheric regions. Thus the polar coronal region is speeded up, while the more massive accompanying active zone region is slowed down in rotation, but by a lesser amount. Furthermore, the top of each region is bent, as though being dragged by the other. According to such a picture we would not expect all polar coronal features at the same latitude to rotate with the same angular velocity. Those that are connected with the active zone features by particularly strong magnetic fields would have the faster rate of rotation. We would conclude that the region studied by Cooper and Billings was particularly strongly bound to the active zone, and might postulate that its long lifetime was further evidence of the strength of its binding.

REFERENCES

Alfvén, H. (1947). Magnetohydrodynamic waves and the heating of the corona. *M. N. R. A. S.* **107**, 221.

Alfvén, H. (1950). "Cosmical Electrodynamics." Oxford Univ. Press (Clarendon), London and New York.

Allen, C. W. (1944). Relation between magnetic storms and solar activity. *M. N. R. A. S.* **104**, 13.

Allen, C. W. (1963). Astrophysical Quantities," 2nd ed. Oxford Univ. Press (Athlone), London and New York.

Anderson, C. (1965). "Representative Models of the Observed Solar Wind." Univ. of Colorado Ph.D. Thesis.

Athay, R. G., and Roberts, W. O., (1955) Coronal line intensities at the Khartoum Eclipse. *Ap. J.* **121**, 231.

Babcock, H. W. (1961). The topology of the sun's magnetic field and the 22-year cycle. *Ap. J.* **133**, 572.

Bazer, J., and Ericson, W. B. (1959). Hydromagnetic shocks. *Ap. J.* **129**, 758.

Bell, B., and Glazer, H. (1954). Geomagnetism and the emission line corona. *J. G. R.* **59**, 551.

Biermann, L. (1946). The meaning of chormospheric turbulence and the UV excess of the sun. *Naturwissenschaften* **33**, 118.

Biermann, L. (1948). Turbulent heating of the solar chromosphere. *Z. Ap.* **25**, **161**.

Billings, D. E. (1963). Spectroscopic limitation on coronal heating mechanisms. *Ap. J.* **137**, 592.

Billings, D. E. (1965). Optical line profiles and radar observations in the corona. *Ap. J.* **141**, 325.

Billings, D. E., and Lehman, R. C. (1962). Line-width temperatures of distinct coronal features. *Ap. J.* **136**, 258.

Billings, D. E., and Lilliequist, C. G. (1963). Coronal temperature gradient and the solar wind. *Ap. J.* **137**, 16.

Billings, D. E., and Roberts, W. O. (1964). The origin of M-region magnetic storms. *Astrophysica Norvegica* **9**, 147.

Blackwell, D. E., and Dewhirst, D. W. (1956). An examination of the observational evidence for the accretion theory of the solar corona. *M. N. R. A. S.* **116**, 637.

Brandt, J. C., Michie, R. W., and Cassinelli, J. P. (1964). Interplanetary gas X coronal temperatures, energy deposition and solar wind. Contribution from the Kitt Peak National Observatory.

Chamberlain, J. W. (1965). On the existence of slow solutions in coronal hydrodynamics. *Ap. J.* **141**, 320.

Chapman, S. (1957). Notes on the solar corona and the terrestrial ionosphere. *Smithsonian Contributions to Astrophysics* **2**, 1.

Chisholm, J. H., and James, J. C. (1964). Radar evidence of solar wind and coronal mass motion. *Ap. J.* **140**, 377.

Cooper, R. H., and Billings, D. E. (1962). A long-lived polar coronal region. *Z. Ap.* **55**, 24.

Cowling, T. G. (1953). Solar electrodynamics, *in* "The Sun" (G. P. Kuiper, ed.), p. 532. Univ. of Chicago Press, Chicago, Illinois.

Cowling, T. G. (1957). "Magnetohydrodynamics." Wiley (interscience), New York.

d'Azambuja, M., and d'Azambuja, L. (1948). Solar prominences and their evolution. *Ann. L'obs. de Paris* **6**, 1.

de Jager, C., and Kuperus, M. (1961). The acoustic energy flux of the sun and formation of the corona. *B. A. N.* **16**, 71.

Evans, J. W., and Michard, R. (1962). Observational study of macroscopic inhomogeneities in the solar atmosphere. III. Vertical oscillatory motions in the solar atmosphere. *Ap. J.* **136**, 493.

Ferraro, V. C. A., and Plumpton, C. (1961). "An Introduction to Magneto-Fluid Mechanics." Oxford University Press, London.

Hansen, R. T. (1966). Private communication.

Hoyle, F. (1949). "Some Recent Researches in Solar Physics." University Press, Cambridge (London).

Hoyle, F., and Wickramasinghe, N. C. (1961). Origin of the sun's polar field (heating of the corona). *M. N. R. A. S.* **123**, 51.

Jensen, E., and Orrall, F. Q. (1963). Observational study of macroscopic inhomogeneities in the solar atmosphere. IV. Velocity and intensity fluctuations observed in the K-line. *Ap. J.* **138**, 252.

Kuperus, M. (1963). Private communication.

Landseer-Jones, B. C. (1961). Viscous damping of hydromagnetic waves in the corona. *M. N. R. A. S.* **122**, 7.

Linhart, J. C. (1960). "Plasma Physics." North Holland Publishing Company, Amsterdam.

Lüst, R., Meyer, F., Treffle, E., and Biermann, L. (1962). Zur Temperatur der Sonnenkorona. *Z. Naturforsch.* **17a**, 259.

Nagasawa, S. (1961). Some relations between the intensity of the green coronal line and sunspot groups. *Publ. Astr. Soc. Japan* **13**, 384.

Noble, L. M., and Scarf, F. L. Hydrodynamic models of the solar corona. *J. G. R.* **67**, 4577.

Noble, L. M., and Scarf, F. L. (1963). Conductive heating of the solar wind. *Ap. J.* **138**, 1169.

Osterbrock, D. E. (1961). Heating of the solar chromosphere, plages and corona by magnetohydrodynamic waves. *Ap. J.* **134**, 347.

Parker, E. N. (1959). Plasma dynamical determination of shock thickness in an ionized gas. *Ap. J.* **129**, 217.

Parker, E. N. (1960). Stallar winds. *Ap. J.* **132**, 821.

Parker, E. N. (1963). "Interplanetary Dynamical Processes." Wiley (Interscience), New York.

Parker, E. N. (1955). Dynamical properties of stellar coronas and stellar winds. IV. The separate existence of subsonic and supersonic solutions. *Ap. J.* **141**, 1463.

Pecker, J. C., and Roberts, W. O. (1955). Solar corpuscles responsible for magnetic disturbances. *J. G. R.* **60**, 33.

Piddington, J. H. (1956). Solar atmospheric heating by hydromagnetic waves. *M. N. R. A. S.* **116**, 314.

Plumpton, C. (1959). The propagation of hydromagnetic waves of finite amplitude in a horizontally stratified atmosphere. *Ap. J.* **129**, 752.

Potasch, S. R. (1963a). The lower solar corona: The abundance of iron. *M. N. R. A. S.* **125**, 543.

Pottasch, S. R. (1963b). The lower solar corona: Interpretation of the ultraviolet spectrum. *Ap. J.* **137**, 945.

Pottasch, S. R. (1964). On the interpretation of the solar UV emission line spectrum. *Space Sci. Rev.* **3**, 816.

Pottasch, S. R. (1965). On the determination of the solar chemical composition from a study of the UV resonance lines. *Ann. d'Ap.* **28**, 148.

Scarf, F. L., and Noble, L. M. (1965). Conductive heating of the solar wind. II. The inner corona. *Ap. J.* **141**, 1479.

Schatzman, E. (1949). The heating of the solar corona and chromosphere. *Ann. d'Ap.* **12**, 203.

Schwarzschild, M. (1948). Noise arising from the solar granulation. *Ap. J.* **107**, 1.

Simon, R. (1958). On the reflection and refraction of hydromagnetic waves at the boundary of two compressible gaseous media. *Ap. J.* **128**, 352.

Spitzer, L., Jr. (1956). "Physics of Fully Ionized Gases." Wiley (Interscience), New York.

Trellis, M. (1957). Contribution to the study of the solar corona. *Ann. d'Ap.* Suppl. 5.

Trellis, M. (1960). East-West dissymetry of the monochromatic coronal intensity. *Compt. Rend.* **250**, 58.

Uchida, Y. (1963). An effect of the magnetic field in the shock wave heating theory of the corona. *Publ. astr. Soc. Japan* **15**, 376.

van de Hulst, H. C. (1949). "Viscous Heating of the Corona—Problems of Cosmical Aerodynamics." I. U. T. A. M. and I. A. U. Symposium, Paris.

Waldmeier, M. (1950). Polar charts of the solar corona. *Z. Ap.* **27**, 24.

Waldmeier, M. (1955). The minimum-structure of the corona. *Z. Ap.* **37**, 233.

Weymann, R. (1960). Heating of stellar chromospheres by shock waves. *Ap. J.* **132**, 452.

Weymann, R., and Howard, R. (1958). Note on hydromagnetic waves passing through an atmosphere with a density gradient. *Ap. J.* **128**, 142.

Whitaker, W. A. (1963). Heating of the solar corona by gravity waves. *Ap. J.* **137**, 914.

CHAPTER 8

DENSITY DISTRIBUTION IN THE CORONA

A. General Problem

The distribution of matter in the corona out to several solar radii is derived more directly from eclipse photographs in white light than from any other datum, using the electron-scattering theory outlined in Chapter 5. In the absence of eclipse, the density has been derived from white-light coronameter measurements and from white-light photographs at very high altitudes. X-ray spectroheliograms, optical monochromatic observations, and radio-noise interferometer measurements also indicate regions of enhanced density—in sharper relief, as a matter of fact, than the white-light measurements, since they respond to the square of the electron density. Unfortunately, they also depend on electron temperature, so can be interpreted to yield electron density only in case the temperature is known with some certainty and the ionization and excitation processes are completely and quantitatively understood. Because of these complications, white-light observations remain the primary source of information concerning electron density. Other observations yield special information, as, for example, the detailed fine structure shown in monochromatic optical photographs. If, in such photographs, the same structure appears in both λ 5303 and λ 6374 emission, it is apparent that it defines a region of enhanced density in which a range of temperatures are present. Intense regions of X-ray or 10–100-cm radio emission, furthermore, will distinguish high-density coronal regions on the disk—a locality that is not available at all to any form of white-light measurements.

The density distribution in the corona is too complex to be easily described in quantitative terms. From a comparison of photographs at various eclipses one infers immediately that the distribution is quite different at sunspot minimum compared to sunspot maximum, and at the poles compared to the equator at sunspot minimum. This inference has led to the practice of specifying one typical density as a function of height for sunspot maximum, another for sunspot minimum at the equator, and a third for sunspot minimum at the poles. Such descriptions necessarily average out a great deal of structure both at the equator and at the poles, fail to bring out the minimum in brightness that is often observable between the equatorial and the polar structures, and ignore the fact that at many sunspot minima the equatorial streamer is cleft so that it is not described in its greatest extent by the equatorial gradient. Nevertheless, these generalizations have proved useful, and seem to be about the only alternative to a degree-by-degree enumeration of the density at different heights for each position on the solar limb for each eclipse. Furthermore, a degree-by-degree tabulation of density vs height would imply a knowledge that does not exist, since any density computation is based on some assumption concerning the distribution of matter along the line of sight.

A second scheme that has been in use for many years for giving a generalized description of the changes in density distribution with the solar cycle is by specifying the smoothed, general shape—expressed quantitatively by the eccentricity of the isophotes. Again, such a description smooths over many interesting features of the corona. For example, a surprising number of coronal observations at times of decline of sunspot activity have followed the general form shown at the 1952 eclipse (see Fig. 3.6) with two or more strong streamers on one side of the sun, spread out in a manner suggestive of sunspot maximum, and only one well-defined equatorial streamer on the other side of the sun.

Any attempt to specify the corona by a limited number of quantities must overlook the great variety of structural features that we have described in Chapter 3, "Observational Aspects of the Corona." Some of these features have been sufficiently well observed that photometry and estimates of density distribution within them have been possible, but the sampling has been so sparse that we cannot profess any knowledge of the "typical" density of any of them.

At distances from the sun beyond 5 or 6 solar radii the problem of separating F-corona, K-corona and instrumentally-scattered light becomes overwhelming. We may obtain some evidence of the coronal density in the scattering of radio waves from such discrete sources as the Crab Nebula. In this case, unfortunately, another parameter—the number of scattering structures along a line of sight—is involved.

At 1 A.U. from the sun the problem again becomes simpler. As a matter of fact, the least ambiguous measurements of coronal density to date have been achieved by space probes operating beyond the earth's magnetosphere.

B. Average Density Distributions Near the Sun

Models Based on the Baumbach Distribution

During the early part of this century several attempts were made to summarize the observations from many eclipses into systematic laws relating coronal brightness with height, and in some cases, to compute from these the density in the corona as a function of height. The results of these efforts were notable in the wide variety of relations they brought forth, depending primarily on whether the data dealt with the inner or the outer corona. The most notable of these syntheses was by Baumbach (1937) who wrote an expression for brightness at the equator as

$$I = \frac{2.58}{r^{17}} + \frac{1.43}{r^7} + \frac{0.053}{r^{2.5}} \quad \text{in units of } 10^{-6} B_\odot \tag{1}$$

without regard to phase in the solar cycle; r is the distance from the center of the sun in solar radii. This expression has the merit that at various distances above the solar limb different inverse powers of distance predominate.

Baumbach applied scattering theory to his brightness model to obtain a corresponding density model for the corona. However, he was unaware of the distinction between the F and K corona, and also used an isotropic rather than an exact scattering function in the computations. Consequently, his density values are no longer considered valid. The brightness model, on the other hand, has served as the basis for more precise computations of density, which have been used repeatedly and are still meaningful. We consider here two density computations based on the Baumbach brightness model—one by Saito (1950), and one by van de Hulst (1950). Both authors made the simplifying assumptions that the F corona is constant with the solar cycle and spherically symmetrical, at least in the neighborhood of the sun; and that for equatorial lines of sight the K corona could also be considered to be spherically symmetrical. Saito introduced a further simplification by assuming that the inverse 2.5-power term in the Baumbach expression represents the F corona in its entirety, and justified the assumption by showing that this term gave an acceptable description to zodiacal-light observations. On this basis he determined the density variation with distance from the sun in this average corona to be

$$N(r) = 10^8 \left[\frac{1.93}{r^2} + \frac{1.47}{r^{16}} \right]. \tag{2}$$

Saito found that this distribution in density yielded polarization-vs-height values that agreed with those observations in which the sky brightness had been evaluated very far from the sun—i.e., with observations in which the F corona was not contributing to the quantity that was erroneously considered to be sky light—thereby leading to an overcorrection for sky brightness. He also concluded, from a comparison of brightness at various eclipses, that the K corona varied in brightness by $\pm 35\%$ with changes in the solar cycle.

Van de Hulst used a somewhat more involved procedure for separation of the F from the K corona. He introduced the approximation that at sunspot minimum the equatorial regions contributed 70% of the total K corona, and that the total scattered light at sunspot maximum exceeded that at sunspot minimum by a factor of 1.84. These data he found to be consistent with

$$K_{\max} = 355.6r^{-17} + 177.8r^{-7} + 7.08r^{-2.5}, \tag{3}$$

$$K_{\min} = 200.0r^{-17} + 100.0r^{-7} + 3.98r^{-2.5}, \tag{4}$$

$$F = 14.86r^{-7} + 4.99r^{-2.5}, \tag{5}$$

in units of $10^{-8} B_\odot$. The equatorial electron densities given in Appendix IV are consistent with these K-corona values. Computed polarizations agree with observed out to about $r = 3$, at which point discrepancies set in—probably due to erroneous corrections for sky light.

Van de Hulst obtained the polar variation of density with height given in Appendix IV by making microphotometer tracings across the poles in the photographs of the 1900 eclipse; then, after converting to brightness and inverting the Abelian integral as described in Chapter 6, on the assumption of cylindrical symmetry with regard to the pole, determined the electron density at various latitudes in the polar regions. The procedure involved first assuming isotropic scattering, then introducing a factor of 1.08–1.05 to correct for this assumption. The procedure is basically much sounder than assuming spherical symmetry over the poles in a sunspot-minimum corona. Polarizations computed from the polar density distribution thus determined depart from observed values somewhat closer to the sun than in the equatorial case. The discrepancy could be alleviated were one to assume that the F corona was more concentrated near the equator than the poles. Subsequent investigators, as we shall see, have also found this assumption to be useful.

Pottasch Model

Pottasch (1960) developed a model corona for the equatorial sunspot minimum that incorporated eclipse observations of 1952 and 1954. The model is interesting in that it extends from within the chromosphere to a distance of more than 10 solar radii from the sun. The chromospheric and inner coronal data are based on spectroscopic observations of the 1952 eclipse, analyzed by Athay, Menzel, Pecker, and Thomas (1955). Further out Pottasch used the 1952 eclipse data obtained by Lyot and associates and analyzed by Michard (1954). These data are of exceptionally high quality, the photographs having been made with an occulting disk to mask the inner corona as well as other precautions having been taken to reduce the scattered light. The sky light was reduced by the use of red and infrared filters, and was carefully determined on the assumption that its isophotes would be parallel to the horizon. The K corona was separated from the F corona by polarimetric means. A striking conclusion from these observations is that the more-slowly varying term for brightness in the K corona should not be an inverse 7th-power term, as van de Hulst and Saito had deduced from the Baumbach model, but an inverse 4th-power in the equatorial and 5.5th-power in the polar zones.

Very far from the sun, Pottasch used densities obtained by Blackwell in 1954 from an airplane flying at 30,000 ft altitude. These data, like those of Michard (1954), were obtained and analyzed with great care. However, since they pertain to a different eclipse the only justification for their incorporation into the model is that they join smoothly onto the other data. Waldmeier (1955) had concluded from his observations that the K corona had decreased in brightness by a factor of about 1.7 between 1952 and 1954, but the decrease may have been closer to the sun.

The Pottasch model suffers from two weaknesses. In the first place the 1952 corona was not a true minimum corona. At least one quite active region was still on the limb, and on one limb the directions of the two streamers departed rather strongly from radial. The second weakness is an inevitable result of the joining together of several data obtained by widely divergent means. Such a union produces irregularities that are more likely to be observational than real. Under the circumstances there was no alternative if such a wide range of heights was to be represented, but care should be exercised in any interpretation of the model that involves the slope of the density curve. This is illustrated in the temperature curve computed by Pottasch from his density curve on the assumption of hydrostatic equilibrium. The computations give a temperature that increases gradually from the chromosphere to almost 200,000 km above the limb. Coronal line emission visible only a few thousand kilometers above the limb suggest, however, that the temperature increase must be much more abrupt. A careful examination of the density curve by Pottasch reveals the reason for the discrepancy. The two sets of data obtained by Athay et al. (1955)—one for the chromosphere, based on a comparison of the continuum on opposite sides of the Balmer jump, and the other for the lower corona, based on the continuum lying outside the line spectrum—have been joined by a smooth curve. However, if the slopes of both segments are projected, they join with an abrupt change in slope at about 15,000 km height, corresponding to an abrupt temperature change from chromosphere to corona.

The van de Hulst model for the equator at sunspot minimum agrees well with the Pottasch model for distances of 0.2 to 1.0 solar radii. Closer to the sun the van de Hulst model is considerably lower in electron density and has a markedly lower gradient. Waldmeier (1956) favored the Pottasch model in this regard by noting that the polarization in the 1954 eclipse was significantly higher than that given by the van de Hulst model, even though observed at a time of extreme minimum.

A plot of the Pottasch model, including the van de Hulst model and models by Michard (1954), Hepburn (1955), and von Klüber (1958) based on the 1952 eclipse, are shown in Fig. 8.1.

A better minimum coronal density model should now be possible, using 1954 data alone, then any presently available. Waldmeier (1961) has combined his own observations of the 1954 event with those of Blackwell (1956) and computed thereby a tabulation of K-corona brightness vs distance for every 10° around the limb. In the process he has tabulated F-corona intensities that show a definite equatorial flattening that increases with distance from the sun—as one would expect if the belt of zodiacal-light particles is a disk only a few solar diameters thick. Specifically, the ratio of polar to equatorial F-corona intensity changes from 0.9 at $r = 1$ to 0.8 at $r = 2.5$; 0.7 at $r = 4.3$; 0.6 at $r = 6.3$; and 0.47 at $r = 18$.

A model to be constructed from the 1954 observations will also have the advantage of the considerations given by Blackwell and Ingham (1961) to the problem of the polarization of zodiacal light at considerable distances from the sun. From a comparison of spectroscopic with polarimetric ob-

servations of the zodiacal light, Blackwell and co-workers concluded that
the light scattered by zodiacal particles at larger angles was significantly
polarized—to the extent that any K-corona computations for $r > 8$ solar
radii which are based on the assumption that the F corona is unpolarized
are in error. The correction of this error involved the simultaneous determination of the zodiacal particle density as a function of distance, the
scattering function, and the polarization function for the particles, then
the elimination of the zodiacal light from the observed corona. Ingham
(1961) gives, for $r > 6$,

$$N_e = \frac{6.75 \times 10^6}{r^3} \tag{6}$$

for the sunspot-minimum, equatorial corona. This is a much slower drop-off
than was predicted by the models based on the Baumbach brightness
distribution.

In addition to the observations of Waldmeier and Blackwell, a minimum
model based on the 1954 eclipse could be checked against observations by
Allen (1956) and Baturova *et al.* (1960). The former were photographs

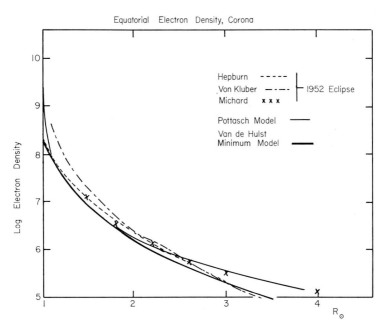

Fig. 8.1. Electron-density models for the intermediate-type 1952 eclipse, compared
with the Pottasch and the van de Hulst minimum models.

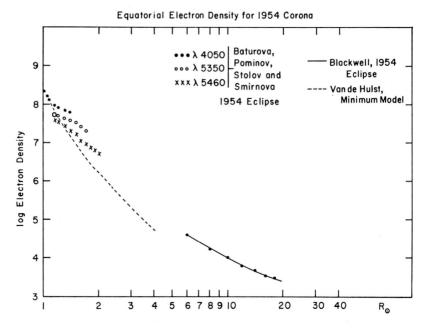

Fig. 8.2. Electron-density models from the extreme-minimum 1954 eclipse, compared to the van de Hulst minimum model.

taken with special precautions to reduce the scattered light from the inner corona; the latter were low-dispersion spectrograms taken with the slit at 23.7° to the solar equator. The former did not have either polarization or spectroscopic observations for separation of the F from the K corona, but the detailed determinations of the F corona by Waldmeier should make additional reduction of the observations possible. The analysis of the data is further complicated by an inadvertent failure to center the outer occulting disk, but Allen has succeeded in computing out the effect of this difficulty. The observations by Baturova *et al.* have been reduced to electron density. They show considerable internal variation. They are plotted in Fig. 8.2, along with the analytical expression for Blackwell's densities, these being the only densities computed from the extensive 1954 observations to date.

Commentary on the Model Coronas

Determinations of coronal densities that have been made since the van de Hulst and Pottasch models were formulated or that were not included in the models provide a considerable body of data for comparison with these models. Two quite different observations during the last sunspot maximum—that by Newkirk (1961) with the white-light coronameter and that by Ney *et al.* (1961) at the 1959 eclipse—agree in indicating that the maximum corona, during the current cycle at least, was about twice as dense at each height as is given in the van de Hulst model. This factor may simply reflect the greater level of activity during the present cycle than during the cycles which were averaged to give the Baumbach corona. Shilova (1961) found that the corona in February 1961 was still brighter than the van de Hulst model.

As we have already stated, the best sunspot-minimum data, namely, those for the 1954 eclipse, are not yet reduced to electron densities. However, the equatorial K-coronal intensities of Waldmeier are almost identical to those of van de Hulst, hence would yield almost identical electron densities on the assumption of spherical symmetry (Fig. 8.3). Waldmeier's

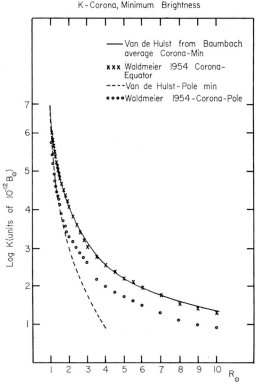

Fig. 8.3. Waldmeier's 1954 K-corona intensities, compared to the intensities used by van de Hulst for computing his minimum model.

polar intensities depart very strongly from those of van de Hulst, however. This may be a consequence of an overcorrection for the F corona by van de Hulst resulting from his assumption of its spherical symmetry. At brightnesses of $10^{-9}B_\odot$ and smaller, at which the two coronal intensities diverge, corrections for instrumental scatter, sky, and F corona all become very important, and it is difficult to find a strong basis for choosing one model or the other. However, in view of the fact that van de Hulst found evidence for a nonspherically symmetric F corona and Waldmeier not only confirmed such evidence but evaluated and used the asymmetry, we are inclined to favor the Waldmeier data.

Finally, we consider the Pottasch model as an example of an intermediate-type corona. We see in Fig. 8.1 that the electron densities of von Klüber near the sun lie well above this model, but drop off more rapidly. Those by Hepburn fit almost exactly on it, which is not particularly surprising since they were adjusted by an arbitrary factor to be brought into coincidence with those of the van de Hulst minimum model at $r = 1.4$—at which height the van de Hulst and the Pottasch models also happen to agree. Nevertheless, the detailed agreement of the Hepburn with the Pottasch densities gives some confirmation of the latter. The large discrepancies with the von Klüber data, on the other hand, are difficult to explain. The latter appear to have been gathered with extraordinary care. Exposures of various length were taken so that each could be used over the best range of densities for photometry, and the absolute calibration was sufficiently consistent internally that adjustments of 0.04 or less in the logarithm of intensity were adequate to bring all photographs into agreement. Three lenses in the camera gave polarized images rotated at 120°, and a fourth gave an unpolarized image. Hence the F corona could be determined from internal measurements, and subtracted out. It showed no clear dependence on latitude, and agreed to a remarkable degree with that of van de Hulst. The coronal densities closest to the sun in the Pottasch model, on the other hand, were determined from the continuum on flash spectrograms in which there were problems of establishing the scale of absolute photometry (see Athay *et al.*, 1954). Also there was the problem of separation of radiation from opposite sides of the sun. These considerations might make one inclined to favor the von Klüber points, except that near the sun the von Klüber densities seem to be abnormally high—not only in comparison with the Pottasch model and the van de Hulst minimum model, but also with the van de Hulst maximum model, with densities derived by von Klüber (1961) from a 1927 sunspot-maximum plate, and even the intensities in the very active sun of 1959, studied by Ney *et al.*

Von Klüber himself suggests that his lower densities far from the sun, compared to van de Hulst, may be more important than his higher densities closer in. Thus, in spite of the numerous careful observations made at the 1952 eclipse, we are not in a position to resolve the serious discrepancies in electron density between the various observers. We suggest that the Pottasch densities in this range may be increased somewhat on the basis of the von Klüber observations, but probably not much. One should at least be justified in smoothing the density curve in the vicinity of $0.1R_{\odot}$ on this basis, and to let the discontinuity in the slope occur nearer the top of the chromosphere.

C. Single-Parameter Designation of Time-Dependent Coronal Density

One of the simplest and most direct coronal measurements is the absolute photometry of the total corona. Such measurements are particularly useful for describing, by a single sequence of numbers, the change of mean coronal density with the solar cycle. In principle the techniques should be readily duplicated at successive eclipses. A difficulty enters, however, in that the outer extent of the "total" corona must be defined in some arbitrary manner—say at $5R_{\odot}$. Observers at different eclipses have not used the same outer limits, and as a result it is necessary to use brightness models for normalizing all observations to a corona of the same extent. The inner boundary of the corona, established by the moon, also proves to be a source of difficulty. Since the brightness of the inner corona is so much greater near the limb than farther out, small changes in the size of the moon projected on the sun between one eclipse and the next can produce large changes in the total radiation being received. Furthermore, when— as in most cases—the moon is not centered on the sun, the correction involves complex geometrical considerations. Van de Hulst (1953), after making the necessary adjustments for inner and outer boundaries, has presented the total emission as a function of the solar cycle (Fig. 8.4). The data show clearly that the intensity of the white-light corona is considerably greater at sunspot maximum than at sunspot minimum—a fact that is not at all evident visually because of the striking character of the equatorial streamers at the minimum phase.

A second quantity that has been used to distinguish maximum from minimum has been the eccentricity of the isophotes in the corona. A basic difficulty with this procedure is that the isophotes are sometimes approxi-

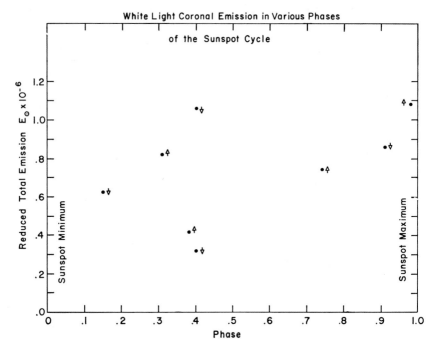

Fig. 8.4. The variation of total coronal brightness with phase of the solar cycle, the values having been corrected by van de Hulst (1953) to equal areas of sky. Arrows indicate whether sunspot number was increasing or decreasing at the time of the eclipse.

mately elliptical and sometimes not, the greatest departure being in the intermediate phases between maximum and minimum. Ludendorff (from van de Hulst, 1953), who introduced the use of eccentricity as a parameter, set up an arbitrary rule for its computation that may be used for any isophote:

$$e = E/P - 1, \qquad (7)$$

where E is the mean of three equatorial diameters making angles of $22.5°$ with each other, and P is a similarly defined mean polar diameter.

One would anticipate, from the general appearance of maxima and minima corona, that the eccentricity would follow the solar cycle, $180°$ out of phase. In attempting to follow the parameter, however, one is confronted by its strong dependence on the distance of the isophote from the sun. The eccentricity first increases with increasing distance, then decreases, passes through a minimum at three or four solar radii from the limb, and finally increases slowly again. Ludendorff concentrated on the initial rise in this complex pattern (which is probably a correct procedure, since the outer minimum and increase involve the dropping off of the K corona and the appearance of the zodiacal effect in the F corona). Thus he expressed the eccentricity as a linear function of distance of the long ends of the isophotes from the limb, $\epsilon = a + b(r_{eq} - 1)$, and finally plotted the sum $(a + b)$ against phase in the sunspot cycle (Fig. 8.5). A strong dependence is apparent. Unfortunately, so many arbitrary decisions have been involved in the choice of parameter that it is impossible to relate it to the physically significant phenomena that must be involved in distinguishing the shape

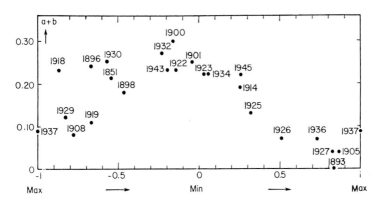

Fig. 8.5. Variation in Ludendorff isophote flattening with the phase of the solar cycle, from van de Hulst (1953). Courtesy, University of Chicago Press.

of the maximum from the minimum corona. Hence the usefulness of the parameter is questionable.

Saito (1950) introduced a parameter for describing the distribution of density as a function of the solar cycle that appears to be a hopeful step between the gross observations as described by the eccentricity of the isophotes and the physical processes involved in the change of the corona with the solar cycle. He wrote an expression for the latitude-dependent portion of the coronal density in the form

$$N(r, \phi) = m \frac{1 - p \sin \phi}{r^n} \cdot 10^8, \tag{8}$$

then evaluated the parameters m and n on the assumption that only the second term in the Baumbach expression depended on latitude, the first term representing the F corona, as previously mentioned, and the last, a spherically symmetric component of the K corona. On this basis he put $m = 1.93 \times \frac{4}{3}$ and $n = 6$. p is a parameter that varies from 0 to 1 as sunspot activity changes from maximum to minimum. The density distribution defined by this equation gives isophotes for $p \simeq 1$ which bear a strong resemblance to sunspot-minimum isophotes. The eccentricity is related to p by

$$\epsilon = 0.090p(1 + p). \tag{9}$$

Vsekhsvayatskii and Ivanchuk (1962) have suggested that the characteristic sunspot-minimum shape of the corona is associated with the development of polar magnetic fields, which begin to appear about the time of sunspot maximum and apparently reach their maximum development at sunspot minimum. Such polar fields not only define the configuration of polar plumes, but also push the remainder of the corona equatorward. An interesting implication of this explanation is that the polar fields, although they appear quite poloidal, are not force-free—for almost the entire magnetic pressure of the polar fields is necessary to maintain the density discontinuity at about 65° during sunspot minimum. Conversely, the much stronger active region magnetic fields must be almost entirely force free. Otherwise, the spherical symmetry in the corona characteristic of sunspot maximum could not be maintained; all of the material would be forced into the polar regions. These considerations lead to the speculation that the polar magnetic fields have their origin entirely in the solar atmosphere—that electric currents in the corona may play a significant role in their existence, whereas the active region magnetic fields are somewhat deeper rooted.

D. Density Models of Coronal Features

A designation of the typical variation of the density of the corona with height over the equator and the poles, or even at every 10° interval on the limb, or a statement of how the integrated brightness or eccentricity changes with the solar cycle all fail to convey any appreciation of the really striking aspects of the corona. A few attempts have been made to determine the density structure of individual features in the corona. These do not cover the whole category of feature types, and there is no assurance that the particular features selected for study are truly typical. Furthermore, the studies are fraught with uncertainties concerning the line-of-sight dimension of the feature or its position in relation to the sky—whether directly on the limb, or in front or back but seen in projection against the sky.

Four models are available for coronal condensations—one drawn by Waldmeier and Muller (1950) from familiarity with features observed in coronal spectrograms, one by Waldmeier (1963) based on the very bright condensation on the west limb at the February 1962 eclipse, and another by Saito and Billings (1964), also based on the latter condensation. The fourth, by Nishi and Nakagomi (1963), is from coronagraph observations and 1420 Mc/sec emission. The regions studied by Newkirk (1961) with the white-light coronameter that form the basis of his "condensation" model would, according to our adopted nomenclature, be termed "enhancements." The Waldmeier-Muller model was devised to explain the slowly varying component of solar radio noise in the 10-cm range. It is based on what the authors considered to be a typical condensation—one 125,000 km in extent and five times as bright as the normal corona. Into such a model, assumed describable by hemispherical shells of equal density, the authors imposed a density range from 63×10^8 at the core to 16×10^8 in the outermost shell. Finally, they computed the radio radiation from the model on two temperature assumptions—(a) a uniform temperature of 1.4×10^6 °, and (b) a varying temperature with 6×10^6 ° at the core— and concluded that either agreed fairly well with observations. The Nishi–Nakagomi model is similar to the Waldmeier–Muller model in that it has at its center a hot, dense core of $4 \times 10^6 \, K$ temperature and $30–100 \times 10^8/cm^3$ electron density. Surrounding layers are of lower density and temperature.

The Waldmeier-Muller model bears a strong resemblance to the condensation at the February 1962 eclipse. This condensation was one of the most spectacular ever available for eclipse observation. It is described by Waldmeier as comparable in brilliance to an adjacent prominence; it is describable as a "white prominence," as a matter of fact, in the manner of a long-forgotten observation by Tacchini in 1883.

The two analyses of the condensation, by Waldmeier (1963) and by Saito and Billings (1964), from separate sets of photographs, yielded almost identical systems of isophotes. The subsequent analysis differed somewhat, however. Waldmeier computed the electron density under the assumption of two different geometrical models: a model with cylindrical symmetry and a model of elliptical horizontal cross section having isodensity contours of the shape of the underlying plage. The cross sections of both the cylindrical and elliptical isodensity contours increase with

height, but at somewhat different rates. As a consequence, the densities
at the center of symmetry in one model are at some heights greater than
in the other model, and at other heights the converse is true. The effect of
the choice of model is not strong, however. The density at the center of
symmetry varies from 63×10^8 at $r = 1.02$ to about 3×10^8 at $r = 1.30$.

Saito and Billings attempted to describe the distribution of density in
the condensation as having cylindrical symmetry with regard to the axis
of the principal loop structure that could be identified in the condensation.
They determined the three-dimensional configuration of the loop as discussed in Chapter 6, and took the departure from the limb into account in
computing electron density (Fig. 8.6). The locus of matter in the condensation was thus more sharply defined than in Waldmeier's analysis, and the

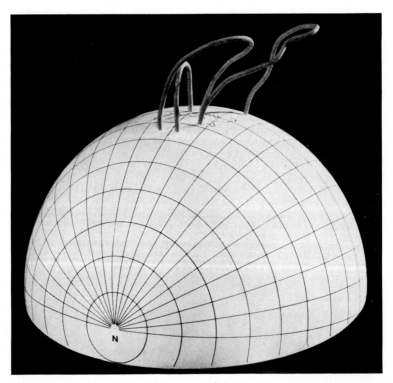

Fig. 8.6. A photograph of a three-dimensional model for the cores or axes of the loop
structures making up the great condensation in the February 1962 eclipse. The model
was constructed by K. Saito on the basis of the analysis outlined by Saito and Billings
(1964).

densities correspondingly were about twice as great. The difference between the two results lies well within the uncertain assumptions concerning the geometric configuration that must be introduced into the analysis. The degree of agreement is sufficient that if we consider the February 1962 condensation to be typical of large, bright condensations we can characterize such condensations as having densities of about 10^{10} electrons/cm^3 in their most intense portions, and a structure that can be described as a complex of loops with overall dimensions of about 100,000 km. The dimensions are comparable to those of the enhancements studied by Newkirk, but the maximum density is an order of magnitude greater. Also, the density gradient is significantly steeper in the lower part of the condensation, but becomes nearly the same beyond the very bright core of the condensation.

The Waldmeier model for the February 1962 condensation confirms the Waldmeier-Muller model quite precisely in both density and dimensions. The peak densities also correspond to those measured from the streaks of continuum in "yellow-line" regions by Waldmeier (1956), Billings (1957), and Zirin (1959). Thus we may consider that the 1962 observations confirm the extensive use of the Waldmeier-Muller model for very bright coronal condensations. However, in the cases in which it is desirable to represent the corona over regions of moderate activity, the Newkirk model is recommended.

Newkirk's model was designed to explain the average variation in polarization in coronal enhancements observed during a two-year period at Climax with the white-light photometer. First, from observations outside of active regions, Newkirk concluded that the electron density could be described as

$$N_Q = N_0 \times 10^{4.32/r} \qquad \text{where } N_0 = 4.2 \times 10^4. \qquad (10)$$

Then he considered the density enhancement in the mean active region to be a Gaussian function of the distance β from the axis of the region, as that

$$N = N_Q[1 + C \exp(-\beta^2/2\sigma^2)]. \qquad (11)$$

Finally, he computed, by least-square analysis, the best-fitting values of C and of σ as a function of height. From these computations he concluded that in the enhancements the density gradient was about the same as that outside, but that the density on the average was about twice as great ($C \simeq 1$). One of the most interesting conclusions was that the values of σ outlined a cusp that bears a strong resemblance to the configuration that many eclipse observers have noted as characteristic of streamers.

Information on the density distribution in streamers and helmets is rather sparse. Furthermore, although highly typical cases of streamers are fairly easy to distinguish from highly typical helmets, most of the extensive features that have been measured are somewhat difficult to identify. There may not be a great deal of difference, as a matter of fact, between the density gradients in streamers and in helmets. Of the four features studied by Saito (1950) on the 1929 eclipse plates of von Klüber, three appear to be identifiable as helmets and one as a streamer. Nevertheless, the density gradients were all so similar that Saito could express them by the single formula:

$$N_e = \frac{0.19 \times 10^8}{r^3} \qquad 1.5 < r < 4.0. \tag{12}$$

The great NE streamer of the 1952 eclipse, studied by Hepburn (1955), was identified by Michard et al. (1954) with a center of activity about $20°$ in front of the limb. It displays a definitely flatter density gradient than the helmet on the SW limb for the same eclipse, the gradient corresponding to a temperature of 2.3×10^6 ° for hydrostatic equilibrium up to a height of two solar radii, beyond which the density drops off more rapidly. The helmet analyzed by Hepburn shows an even more rapid drop off at $r = 2$ than the streamer. The sharper termination of helmets is apparent to the eye, and is one of the distinguishing features between the two extensive structures. In general, out to one solar radius beyond the limb, streamers and helmets show density gradients that are either equal to (Newkirk) or lower than (Hepburn) the gradients in the ambient corona. Schmidt (1953) finds steeper gradients in the range $2.5 < r < 5$ for the "streamers" than for the general K corona. However, because of difficulties in precise correction for sky, instrumental, and F corona over this range, a considerable degree of uncertainty enters into any such comparison.

Von Klüber (1961) has estimated the electron density in the dark zone overlying a prominence in a 1927 eclipse photograph, and arrived at the very interesting conclusion that essentially no electron scattering takes place within the dome. From this observation we can draw an inference concerning the support of the prominence against gravity. If the prominence is a typical height of 30,000 km and has a density of 10^9 electrons/cm³ (see Chapter 11), the weight of a vertical column of prominence material 1 cm² in cross-section is about 0.15 dynes, which is less than the pressure of a coronal gas of density 10^9/cm³ and temperature of $2,000,000°$ that might be expected at the base of the prominence. Thus, in a crude way at least, we can say that the prominence is supported by the vacuum lying over its top! The vacuum in turn originates when sufficient material accumulates on a horizontal magnetic field to settle down, carrying the magnetic field with it, but leaving an evacuated cavity above.

Finally, some determinations have been made of the density of polar rays. Van de Hulst (1950) found, in tracing across the polar regions of the 1900 eclipse plate, that brightness fluctuations were of the order of 30% of the background K corona. The stronger fluctuations appeared to result from the compounding of rays along the line of sight, however. Single plumes enhanced the corona by about 10%. Thus, since the cross-section of a single ray appeared to be about 7000 km, or $\frac{1}{40}$ the effective depth of the polar corona, he concluded that the density in a plume was about $4\times$ that of the surrounding material. Waldmeier (1961), from a similar argument, applied to the 1954 eclipse, determined the density in the plume to be $5\times$ that of the environment—a figure similar to that determined by Hepburn (1955) from the 1952 eclipse for $1.04 < r < 1.34$. Since the density in a plume is in about the same ratio with that in the surroundings at various heights, both van de Hulst and Hepburn have concluded that the equation of continuity does not hold along the plume—in other words, the plume cannot be considered to be a jet of material, but rather a confined region in the solar atmosphere in a state of hydrostatic equilibrium. With the advent of the solar-wind theory we would now modify the statement to "a state of hydrodynamic equilibrium."

Nesmyanovich (1963), from a study of 38 eclipse photographs, concluded that the polar ray/inter-ray electron density ratio changes with the solar cycle, and that the polar magnetic field is not symmetric with respect to the equator. The later conclusion is certainly confirmed by magnetograph measurements of the solar photosphere during the last sunspot cycle.

E. Coronal Densities Far from the Sun

The Region 6–60$R_\odot$

We have already noted that the best white-light determinations of coronal density at more than a few solar radii are derived from the measurements of Blackwell and Ingham and summarized by Ingham (1961) in Eq. (6). However, the observations that bring the corona most into evidence in the regions 6–60$R_\odot$ are those of the scattering of radio noise from the Crab Nebula. Normally, as a radio interferometer antenna sweeps past the nebula, it will give a signal of a width that depends on the dimensions of the radio source and the antenna pattern. During each year, as the Crab Nebula draws close to the sun, this pattern is observed to broaden significantly. The broadening is attributed to scattering of the radio-frequency radiation by the density irregularities in the extended corona.

We can explain the scattering effect of a single irregularity if we consider two paths for the radiation, one through the center of an irregularity of density N_e and dimension l and the other path just skimming this irregularity through an environment assumed for simplicity to be a vacuum. Since the velocity of an electromagnetic wave of frequency f in plasmas of plasma frequency f_p is given by

$$V^2 = \frac{c^2}{1 - f_p{}^2/f^2} \tag{13}$$

(Spitzer, 1956), the index of refraction within the irregularity differs from that outside by

$$\Delta\mu = \frac{4 \times 10^7 N_e}{f^2}, \tag{14}$$

where we have evaluated the plasma frequency according to Section E, Chapter 6. The wave front along the path through the irregularity is advanced by $l\,\Delta\mu$ over that which skims the irregularity. Thus, to a rough approximation, the front is rotated through an angle $l\,\Delta\mu \div l/2$. We can approximate the distance between the two paths better by $l/4$ than by $l/2$, however, since the front is bent an increasing amount from the center to the edge of the irregularity. If the deflection is through a large angle, a ray-tracing technique, rather than the simple argument that we have just used, must be employed. In either case, however, the deflected radiation, upon passing through other irregularities, will experience further deflection, and will thus experience a random walk through n irregularities in the extended corona. The final deflection will be

$$\theta = \frac{16 \times 10^7 N_e\sqrt{n}}{f^2}. \tag{15}$$

Equation (15) can be used directly to determine coronal density from observed scattering only if some assumptions are made about the number of scattering features. Hewish and Wyndham (1963) considered the extreme range of plausible assumptions that might be made, and concluded that at $20R_{\odot}$ the density in the scattering filaments lay between 0.02 and $300/\text{cm}^3$. Erickson (1964), in effect, assumed that the number of scattering elements along a line of sight remained constant for distances from 8 to $60R_{\odot}$. From this assumption he concluded that the half-width of the scattered beam was proportional to the electron density. Then, using Blackwell's electron density at $8R_{\odot}$ and his own scattering observations at 8 and $60R_{\odot}$, he concluded that the electron density at $60R_{\odot}$ was about $200/\text{cm}^3$.

Densities in the Vicinity of the Earth

Any statement that we make at the time of writing of this section concerning the density of the corona at distances of about one astronomical unit from the sun can be of little more than historic interest to the reader. A few days from now *Mariner IV* will have completed its journey to Mars. We may anticipate that it will have contributed information concerning the density structure of the corona between 1 and 1.5 A.U. The corresponding information between the orbits of Earth and Venus was one of the most important contributions of *Mariner II* (Neugebauer and Snyder, 1963). The space probes, such as the *IMP* satellites, are adding information continually on coronal densities near the earth.

We know at the moment that proton densities range from 2 to 20 cm^{-3} in the vicinity of the earth, and that they are highly variable. There has not been published, as yet, any clear cut association of density at 1 A.U. with features of the solar disk or the inner corona, although magnetic fields have been rather well associated as will be discussed later. Also, the corona at the earth's orbit has not been under observation for a sufficiently long time to determine the relation of its density with the phase of the solar cycle. These questions need to be answered before the observed density at the earth can play definitive roles, when used in solar wind theory, in determining the overall characteristics of the corona.

REFERENCES

Allen, C. W. (1956). Coronal photometry of the eclipse of 1954 June 30. *M. N. R. A. S.* **116,** 69.

Athay, R. G., Billings, D. E., Evans, J. W., and Roberts, W. O. (1954). Emission in hydrogen balmer lines and continuum in flash spectrum of 1952 total solar eclipse at Khartoum, Sudan. *Ap. J.* **120,** 94.

Athay, R. G., Menzel, D. H., Pecker, J.-C., and Thomas, R. N. (1955). The thermo-dynamic state of the outer solar atmosphere. V. A model of the chromosphere from the continuum emission. *Ap. J. Supplement* **1**, 505.

Baturova, G. S., Pominov, I. S., Stolov, A. L., and Smirnova, N. N. (1960). Spectroscopic observations of the solar corona during the total solar eclipse of June 30, 1954. *Sov. Astr.-A. J.* **3**, 247.

Baumbach, S. (1937). *N. A.* **263**, 121.

Billings, D. E. (1957). Profile of the yellow coronal line. *Ap. J.* **125**, 817.

Blackwell, D. E. (1956). A study of the outer solar corona from a high altitude aircraft at the eclipse of June 30, 1954. *M. N. R. A. S.* **116**, 56.

Blackwell, D. E., and Ingham, M. F. (1961). Observations of the zodiacal light from a very high altitude station. *M. N. R. A. S.* **122**, 113.

Erickson, W. C. (1964). Radio wave scattering properties of the solar corona. *Ap. J.* **139**, 1290.

Hepburn, N. (1955). A photometric study of the solar corona. *Ap. J.* **122**, 445.

Hewish, A., and Wyndham, J. D. (1963). The solar corona in interplanetary space. *M. N. R. A. S.* **126**, 469.

Ingham, M. F. (1961). Observations of the zodiacal light from a very high altitude station IV. The nature and distribution of the interplanetary dust. *M. N. R. A. S.* **122**, 157.

Michard, R. (1954). Electron densities in the outer corona on February 25, 1952. *Ann. d'Astrophys.* **17**, 429.

Michard, R., Dollfus, A., Pecker, J.-C., Laffineur, M., and d'Azambuja, M. (1954). Optic and radio observations of the total eclipse of February 25, 1952. *Ann. d'Astrophys.* **17**, 320.

Nesmyanovich, A. T. (1963). Some peculiarities of the magnetic field in the solar corona. *Sov. Astr.-A. J.* **6**, 774.

Neugebauer, M., and Snyder, C. W. (1963). The mission of Mariner II Preliminary observations. *Science* **138**, 1095.

Newkirk, G., Jr. (1961). The solar corona in active regions and the thermal origin of the slowly varying component of solar radio radiation. *Ap. J.* **133**, 983.

Ney, E. P., Huch, W. F., Kellogg, P. J., Stein, W., and Gillett, F. (1961). Polarization and intensity studies of the eclipse of October 2, 1959. *Ap. J.* **133**, 661.

Nishi, K., and Nakagomi, Y. (1963). A model of the coronal condensation. *Pub. Astr. Soc. Japan* **15**, 56.

Pottasch, S. R. (1960). Use of the equation of hydrostatic equilibrium in determining the temperature distribution in the solar atmosphere. *Ap. J.* **131**, 68.

Saito, K. (1950). Brightness and polarization of the solar corona. *Ann. Tokyo Astr. Obs.* **3**, 3.

Saito, K., and Billings, D. E. (1964). Polarimetric observations of a coronal *condensation*. *Ap. J.* **140**, 760.

Schmidt, M. (1953). Brightness, polarization and electron density of streamers in the solar corona. *B. A. N.* **12**, 59.

Shilova, N. S. (1961). Polarization of the outer corona from airplane observations of the solar eclipse of February, 1961. *Geomagnetism and Aeronomics* **1**, 576.

Spitzer, L., Jr. (1956). "Physics of Fully Ionized Gases." Wiley (Interscience), New York.

van de Hulst, H. C. (1950). Electron density of the solar corona. *B. A. N.* **11**, 135.

van de Hulst, H. C. (1953). The chromosphere and corona, *in* "The Sun" (G. P. Kuiper, ed.), p. 207. Univ. of Chicago Press, Chicago, Illinois.

von Klüber, H. (1958). Intensities, polarization, and electron density of the solar corona from photographs taken at the total eclipse of February 25, 1952. *M. N. R. A. S.* **118**, 201.

von Klüber, H. (1961). Photometric investigation of the inner solar corona using an eclipse plate of June 29, 1927. *M. N. R. A. S.* **123**, 61.

Vsekhsvayatskii, S. K., and Ivanchuk, V. I. (1962). Overall structure of the solar corona of February 15, 1961. *Sov. Astr.-A. J.* **5**, 655.

Waldmeier, M. (1955). Results of the Zurich eclipse expedition 1954. *Z. Ap.* **36**, 275.

Waldmeier, M. (1956). Results of the Zurich eclipse expedition 1954. *Z. Ap.* **40**, 120.

Waldmeier, M. (1956). Analysis of a coronal condensation. *Z. Ap.* **40**, 221.

Waldmeier, M. (1961). Photometry of the polar rays. *Z. Ap.* **51**, 286.

Waldmeier, M. (1963). The coronal condensation of the eclipse of February 5, 1962. *Z. Ap.* **56**, 291.

Waldmeier, M., and Muller, H. (1950). The solar radiation in the neighborhood of $\lambda = 10$ cm. *Z. Ap.* **27**, 58.

Zirin, H. (1959). Physical conditions in limb flares and active prominences. *Ap. J.* **129**, 414.

CHAPTER 9

THE TEMPERATURE OF THE CORONA

A. Temperatures by Degree of Ionization

The computation of the temperature of the corona from its degree of ionization has had a hectic history. One of the earliest attempts was made by Waldmeier in 1945, then by a revised method in 1946, in each case getting temperatures of several hundred thousand degrees.

The early work of Waldmeier was followed by six studies of the relation of degree of ionization to temperature in the corona, all based on the concept of the degree of ionization in statistical equilibrium as discussed in Chapter 5. These studies were by Biermann (1947), Woolley and Allen (1948), Miyamoto (1949), Shklovskii (1949), Hill (1951), and Elwert (1952). With the exception of Miyamoto, this group of investigators found coronal temperatures in the range 5–11 $\times$ 10⁵ °K. The approaches to the problem by these investigators differed from one another primarily in the manner in which the collisional ionization rate was computed. Biermann and Miyamoto both used cross sections for collisional ionization obtained from Bethe, but the two are not identical. Bethe's cross sections, in turn, are computed by the Born plane-wave approximation. This approximation is valid for high-energy particles only, whereas only a small fraction of the electrons in a plasma at coronal temperatures exceed the threshold for producing the ionizations found in the heavy ions in the corona.

Both Woolley and Allen and Shklovskii, in recognition of the difficulties with the Born approximation, used the classical ionization cross section (see Chapter 5) with a disposable factor introduced to care for known discrepancies between the theoretical and experimental values. We have already noted, in Chapter 5, the various refinements introduced into the use of the classical cross section by Elwert.

The expressions derived by the various investigators for the collisional cross-section, both from the Born approximation and from classical theory, contained undetermined factors "appropriate for the ion involved." Since laboratory measurements of various cross sections for coronal ions were not available, it was necessary to evaluate the undetermined factors by rather large extrapolations. For example, Woolley and Allen extrapolated experimental data for hydrogen and helium.

Hill, like Miyamoto and Biermann, used a Born plane-wave approximation for computing the ionization cross section. Her cross sections had the advantage that the computations were carried out explicitly for highly ionized iron atoms, hence contained no undefined parameters. Her method had the weakness that we have already mentioned of all Born approximation computations for the corona. In addition, her cross-section computation was carried out for one energy value only, then was adjusted to other energy values by use of an average experimental cross section–vs–energy curve obtained by putting together all available data for ionization processes. However, the various curves that she used in the averaging differed quite strongly from one another, and none pertain to very highly ionized atoms.

Several years after the work of Elwert, Schwartz and Zirin (1959) reopened the question of the cross section for collisional ionization of coronal ions. In recognition of the difficulties in both the classical and Born approximation, these authors undertook the recomputation of the cross section for Fe XIV, using Coulomb waves instead of plane waves for the incident electrons. Because of the great labor involved, they were unable to carry out the computation for angular momentum states of the incident electrons other than the lowest (S wave). The cross sections at which they arrived were much smaller than those previously computed. However, in 1960 Burgess reported the results of computations similar to those of Schwartz and Zirin on hydrogen-like ions in general. He found that the contributions of the higher angular momentum states to the cross-sections were several times as great as the S-wave contribution (a result subsequently confirmed by Schwartz). Hence he concluded that the cross sections for collisional ionization of coronal ions were not greatly different from those determined by classical theory. Athay and Hyder (1963) introduced the additional consideration that two-step ionization processes, via metastable levels, when present, increase the ionization cross section still further. As a result of their work, along with that of Burgess, the idea that the discrepancies in coronal temperatures could be explained by too high an ionization cross section was dropped.

During the period in which the ionization rate was being scrutinized, the recombination rate was considered to be well determined. When recombination processes were reexamined by Burgess and Seaton (1964), however, the situation was completely reversed. We have already seen, in Chapter 5, the enormous contribution to the recombination rate by dielectronic recombination. This one discovery has revolutionized the entire coronal temperature scale as determined from ionization processes.

There are two general methods for applying ionization theory to the determination of temperature in the corona. One method is to compute the temperature at which two coronal lines from different stages of ionization of a given atom have brightness in an observed ratio. We have discussed in Chapter 5 and elsewhere the observational difficulties involved here. The other is to determine the temperatures at which various ions of an element are the most abundant, then to decide from observations which ion is the most abundant.

The two coronal lines most frequently used for the first method are $\lambda 5303$ of Fe XIV and $\lambda 6374$ of Fe X—the green line and the red line—the temperature index being the green/red ratio. These lines are both clearly visible under most conditions in which coronagraphs are operated, and are easily photographed on common photographic emulsions. Also, at the height at which observations are commonly made the $\lambda 5303$ polarization is less than 15%. In determining the temperature significance of an observed green/red ratio we multiply four equations from Eq. (21), Chapter 5, getting

$$\frac{N_{\text{XIV}}}{N_{\text{X}}} = \frac{R_{13 \to 14}}{S_{14 \to 13}} \cdot \frac{R_{12 \to 13}}{S_{13 \to 12}} \cdot \frac{R_{11 \to 12}}{S_{12 \to 11}} \cdot \frac{R_{10 \to 11}}{S_{11 \to 10}}. \tag{1}$$

Equation (1) expresses the ratio of the density of Fe XIV to Fe X ions. This ratio, being the product of four strongly increasing functions of temperature, is in turn a very sharp function of temperature. Each line intensity depends on the number of appropriate ions, the degree of excitation to the upper energy level for production of the line, and the transition probability. Excitation may be either collisional or radiative. The temperature dependence of the excitation is not strong. Schwartz (1959), using collisional excitation only, writes the ratio of the intensities in the two lines as

$$\frac{I_{\lambda 5303}}{I_{\lambda 6374}} = 2.4 \frac{N_{\text{XIV}}}{N_{\text{X}}} \exp\left[-\frac{4.63 \times 10^3}{T} \right]. \tag{2}$$

At coronal temperatures the exponential term is very near unity. Also,

2.4 is a fairly typical ratio for the green/red line intensity. Hence a typical line ratio temperature for a coronal enhancement would be one in which the numbers of Fe X and Fe XIV ions are equal. This takes place at about 1.6×10^6 °K.

In order to apply Eqs. (1) and (2) in determining the temperature at a given point in the corona, we should know the ratio of emission in the two lines from an infinitesimal volume of the coronal gas. Unfortunately, such knowledge is not possible. We must be content with knowing the intensity of the integrated radiation in each line over a very long optical path. Thus, when we apply Eqs. (1) and (2) to actual coronal observations of two line intensities, we make the tacit assumption that the ratio of emission in the two lines is constant along the line of sight; or, in other words, that temperature is constant along the line of sight. One observation, familiar to all coronagraphic observers, gives some justification to this assumption— namely, that in many regions of bright coronal emission the two lines brighten simultaneously and in about the same proportion, indicating changes of density from point to point in the corona without changes in temperature. Billings and Lehman (1962) have found, however, that even in such regions the width of the red coronal line corresponds to a consistently lower temperature than that of the green coronal line. Thus, whether the line widths are to be interpreted as due to thermal or macroscopic motion, it follows that the emission in the two lines must arise in different portions of the corona, even though the different regions emitting enhanced radiation in the two lines are both within a space too small to be resolved by present coronagraphic techniques. We conclude that the most we can hope to learn from an application of Eqs. (1) and (2) is a crude average temperature along a line of sight.

The most abundant ion of a given element can be determined by simultaneous measurements of the intensity of emission lines from several successive stages of ionization. Firor and Zirin (1962) found that the distribution of iron ions among the various stages of ionization varied from observation to observation, but in every case passed through a broad maximum at or not more than one ion removed from Fe XIII. All observations were made near sunspot maximum. The most abundant stage of ionization could be quite different at sunspot minimum. Their observations are somewhat in conflict with XUV observations that show a large amount of Fe XV and considerable Fe XVI in active regions (Neupert, 1965).

A second device for determination of the most abundant ion was that used by Athay and Roberts (1955)—the determination of which emission line showed the strongest correlation with continuum emission. Since the continuum emission is a direct measurement of the number of electrons along the line of sight scattering photospheric light, the method is equivalent to finding which ion has a density most strongly correlating with electron density. In a completely isothermal corona the densities of all ions would have the same correlation to electron density. In a nonisothermal corona, however, the ion density that correlates best with electron density is that with the smallest rate of change with temperature. If the densities of the various stages of ionization are plotted against temperature, each passes through a maximum at the temperature at which the ion is most abundant. Thus the most abundant ion, being least affected by small temperature changes, will show the best correlation with electron density. In active regions in the 1952 eclipse, Athay and Roberts found the yellow line best correlated with continuum, whereas in other regions λ 5303 fit best.

The temperature that we determine from a knowledge of the most abundant ion depends, of course, on the collisional cross sections for ionization and recombination used in the computation. Firor and Zirin point out that the width as well as the position of the maximum in their ion-population distribution curves depends on these cross sections. Thus, by assuming that the temperature was uniform along a line of sight, they were able to use the two observable quantities, distribution width and distribution maximum, to determine the two unknown quantities, temperature and ionization cross section. A more modern version of the same work would probably have given a determination of temperature and recombination cross section. The temperatures thus found are necessarily a maximum, since the distribution can be broadened, as some of theirs obviously were, by variations in temperature along the line of sight.

The sequence of iron ions that emit measurable coronal lines—Fe X, XI, XIII, XIV, and XV—is the most complete in the corona. Its chief limitation is that it does not extend to sufficiently high ionization potentials to measure the temperature in very active regions. In principal the ratio of the intensity of the two lines of ionized Calcium—λ 4086 from Ca XIII and λ 5694 from Ca XV—could be used in a way analogous to the use of the red and green lines of Fe X and XIV. Unfortunately, the λ 4086 line is quite difficult to measure by coronagraphic techniques, since it is superimposed on a complex of Fraunhofer lines in the scattered-light spectrum. Also, in principal, if all pertinent atomic parameters and chemical abundances were well known, one could determine the temperature from the ratio of the brightness of the yellow line of Ca XV, λ 5694, to that of one of the iron lines, but uncertainties in chemical abundance makes this technique of little value.

The relatively small regions that emit λ 5694 brightly also show an enhanced scattering of photospheric radiation from which we can determine the electron density. From such an observation, Billings (1957) has concluded that a rather large percentage of calcium ions participate in the emission of λ 5694. Hence in such circumstances the temperature cannot differ greatly from the value that renders Ca XV the most abundant ion of that element.

If we accept the hypothesis that the emission in any coronal line is most likely to come from a temperature regime in which the ion emitting that line is most abundant, we conclude that along almost every line of sight a considerable range of temperatures is to be found. On the basis of current ionization and excitation coefficients we would conclude further that at times of extreme sunspot minimum the most prevalent temperature may be about 1 million degrees, with a smaller amount of material having higher temperatures extending up to about 2 million degrees. Occasional active regions very early in a new cycle that display unusually bright red-line emission may also have such a temperature range.

For a quite common type of coronal enhancement, more likely to occur during the rise or decline of sunspot activity than at sunspot maximum, in which the green-to-red coronal-line intensity is about in the ratio 2.5/1, we suggest a rather uniform distribution in temperature from 10^6 to 2.2×10^6 °K. In estimating the temperature of such regions an observation by Billings and Lehman may be significant, however. Whereas the widths of the green line customarily correspond to temperatures 200,000–400,000° higher than the temperature computed by Burgess and Seaton (1964) as that for which Fe XIV is most abundant, the widths of the red line are 600,000–800,000° higher than their corresponding ionization temperature. Since there is no obvious reason why macroscopic line broadening should be more pronounced in red- than in green-line sources, we perceive an implication that most of the red-line emission arises from temperatures closer to 1.4 or 1.5 million degrees than to 1 million degrees. This temperature is sufficiently far removed from the temperature of maximum Fe X that in order to keep the red- and green-line ratios in proper balance it is desirable either to postulate a distribution that maximizes strongly around 1.4 million degrees or to drop off the high end of the distribution below the temperature at which Fe XIV maximizes. The latter process gives a somewhat narrower distribution than that which we first considered—one in which the plateau extends from about 1.3×10^6 to 2.0×10^6 °K.

In enhancements that are more typical of sunspot maximum than the one just described, the red-line emission is repressed. For such enhancements we suggest a temperature range from 2 to 3 million degrees. It is probably such enhancements that provide the strong correlation found by Neupert (1965) between calcium plage and Fe XV XUV emission. This Fe XV emission persists for at least a solar rotation after the activity declines, indicating a slow decay of temperature in the active regions of the corona.

Very active regions are even hotter, as indicated by the association of XUV Fe XVI emission and flares, and by the presence of Ca XV emission in coronal condensations. The abundance of the Ca XV ion maximizes at about 5×10^6 °K (Boardman and Billings, 1966). Young regions also appear to be hotter than old, for they are more strongly associated with Fe XVI emission (Neupert, 1965).

B. Temperatures from Line Profiles

When we measure the temperature of the corona by the use of line profiles, we confront rather directly the basic question of the meaning of "temperature" in this nonuniform, nonequilibrium gas. Since we are dealing with line-of-sight velocities only, we shall consider only the component v_x of motion of the coronal particles along the line of sight—the x axis. We shall consider a region in space small enough that the properties of the coronal gas are homogeneous throughout the region, yet large enough to contain a considerable number of each species of coronal particle. If N_j is the number of particles of the jth kind per unit volume and $\bar{v}_{x,j}$ is the rate of drift of this species, either through wind or diffusion, then $V_{x,j} = (v_{x,j} - \bar{v}_{x,j})$ may be considered to be the "thermal" line-of-sight velocity of a particle in the species. The momentum transferred in unit time to a surface of unit area normal to the line of sight and moving with the drift velocity is $N_j m_j \overline{V^2}_{x,j}$, which we equate to the partial pressure exerted by the species, $N_j kT$. Thus, from a very fundamental point of view, the kinetic temperature of the jth species is

$$T = \frac{m_j \overline{V^2}_{x,j}}{k} = \frac{m_j}{k} \frac{c^2 \overline{(\Delta\lambda)^2}}{\lambda^2}, \tag{3}$$

where $\Delta\lambda$ is measured from the mean position rather than the normal position of the center of the profile. Equation (3) is applicable to any profile, whether Gaussian or not, and indicates that line-profile measurements will give temperatures that are consistent with the gas laws, even though the gas may not be described by a Maxwell-Boltzmann distribution of velocities.

We have pointed out in Chapter 5 that if the corona is heated by successive passages of hydrodynamic or hydromagnetic shocks, there will be a period of time immediately after the passage of each shock during which the kinetic temperatures of the various species of particles will not be equal. Furthermore, if the electrons in the corona must receive their thermal energy from the protons but give it up through inelastic (exciting and ionizing) interactions with the heavy ions, there will be a tendency for the high-energy tail of the (electron) Maxwell distribution to be depleted. House (1965), who has been considering the problem in some detail, believes that a serious departure from a Maxwellian distribution would result—so serious as to require other means of heating the electrons than through collisions with the protons in order to explain observed excitation and ionization effects.

We shall watch with interest the development of the questions raised by House, and in the meantime consider the case in which the thermal kinetic energy associated with each degree of freedom in the jth species of particles is distributed among the particles according to a Boltzmann distribution:

$$N(E) \propto \exp\left(\frac{-E}{kT}\right) = \exp\left(\frac{-m_j V_x^2}{2kT}\right)$$

$$= \exp\left(\frac{-m_j}{2kT}\frac{c^2(\Delta\lambda)^2}{\lambda^2}\right) = \exp\left(\frac{-(\Delta\lambda)^2}{(\Delta\lambda_D)^2}\right). \quad (4)$$

Thus, if the profile has the shape of a Gaussian curve, the parameter $\Delta\lambda_D$, the "Doppler half-width," which describes the width of the profile, is related to the temperature by

$$T = \frac{m_j c^2}{2k}\frac{(\Delta\lambda_D)^2}{\lambda^2}. \quad (5)$$

In Chapter 4 we described various techniques for determination of $\Delta\lambda_D$ from actual line profiles.

The determination of coronal temperature by line-profile analysis has the advantage over degree of-ionization techniques that the only atomic parameter involved is the atomic weight of the emitting ion. Furthermore, since the corona is optically thin in the visual emission lines, the profile breadths may be interpreted unambiguously as arising from motion of the emitting ions. The real difficulty arises from the identical Gaussian character of profiles arising from thermal or small-scale random macroscopic motion. If the motion is not small scale, observable gross Doppler displacements of the coronal lines and distortions of the profiles will occur. If it is not random, systematic line displacements related to coronal structures should be observed. In Chapter 7 we considered the question of line broadening vs gross Doppler displacements due to small-scale random motions in the corona, and in Chapter 4 we discussed a technique for determining the line-broadening effect of certain types of nonrandom macroscopic motion. The technique depends on the detection of small departures of the profile shapes from Gaussian—an effect that is likely to be masked by the superposition along the line of sight of Guassians of different widths. Consequently, it must be considered to be only a minor first step in solving the difficult problem of separation of thermal from macroscopic motion.

Fortunately, the problem of the effect of macroscopic motion on coronal-line profiles does not now seem as severe as it did prior to the consideration of dielectronic recombination. The discrepancy between ionization and line-width temperatures is now a fraction of its earlier value. Moreover, in the case of λ 5303 a considerable part of the discrepancy can be explained by assuming that the motions in the corona observed by radar by Chisholm and James (1964) are radial (Billings, 1965), with the broadening of the profiles resulting from the summation of the line-of-sight components of these motions throughout the corona. Unfortunately, the argument breaks down for those cases in which the emission from a thin filament of coronal material also has a broad profile.

Historically, the use of line profiles is one of the oldest schemes for determining the temperature of the corona. We have already noted the early suggestion by Lyot (1937) that the broadening of the coronal lines may be thermal. In the following year, Waldmeier interpreted this broadening as a result of radial streaming of material from the sun. In 1941 he reported his own measurement of the half-width of the λ 5303 line—0.65 Å —and concluded that this was an indication of high turbulence in the corona, since it corresponded to random motions of 37 km/sec, whereas the thermal motion would be only 1.2 km/sec (in a 5000° corona). By 1945 Waldmeier, like Lyot, explained the line broadening as thermal, indicating a temperature of 2,100,000 °K. Later he used temperatures obtained from the degree of ionization according to Biermann's computations, and explained the residual broadening of the emission lines by macroscopic motion.

Pecker et al. (1954), Billings (1957), and Zirin (1959) have measured the widths of λ 5694 Ca XV and have found in all cases that they correspond

to temperatures in the range 3.5–4.5 million degrees. In a more comprehensive study, Boardman and Billings (1966) have found some line profiles
indicating even higher temperatures. They were able, through the use of
the ratio of the two yellow-line intensities (λ 5694/λ 5445), to compute
electron density, and from the ratio of line/continuum intensity, the degree
of ionization in the condensations. Consequently, they could plot a degree-
of-ionization vs line-width temperature-scatter diagram, compare it with a
theoretical degree-of-ionization curve, and thereby analyze the internal
motion, which they found to be very small.

Dollfus, in 1953, studied the distribution in widths of the red-line profiles,
and found that the stronger red lines had profiles corresponding to 1.7 or
1.8 $\times$ 10^6 °K. Billings (1959a) confirmed the conclusions of Dollfus, and
found in addition that the most prevalent λ 5303 emission profiles corresponded to 2.4 $\times$ 10^6 °. The distribution of radiation with width in the two
lines was found by Billings to be explainable by a unimodal distribution of
matter with temperature that maximized at 2.4 $\times$ 10^6 °. The distribution
persisted in both the sunspot latitudes and the polar regions, but was
shifted to somewhat higher temperatures in very active regions.

Considerable effort has been devoted at the High Altitude Observatory
to looking for variations in line profiles with position in the corona. In
these studies we have tried an assortment of the techniques for fitting
Gaussian curves to the observed profiles that are discussed in Chapter 4.
Some of the conclusions from this study are

(1) In regions of low to moderate activity the line profiles are no
broader in the center of the region than in the outer edge.

(2) The breadth of the lines in sharply defined emission features is
essentially the same as outside the features.

(3) There is, on the average, a small decrease in line width with height
which, if due to temperature changes, corresponds to a few degrees per
kilometer temperature gradient.

(4) There is vague evidence of an oscillatory change of line width
with height (Billings, 1959b), the first maximum occurring at a height of
30,000–40,000 km. Such a maximum appeared in two of three regions
studied, but at different heights. Repeated observations in one of these
regions did not show a change in this maximum with time.

(5) Net macroscopic line-of-sight motion, as indicated by Doppler
shifts in the coronal lines, is very small.

(6) The dispersion in temperature corresponding to line widths of the
λ 5303 line is only about 200,000°. There are systematic differences in
measurements arising from different techniques used for determination of

the best Gaussian curve, but with any consistent set of measurements the widths of the lines are surprisingly uniform. Occasional exceptions occur. For example, in regions in which the green-line emission is bright and the red-line emission faint, or in regions in which yellow-line emission is evident, the green line is likely to be considerably wider than in other regions.

From a consideration of line profiles only, we would conclude that the temperature at which Fe XIV is most prevalent is about 2.5×10^6 °K; Fe X, 1.8×10^6 °K; and Ca XV, 5×10^6 °K. We would conclude, furthermore, that most of the emission in each line comes from temperature regimes at which the appropriate ion is near maximum abundance, whether in or outside of active regions, or in the polar regions. We shall defer consideration of line-profile data jointly with other data until later in the chapter.

C. The Radio Temperature of the Corona

One of the striking characteristics of the radio sun, appreciated during the early years of solar radio astronomy, was that the apparent temperature of the sun increases with wavelengths, from centimeter to meter waves. This effect was attributed correctly to an increased contribution to the emission from the corona, and the observation provided one of the early pieces of evidence that the temperature of the corona was in the million-degree range. Smerd, in 1950, carried out a rather detailed analysis of the problem in which he traced rays of various wavelengths through various model isothermal quiet coronas, and computed the intensity of the emergent rays as a function of distance from the center of the solar disk by the relationship

$$I_{\mathrm{Em}} = B(T_c)(1 - \exp{-\tau_c}) + B(T_{\mathrm{ch}}) \exp{-\tau_c} \qquad (6)$$

Here I_{Em} is the intensity of the emergent beam, $B(T_c)$ the Planck function at the assumed model coronal temperature, $B(T_{\mathrm{ch}})$ the Planck function at the chromospheric temperature, and τ_c the optical depth in the corona along the trajectory of the ray being studied. The computed apparent temperature T_{ap} at a given wavelength is the temperature of the black body that would emit I_{em} at that wavelength. In passing from centimeter to meter wavelengths, T_{ap} first increases strongly as the contribution to the emission from the corona increases relative to that of the chromosphere. For wavelengths so long that their trajectories never extend to the chromosphere, however, I_{em} decreases with increasing wavelength, since the optical depths along the trajectories decrease. Thus each curve of T_{ap} vs λ passes through a maximum. The problem is: given an observed apparent temperature at a given wavelength, to find which computed curve (T_{ap} vs λ) determined by the parameter T_c passes through the observed point (T_{ap}, λ). Here one has the choice of a curve passing through the point in either its ascending or descending part. Thus each observed apparent temperature is consistent with two model temperatures. As a result, the considerable range of observed apparent temperatures corresponds either to a lower or to a higher range of model temperatures, either from 3×10^5 to 3×10^6 °K, or from 2×10^6 to 3×10^7 °K. Smerd felt that the lower range of model temperatures was the more plausible, but did not rule out the higher range as impossible. There is no reason that all observations must be fit by either the rising or the descending part of the theoretical curves. It would be more consistent with our present concepts of coronal temperature to fit the more intense observed brightness temperatures with the descending curves and the less intense with the rising curves, thereby bringing all coronal temperatures into the range from 2 to 3 million degrees. All we can really say, of course, is that the various brightness temperatures that Smerd considered do not contradict any model temperature derived either from ionization or line profiles.

A further complication pointed out by Oster and Sofia (1965) is that the simple transfer equation used by Smerd in deriving equation (6) is inadequate, since the radiation, being near the plasma frequency over at least a part of its path, is passing through a highly dispersive medium. Using a revised form of the transfer equation over the wavelength range from 2.5 to 10 meters, these authors conclude that the apparent temperature is only 0.6–0.25 the actual electron temperature. Thus an observed apparent temperature of about 1,000,000° corresponds to an electron temperature of 2,000,000° or more. If we accept this new element into the picture, we conclude that radio-astronomical observations indicate temperatures comparable to those obtained from present ionization theory, using dielectronic recombination, or from coronal-line profiles.

The same considerations introduced by Oster and Sofia in dealing with the entire quiet sun would also modify the conclusions reached by Newkirk (1961) concerning the sources of the slowly varying component of radio noise. Thus, whereas Newkirk concluded that the spectrum of the slowly varying component indicates temperatures somewhere in the region between 1 and 2,000,000°, but could not distinguish between the higher or the lower of these values, we would expect ray tracing carried out by Oster and Sofia's procedure to lead to a higher range of temperatures.

The idea that the radio temperature of the active regions in the corona should range upward from 2,000,000° had already received observational support from the work of Swarup et al. (1963). In this work dealing with pencil- and fan-beam observations at wavelengths of 10.7, 9.1, 7.5, and 3.2 cm, as well as in earlier publications by Swarup and associates, it is apparent that active regions that are optically deep in the centimeter wavelength range, when studied with sufficient resolution to eliminate the contribution from the optically thin environment, show brightness temperatures in the range from just under two million to several million degrees.

Several different aspects of Type-III radio-noise bursts give information on the coronal temperature. This information is particularly valuable, since it deals with coronal heights in the range 0.2–1.4 solar radii. Malville (1961) has attributed the sharp cutoff in burst velocity at about $0.2c$ to Landau damping, from which he has computed that the coronal temperature is in the range $2\text{–}4 \times 10^6$ °K. Also, by assuming that the apparent decrease in mean burst velocity with decreasing frequency is due to a change in the velocity cutoff, he concluded that the corona had a negative temperature gradient of about 3°/km. Finally, Pawsey and Smerd (1953) and Malville (1961) have computed the coronal temperature as a function of height from the decay time for Type-III bursts at a given frequency. This decay time is inversely proportional to electron density and directly proportional to $T^{3/2}$. These investigators found a decrease in decay time with frequency that would correspond to a rather marked negative temperature gradient.

D. Temperature from Density Distributions

In Chapter 8 we discussed the determination of electron density in the corona. Most of the computations of temperature from electron-density distribution are based on the assumption that the corona is in hydrostatic equilibrium, and if density distribution constitutes the only available data, such an assumption is necessary. If we do not assume hydrostatic equilibrium, we may, following Parker (1960), write the hydrodynamic equation in the form

$$\frac{1}{T}\frac{dT}{dr} = -\frac{1}{N}\frac{dN}{dr} - \frac{\mu}{kT}\left(g + v\frac{dv}{dr}\right), \tag{7}$$

where μ is the mean particle mass and v the rate of radial expansion of the corona. We see from this equation that since the term $v\,(dv/dr)$ adds to g, the effect of an expanding corona, accelerated outward as postulated by Parker, is to increase g, hence T, for a given density distribution. Thus the temperature derived from a hydrostatic assumption is less than that which would be derived if a solar wind is taken into account. Conversely, measurements of solar winds by space probes, coupled with electron-density measurements in the corona, should lead to higher temperature values than those from the hydrostatic assumption alone.

The solar-wind effect whereby the hydrostatic assumption leads to a lower than actual temperature is opposite to the effect of most macroscopic motions that have been suggested. McCrea (1929) considered the effect of turbulence on the scale height of the chromosphere. His arguments may also be applied to the corona. More recently, Lüst et al. (1962) considered radial shock waves and their effect on the coronal scale height. In either case the scale height is increased by the macroscopic motion; thus a temperature computed by the hydrostatic assumption tends to be higher as a result of these effects than the actual temperature. The difference between the effect of turbulence or shock waves and of the solar wind is that the turbulences or shock waves impart vertical upward momentum to the coronal gas, which is equivalent to pressure in increasing the scale height. The solar wind, on the other hand, is being accelerated outward and is therefore receiving momentum from the corona as a whole.

In addition to solar wind, turbulence and radial shocks as factors that may cause the hydrostatic equilibrium temperature in the corona to be different from the true temperature, a fourth factor has been suggested by Unsöld (1960). This is the effect of density irregularities in the corona when spherical symmetry has been assumed. Unsöld considers that only a fraction of the volume in the corona along a line of sight will be occupied by coronal gas, and that this fraction diminishes with height. Thus the apparent density variation with height is steeper than that actually existing within any given coronal structure, and the resulting temperature computation gives too low a value. We shall consider the possible importance of these four effects—solar wind and density irregularities leading to too low temperatures, and turbulence and radial shocks leading to too high temperatures—after we have discussed the determination of temperature under the assumption of hydrostatic equilibrium.

If we set $v \, (dv/dt) = 0$ in Eq. (7), the resulting differential equation may be expressed, as shown by van de Hulst (1950), in the form

$$\frac{T_1}{T} = \frac{d}{d(1/x)} \ln N + \frac{d}{d(1/x)} \ln T, \qquad (8)$$

where $T_1 = g_\odot R_\odot \mu m / k \cdot g_\odot$ is the acceleration of gravity at the solar surface,

μ the mean atomic weight, and m the mass of unit atomic weight. Thus if ln N plotted as a function of $1/x$ is a straight line over a significant interval we may assume that the temperature is constant over that interval, and from the slope of the function, evaluate T.

Waldmeier (1945) was one of the first to use density gradients for determination of temperature. His value was 1.3×10^6 °K. Van de Hulst (1953), using empirical formulas for electron density that he had presented in 1950, differentiated between a sunspot-maximum and a sunspot-minimum temperature. For the former he obtained 1.62×10^6 °K; for the latter 1.15×10^6 °K.

The computations of temperature from electron-density gradients by Waldmeier and van de Hulst were both based on electron densities averaged around the sun. Following chronologically are two studies in which the density gradients are measured in specific locations. Hepburn (1955), from measurements of a 1952 eclipse photograph and separation of the K and F corona by a somewhat circuitous method that is discussed in Chapter 8, found electron-density gradients corresponding to temperatures of 1.73×10^6 ° at the equator, 1.44×10^6 ° at the poles, and 2.3×10^6 ° in a great streamer. She found these temperatures to hold out to about 2 $R_\odot$, then apparently drop off abruptly.

Evidence of a similar abrupt decrease in temperature with height was found by Baturova *et al.* (1960) from a spectrogram taken at the 1954 eclipse. The broad slit of a low-dispersion spectrograph was set radial to the sun at an angle of 23.7° with the solar equator. Intensity in the continuous spectrum, normal to dispersion, was then measured at three different wavelengths, F and K were assumed to be in ratios based on Allen and Alfvén, and resulting electron densities were computed. The density gradients correspond to temperatures of 3 to 5 million degrees for distances less than 1.5 $R_\odot$ and to 2 million degrees for 1.5 to 2.0 $R_\odot$. There is considerable variation in electron density from one wavelength to another and from one spectrogram to another, but the gradients are quite well defined.

The Pottasch (1960) density model discussed in Chapter VIII leads to a temperature that increases steadily to 1.43×10^6 ° at 200,000 km above the limb, remains constant for the next 500,000 km, then drops slowly toward 10^5 ° at the outer limits of his computations. We have already noted that a small modification in the Pottasch model would give a much more abrupt increase in temperature.

Von Klüber (1961) carried out a very careful analysis, near the limb, of coronal brightness on a photograph of the 1927 sunspot-maximum eclipse. From these measurements he computed electron densities, without, apparently, first separating the F corona, although it may be that this was unnecessary so close to the limb. From the resulting density gradients he determined temperatures ranging from 1.4 to 2.1 $\times$ 10^6 ° above different portions of the limb.

Very few of the determinations mentioned above are based on observations in which the separation of the K and F components were incorporated into the observing program. The photoelectric polarization measurements of Ney *et al.* (1961) are exceptional in that such provisions were carefully made in observing the 1959 eclipse. From their study they found, at the equator, an electron-density gradient corresponding to a temperature of 1.22 $\times$ 10^6 ° at 1.3 $R_\odot$, and 0.91 $\times$ 10^6 ° at 1.8 $R_\odot$. There is also evidence that closer to the limb than 1.3 $R_\odot$ the temperature is higher than either of these values.

Billings and Cooper (1957) carried out a study in the monochromatic corona that should be compared with the measurements by Hepburn in the coronal streamer. This study involved measurements of intensity gradients in λ 5303 and λ 6374 in regions of bright line emission. The measurements were taken, at each height, at the point of maximum brightness in the respective line in the region. On the assumption that the emission was proportional to the square of the electron density in an isothermal corona, the authors found mean density gradients corresponding to temperatures in the range 1.8–2.2 $\times$ 10^6 °. A great deal of scatter in the data gave evidence of possible thermal and magnetic structures causing density and brightness fluctuations about mean values. It is impossible to detect, in this method of analysis, the effect of changes in the degree of ionization of the ion being observed.

Any conclusions that we draw from the above seven determinations must be tempered by an evaluation of the various factors that may make the distribution different from that of hydrostatic equilibrium. We consider first the hydrodynamic effect. More recent measurements of solar wind, as by Neugebauer and Snyder (1963) confirm the earlier observation by Gringauz *et al.* (1961) of a flux of about 2 $\times$ 10^8 positive solar particles of energy greater than 15 eV per square centimeter per second near the earth. We find from this, by continuity considerations, that the velocity at a point near the sun where the density is 10^7 cm^{-3} is about 0.8 km sec^{-1}. From Fig. 10 in Parker's 1960 paper we estimate dv/dr to be 4 $\times$ 10^{-5} per second. Thus v (dv/dr) is of the order of 0.001 g and may be ignored.

The other factor that could cause the observed temperature to be less than the actual temperature is the effect of density inhomogeneities in the corona along the line of sight. Unsöld (1960) has estimated this effect from a two-point evaluation of the fraction of the line of sight occupied by matter. He makes rough estimates of this fraction near the sun from visual observations by Allen, and far from the sun by radio observations of the occultation of the Crab Nebula. From these data he computes that a corona of 2.4×10^6 ° could have an apparent density gradient corresponding to 1.6×10^6 °. Although the data that he puts into these computations are fraught with uncertainty, we see a possible confirmation of his conclusions in the temperature found by Hepburn for the large streamer. If we interpret the streamer, not as a high temperature feature, but as a region in the corona in which the structural features do not diverge (and visual appearance of the streamers makes such an interpretation very plausible), we could expect to observe the same density gradients in the streamer that Unsöld computes to be within the otherwise diverging structural features. This, indeed, is what Hepburn did observe.

We cannot rule out the possibility that the density gradient is decreased by either turbulent motions or directed shocks, but we can refute an explanation of both the observed line-profile widths and the observed height gradients as resulting from a simple pattern of macroscopic motion in a five- or six-hundred-thousand degree corona. Let us first consider that the motion is an isotropic turbulence of rms velocity c. Let T_H be the temperature computed from electron height gradient observations; T_{fe}, the temperature computed from the profile of an iron–ion coronal line; T, the true temperature; μ, the mean molecular weight. Then

$$T_H = T + \frac{1}{3}\frac{\mu}{k} c^2 \tag{9}$$

and

$$T_{fe} = T + \frac{1}{3}\frac{m_{fe}}{k} c^2. \tag{10}$$

If we eliminate c between (9) and (10), we have

$$T_H = T\left(1 - \frac{\mu}{m_{fe}}\right) + \frac{\mu}{m_{fe}} T_{fe}. \tag{11}$$

Thus, since $\mu/m_{fe} \sim 0.01$, and $T_{fe} \sim T$, we see that the temperature computed from height gradients will differ by a negligible amount from the true temperature.

In summary, we note that there is general agreement between temperatures found from height-gradient measurements and those from degree of ionization or line profiles. The temperatures found from height-gradient averages over the limb lie well below 2,000,000°. Whether this results from the presence of the cooler red-line–emitting constituents of the corona or from the inhomogeneity effect suggested by Unsöld is hard to say. The densities in streamers, analyzed by Hepburn, give temperatures in good agreement with the ionization temperatures for features of this type, and only a little below the line-width temperatures.

E. Radar Determination of Coronal Temperature

The use of radar for determination of the temperature of the corona has interesting possibilities. Abel *et al.* (1961) have already made one rough determination using this technique. They computed, from the signal/noise ratio and the known noise level, the apparent cross section for reflection of the radar signals offered by the sun. One of the major phenomena limiting the reflectivity is the absorption, which in turn depends on the collision frequency of electrons with protons in the corona, a strong function of temperature. Thus, from their rough results, they concluded that the absorption agreed better with half a million than with a million-degree corona.

Eshleman *et al.* (1960), in the first successful reflection of radar from the sun, noted that the reflected signal was spread over at least 2000 cycles/sec. Such observations could have significant bearing, indirectly, on the determination of the coronal temperature. If the Doppler spreading of frequencies due to solar rotation and that due to macroscopic motion can be separated, a number of questions concerning turbulence in the solar atmosphere and its effect on various types of temperature measurement may perhaps be determined. Chisholm and James (1964), as we have already noted, have presented radar data of just this type, and Billings (1965) has attempted to interpret it in relation to line width and ionization temperatures.

F. Space-Probe Measurements of Coronal Temperature

As with radar measurements, the use of space probes for temperature measurements is in its infancy. Neugebauer and Snyder (1963) made some determinations of the coronal temperature between Earth and Venus from the width of the velocity distribution of the particles in the solar wind, although they felt that the velocity intervals in the distribution were too broad to give them very much precision. In one of the two sample results they give, the mean velocity was 460 km/sec, the density, 2.5 cm^{-3}, and the temperature, 1.9 $\times$ 10^5 °K. In the second case the velocity was 810 km/sec, the density, 4.5 cm^{-3}, and the temperature 7.4 $\times$ 10^5 °K. If these temperatures are valid, they show a remarkably small decline between the sun and the earth. It is best, perhaps, to withhold a consideration of their implications to solar-wind theory until they are confirmed by further observations.

One asks immediately whether the distribution of radial velocities in the solar wind is truly a measure of temperature. The crucial question is whether the distribution is isotropic in a frame of reference moving with the wind. If it is, it is appropriately described by a kinetic temperature; if not, it can be represented as a temperature in a very limited sense only. We hope that space probes have been or soon will be designed to determine the transverse as well as the radial distribution of velocities.

G. A Thumbnail Summary of Coronal Temperatures

The methods of measurement outlined in this chapter point to a fairly consistent set of temperatures for the corona close to the sun. On the basis of our own rather subjective evaluation of these results we suggest the following table for temperatures of features of the inner corona:

(1) *Red line region.* A region of this type is characterized by heightened emission in λ 6374, with a much less pronounced enhancement, if any, in λ 5303. It is found in the polar regions or at the equator near sunspot minimum and on occasions, highly localized, in the early days of new cycle activity. Temperature: 1.2 $\times$ 10^6 °K.

(2) *Moderate enhancement.* This region shows heightened emission in both λ 6374 and λ 5303. It may appear at almost any time in the sunspot cycle except at times of extreme activity or extreme inactivity. It is associated with sunspot groups of small to moderate activity. Temperature: a range of temperatures within the feature, from 1.4 $\times$ 10^6 to 2.0 $\times$ 10^6 °K.

(3) *Active enhancement.* This region, which occurs over quite active sunspots, shows heightened emission in λ 5303, diminished emission in λ 6374, and some evidence of emission in λ 5694. Temperature: 3 $\times$ 10^6 °K.

(4) *Yellow-line condensation.* The λ 5694 emission is intense, the λ 5303

emission is diminished, and the λ 6374 emission is essentially absent. Temperature: 4.5 × 10⁶ °K.

Within this framework it should be possible to assign temperatures to within two or three hundred thousand degrees to a very large number of coronal regions for which spectroscopic data are available. Knowledge of the variation of coronal temperature with distance from the sun is still very meager. Our own work on line widths indicates that the temperature maximum is quite close to the sun—within 20,000 to 30,000 km above the photosphere. A number of density gradients, as well as the lifetimes of Type-III bursts, also show declining temperatures over the height ranges studied. Contrary evidence in other density gradients, as well as in the intensity distribution with height of red vs green-line emission, suggest that the maximum temperature may be 100,000 to 200,000 km above the photosphere. The temperature structure as a function of height may vary strongly from one region type to another. At the moment we can say very little on the subject.

REFERENCES

Abel, W. G., Chisholm, J. H., Fleck, P. L., and James, J. C. (1961). Radar reflections from the sun at very high frequencies. *J. G. R.* **66**, 4303

Athay, R. G., and Hyder, C. L. (1963). Coronal ionization by two-step collision processes. *Ap. J.* **137**, 21.

Athay, R. G., and Roberts, W. O. (1955). Coronal line intensities at the Khartoum Eclipse. *Ap. J.* **121**, 231.

Baturova, G. S.,Pominov, I. S., Stolov, A. L., and Smirnova, N. N. (1960). Spectroscopic observations of the solar corona during the total solar eclipse of June 30, 1954. *Sovi. Astr-A. J.* **3**, 247.

Biermann, L. (1947). *Naturwissenschaften* **34**, 87.

Billings, D. E. (1957). Profile of the yellow coronal line. *Ap. J.* **125, 817**.

Billings, D. E. (1959a). Distribution of matter with temperature in the emission corona. *Ap. J.* **130**, 961.

Billings, D. E. (1959b). Velocity fields in a coronal region with a possible hydromagnetic interpretation. *Ap. J.* **130**, 215.

Billings, D. E. (1965).Optical line profiles and radar observations in the corona. *Ap. J.* **141**, 325.

Billings, D. E., and Cooper, R. H. (1957). Height gardient of the emission corona. *Z. Ap.* **43**, 218.

Billings, D. E., and Lehman, R. C. (1962). Line-width temperatures of distinct coronal features. *Ap. J.* **136**, 258.

Boardman, W. J., and Billings, D. E. (1966). Ionization and excitation of yellow-line coronal regions. *Ap J.* (in press).

Burgess, A. (1960). Note on the calculation of coronal ionization cross sections. *Ap. J.* **132**, 503.

Burgess, A., and Seaton, M. (1964). The ionization equilibrium for iron in the solar corona. *M. N. R. A. S.* **127**, 355.

Chisholm, J. H., and James, J. C. (1964). Radar evidence of solar wind and coronal mass motion. *Ap. J.* **140**, 377.

Dollfus, A. (1953). *Compt. rend.* **236**, 996.

Elwert, G. (1952). Concerning the ionization-recombination process in a plasma and the ionization formula for the solar corona. *Z. Naturforsch.* **7a**, 432.

Eshleman, V. R., Barthle, R. C., and Gallagher, P. B. (1960). Radar echoes from the Sun. *Science* **131**, 329.

Firor, J., and Zirin, H. (1962). Observations of five ionization stages of iron in the solar corona. *Ap. J.* **135**, 122.

Gringauz, K. I., Bezrukikh, V. V., Ozerov, V. D. and Rybchinskii, R. E. (1961). A study of interplanetary ionized gas, high energy electrons and corpuscular radiation of the sun, employing three-electrode charged particle traps on the second soviet space rocket. *Artificial Earth Satellites USSR* **6**, 101.

Hepburn, N. (1955). A photometric study of the solar corona. *Ap. J.* **122**, 445.

Hill, E. R. (1951). Collision processes involving highly ionized atoms. *Aust. J. Sci. Res.* **4A**, 437.

House, L. L. (1965). Personal communication.

Lüst, R., Meyer, F., Trefftz, E., and Biermann, L. (1962). Zur Temperatur der Sonnenkorona. *Z. Naturforsch.* **17a**, 259.

Lyot, B. (1937). Some observations of the solar corona and of prominences in 1935. *L'Astronomie* **51**, 203.

McCrea, W. H. (1929). *M. N. R. A. S.* **89**, 718.

Malville, J. M., (1961). Studies of fast drift radio bursts and related phenomena. Ph.D. Thesis, University of Colorado.

Miyamoto, S. (1949). Ionization theory of solar corona. *Publ. Astr. Soc. Japan* **1**, 10.

Neugebauer, M., and Snyder, C. W. (1963). The mission of mariner II reliminary observations. *Science* **138**, 1095.

Neupert, W. M. (1965). Intensity variations in the extreme UV spectrum observed by OSO-1. *Ann d'Aph.* **28**, 446.

Newkirk, G., Jr. (1961). The solar corona in active regions and the thermal origin of the slowly varying component of solar radio radiation. *Ap. J.* **133**, 983.

Ney, E. P., Huch, W. F., Kellogg, P. J., Stein, W., and Gillett, F. (1961). Polarization and intensity studies of the eclipse of October 2, 1959. *Ap. J.* **133**, 616.

Oster, L., and Sofia, S. (1965). The emission of the quiet corona at meter wavelengths. *Ap. J.* **141**, 1139.

Parker, E. N. (1960). The hydrodynamic treatment of the expanding solar corona. *Ap. J.* **132**, 175.

Pawsey, J. L., and Smerd, S. F. (1953). Solar radio emission, *in* "The Sun (G. P. Kuiper, ed.), p. 466. Univ. of Chicago Press, Chicago, Illinois.

Pecker, C., Billings, D. E., and Roberts, W. O. (1954). Identification of the yellow coronal line. *Ap. J.* **120**, 509.

Pottasch, S. R. (1960). Use of the equation of hydrostatic equilibrium in determining the temperature distribution in the solar atmosphere. *Ap. J.* **131**, 68.

Schwartz, S. B. (1959). The ionization cross section of Fe XIV in the solar corona by electron collision and its relationship to the temperature of the corona. Ph.D. Thesis, University of Colorado.

Schwartz, S. B., and Zirin, H. (1959). Collisional ionization cross section for Fe XIV in the solar corona and the coronal electron Temperature. *Ap. J.* **130**, 384.

Shklovskii, I. S. (1949). *Izv. Krymsk. Astrofiz. Obs.* **4**, 80.

Smerd, S. F. (1950). Radio frequency radiation from the quiet sun. *Aust. J. Sci. Res.* **A3**, 34.

Swarup, G., Kakinuma, T., Covington, A. E., Harvey, G. A., Mullaly, R. F., and Rome, J. (1963). High-resolution studies of ten solar active regions at wavelengths of 3-21 CM. *Ap. J.* **137**, 1251.

Unsöld, A. (1960). Temperature of corona. *Z. Ap.* **50**, 48.

van de Hulst, H. C. (1950). Polar rays of the corona. *B. A. N.* **11**, 150.

van de Hulst, H. C. (1953). The chromosphere and corona, *in* "The Sun" (G. P. Kuiper, ed.), p. 207. Univ. of Chicago Press, Chicago, Illinois.

von Klüber, H. Inner solar corona. *M. N. R. A. S.* **123**, 61.

Waldmeier, M. (1941). Report of the activities of the arosa Observing station. *Astr. Mitt., Zurich* N. 141.

Waldmeier, M. (1945). *Mitt. der Aarg Natur. Ges.* **22**, 185.

Waldmeier, M. (1946). A new determination of coronal temperature. *Experientia* **2**, 1.

Woolley R. v. d. R., and Allen, C. W. (1948). The coronal emission spectrum. *M. N. R. A. S.* **108**, 292.

Zirin, H. (1959). Physical conditions in limb flares and active prominences. *Ap. J.* **129**, 414.

CHAPTER 10

MAGNETIC FIELDS IN THE CORONA

A. Postulation of Magnetic Fields

The most striking aspect of the subject of magnetic fields in the corona is the frequency and variety of situations for which they are postulated, compared to the scarcity of any definite information concerning them. Magnetic fields are invoked more often than not in hypotheses for the heating of the corona, since a favorite heating mechanism is hydromagnetic waves. Sometimes such fields are postulated only in the active regions; at other times, over the entire sun and involved in the production of spicules. In some cases they are postulated merely to channel wave energy into the corona (Uchida, 1963), in other cases they are pictured as accelerating particles by the Fermi mechanism (Parker, 1958), not only to thermal energies, but to the superthermal energies necessary for explaining the existence of Type-III, -IV, and -V bursts.

Magnetic fields are invoked to explain the existence and shape of polar plumes at sunspot minimum (van de Hulst, 1950) and the existence of polar regions of coronal enhancement at sunspot maximum. They are employed, as a matter of fact, to explain all departures from a nonspherical distribution of matter in the corona, including the loop structure of the corona over active regions, the streamers, and helmets over quiescent prominences (Mustel, 1962). The poleward and equatorward movement of zones of principal and secondary coronal emission are assumed to be associated with the development of polar and sunspot magnetic fields; and the apparent differential rotation rate between the polar corona and the underlying photosphere, with magnetic fields extending from the sunspot zone into the corona (Cooper and Billings, 1962). At the great distances from the sun studied by occultations of the Crab Nebula radio source, magnetic fields are used to explain the filamentary structure, implied by the observed scattering processes in this extended coronal material.

In solar–geophysical relationships, looped mognetic fields in coronal enhancements have been postulated to reduce the thermal conductivity, thereby diminishing the solar wind and producing the "zones of avoidance" of geomagnetic activity observed during the declining years of a solar cycle (Billings and Roberts, 1964). They have also been visualized as becoming detached from the sun, or greatly extended, to pass through interplanetary space, scatter relativistic solar protons, enhance the effect of solar wind on comet tails, and disturb the terrestrial magnetic field more effectively than nonmagnetic clouds would do.

Explanation of the various polarization phenomena in coronal radio noise has required a magnetic field in the corona. The relative intensity and polarization of thermal radiation at centimeter wavelengths is explained by an increase in the optical depth of the corona for certain frequencies as a result of resonant absorption at the gyromagnetic frequency and its harmonics (Kakinuma and Swarup, 1962). The polarization of Type-III bursts is explained by a postulated magnetic field at the point of origin of the bursts; variation in polarization with frequency is explained in terms of a change in the magnetic field along the path of the burst source; and a decrease in polarization with band width, as resulting from Faraday rotation of the radiation due to magnetic fields through which the radio waves pass (Cohen, 1961). Type-IV and Type-V bursts are explained as synchrotron radiation from relativistic particles in magnetic fields high in the corona; and visible radiation polarized with its magnetic vector apparently other than radial (probably due to observational difficulties; Ney *et al.*, 1961) has similarly been explained as synchrotron radiation (Kellogg and Ney, 1959) from high-energy particles in very strong magnetic fields in the corona.

Many Hα phenomena in the solar atmosphere are explained in terms of magnetic fields in the corona. They appear to be the only adequate reservoir of energy present in the atmosphere for the production of flares, and many hypotheses have been devised for explaining how the magnetic-field energy is converted into other forms of energy during flares, or how the fields get into such a configuration that this conversion could take place with the observed violence. Magnetic fields are postulated to provide mechanical support for quiescent prominences (Kippenhahn and Schluter, 1957), to determine the trajectories of active prominence material, and to play a role in the condensation of prominence material from the corona (Lüst and Zirin, 1960).

Finally, a number of assorted phenomena in the corona have been explained by magnetic fields. The correlation of Doppler effects in coronal and prominence lines for motion transverse to, but not along loops is explained as the displacement of the magnetic field in both media (Newkirk, 1957). The propagation of pulses from flares that excite and agitate prominences and spicules appears to be attributable to hydromagnetic waves or shocks in the corona; and hydromagnetic waves have been used to explain the well-known phenomenon of a succession of bright and dark arches over quiescent prominences in the white-light helmets that overlie such prominences (Obashev, 1961). Similarly, standing hydromagnetic waves have been invoked to explain the periodic broadening of emission lines with height in the corona (Billings, 1959).

B. Evidence for the Presence of Magnetic Fields

In a sense, every successful application of the assumption of magnetic fields in the corona to explain observed phenomena constitutes an indication that such fields exist, and the aggregate of such hypotheses constitutes overwhelming evidence not only that they exist but that they are prevalent throughout the corona. Some solar features provide much more definitive evidence than others, however. Whereas, for example, a loop structure of coronal material could not maintain its observed stability without the intervention of magnetic forces, the usefulness of magnetic fields in wave or shock theories for heating the corona does not establish that the corona is necessarily heated by a wave or shock phenomenon—or that such waves exist in the corona at all.

One need mention only a few unambiguous manifestations of magnetic forces to establish their presence in active regions of the corona. The simplest and most obvious is the distribution of coronal material. Loops that are hotter than the surrounding coronal material and several times as dense would expand with explosive violence if they were not magnetically constrained. A greater concentration of material could arise in active regions than outside simply because of a greater input of matter from the chromosphere, but it would not follow well-defined trajectories without being constrained. Also, none of the polarization phenomena in radio noise from the corona could be explained except by active region magnetic fields. The existence as well as the character of Type-IV and -V bursts appear to depend on magnetic fields—this conclusion being substantiated by a strong correlation between the intensity of Type-IV bursts and the percent of sunspot umbrae covered by flares.

The positive identification of calcium plages in the chromosphere with extended photospheric fields, coupled with the very strong correlation of such plages with regions in the corona bright in λ 5303 emission, leads one automatically to the conclusion that the most fundamental characteristics of active regions in the corona, as in sunspots, is the presence of the magnetic field.

In the corona outside of active regions the magnetic fields would be expected to be less intense, and their role may be somewhat less dominating. The existence of polar plumes at sunspot minimum depends on magnetic constraint, and their general configuration has long been highly suggestive of the field of an extended dipole. Also, the general pattern of the sunspot-minimum corona implies that the extended portions of the corona are being forced into the equatorial regions by the pressure of the polar magnetic field, as we pointed out in Chapter 8. The polar plumes may be identified with the polar photospheric fields observed at sunspot minimum, and with the polar faculae, and are therefore not true indicators of magnetic field in the absence of activity. Evidence for fields under the latter circumstances is considerably more indirect. We consider here three separate indications:

(1) The support of quiescent prominences. It has not yet been clearly established whether fields that support filaments thread the filaments normal to or along their long axis. If it is the latter, we could not say that the field exists in the corona as such, but only in the filament. However, the Kippenhahn and Schluter theory for prominence support, which we prefer, is based on the concept that the field is normal to the long axis of the filaments. This concept is borne out by the tendency of filaments to lie along isogauss contours. It is also confirmed by the appearance in prominences seen edgewise on the limb of the sun of streams of material issuing from the sides of the prominences and following curved trajectories toward active regions (Fig. 10.1).

(2) Spicules appear to be tilted from normal to the sun's surface when in the vicinity of active centers or the poles, indicating that they partake of very extensive magnetic fields. Moreover, since clumping of spicules appears to accompany such photospheric fields, one might conclude that all spicules carry magnetic field through the chromosphere, and that the distribution of magnetic fields in the corona is more or less proportional to spicule density.

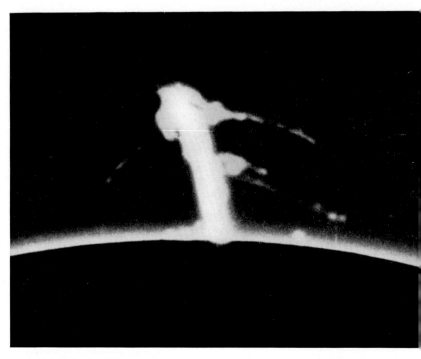

Fig. 10.1. End-on prominence with streams of material from sides outlining supporting magnetic fields. The existence of prominences of this type gives evidence in favor of the Kippenhahn–Schluter theory for the support of quiescent prominences.   Courtesy High Altitude Observatory.

(3) Impulses that pass outward from solar flares to great distances on the sun appear to avoid active regions and regions of intense photospheric magnetic fields. Nevertheless, they are propagated with velocities that are appropriate for hydromagnetic waves, but not mechanical waves, through the corona.

A promising technique for the detection and measurement of magnetic fields is through the study of the polarization in coronal emission lines (Warwick and Hyder, 1965; Hyder, 1965a). If an atom is excited by polarized radiation in the absence of a magnetic field, or if it is excited by nonisotropic unpolarized radiation, the emitted radiation will be more or less strongly polarized, depending on the term types involved in the transition (Zanstra, 1950). If, however, a magnetic field is present along the line of sight, the magnetic moment of the atom precesses about the field

If the field is so weak that the precession period is long compared to the lifetime of the excited state, a rotation of the plane of the emitted radiation may result; but in the case of coronal ions with small transition probabilities, hence long lifetimes, the field for such a process is very small, less than 10^{-5} gauss. For larger fields the orientation of the atom is smeared out during the process of emission, and no polarization is observed.

If, on the other hand, the magnetic field is normal to the line of sight, strong polarizations may be observed. Hyder has computed the polarizations that could occur under most favorable conditions, for various transition types, at various distances from the center of the sun (Fig. 10.2). We see from the figure that in an observation capable of detecting polarizations as small as 1%, at a height in the corona of 1.4 $R_\odot$ or more—sufficiently high that collisional excitation does not play a significant role—an absence of polarization in λ 5303 is positive evidence of at least a small magnetic field along the line of sight. Observations in the 1965 eclipse by Hyder confirm this conclusion, but it is not clear that collisions are not responsible for the observed depolarization.

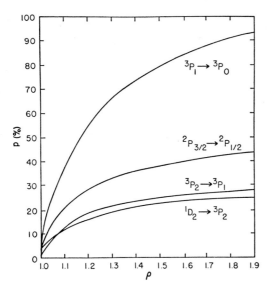

Fig. 10.2. Theoretical upper limits for the polarization of coronal emission lines (Hyder, 1965a). The most extreme polarizations that could occur are found in the $^3P_1 \rightarrow {}^3P_0$ transitions, of which the lines λ 10747 of Fe XIII and λ 5694 of Ca XV are representative. λ 5303 $(^2P_{3/2} \rightarrow {}^2P_{1/2})$ is also capable of considerable polarization. Courtesy, *Astrophysical Journal*.

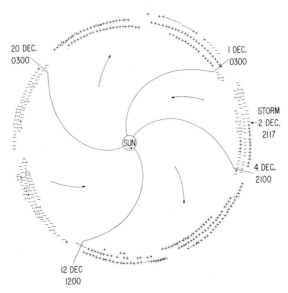

Fig. 10.3. Quasistable pattern in magnetic field direction at one astronomical unit from the sun. This pattern, detected by the *IMP*-1 satellite, persisted for almost three solar rotations.   Diagram courtesy *J*. M. Wilcox.

The only region in the corona in which magnetic fields have been demonstrated by direct observation is that at about one astronomical unit from the sun. In this region, magnetometers mounted on space probes (notably *IMP–1*) operating outside the earth's magnetosphere have not only detected magnetic fields in the extended corona but have measured their magnitude and direction with considerable precision. Furthermore, from these observations Ness and Wilcox (1965) have demonstrated a strong correlation between the direction (outward or inward) of magnetic fields at 1 A.U. and photospheric fields that have passed the central meridian of the sun about $4\frac{1}{2}$ days earlier. The lag time implies that solar plasma carrying photospheric magnetic fields traverses the sun–earth distance at a little more than 300 km/sec—a speed that agrees well with Parker's solar wind. Furthermore, the magnetic fields are oriented away from radial to the sun in precisely the direction of Archimedes spirals that would map the loci of plasma streams moving radially outward from a rotating sun with the indicated speed.

Ness *et al.* (1965) have demonstrated that these fields have a considerable degree of stability at times of low sunspot activity, showing a very similar pattern for at least three solar revolutions (Fig. 10.3). Wilcox and

Ness (1965) have studied the detailed characteristics of the persistent features that they thus found. They identified four longitudinal zones of alternating polarity encircling the sun, and noted that within each zone a characteristic pattern of field intensity, solar-wind velocity, density, and flux occurred. They associated the zones with geomagnetic activity and discovered that one of the four contained MeV protons upon each solar rotation.

Since the magnetic fields detected by *IMP-1* observations are not only associated with photospheric features but have a permanence lasting over several rotations, we can conclude with considerable certainty that they extend outward through the corona for at least one astronomical unit. Biermann and Lüst (1964) find in the behavior of comet tails evidence that the fields extend to 2 or 3 solar radii. They postulate magnetic fields in the solar wind at these distances in order to explain the coupling between the wind and the comet tails.

C. Quantitative Information on Magnetic Fields

The arguments for the existence of magnetic fields in the corona are overwhelming. Quantitative information concerning such fields, on the other hand, is very scarce, conflicting, and in most cases, inconclusive.

An evaluation of the direction of the magnetic field in the lower corona is somewhat easier to arrive at than the intensity. Billings, using intensity of emission in λ 5303 and assuming that this emission was proportional to the square of electron density, the temperature being constant, used the theory of Chapter 7 to determine the projected direction of the magnetic field in a rather typical coronal enhancement (Fig. 10.4). The evidence of a loop structure is quite apparent, even though no such loop was obvious in the brightness distribution in the region. Saito and Billings (1964) used the same basic approach to map the magnetic field in an intense coronal condensation observed in the February 1962 eclipse. In this case the data were the pattern of electron densities computed from polarimetric observations of the white light corona. In either case the fields bear strong resemblance to loop prominences (Correll and Roberts, 1958).

The configuration of polar plumes has led to a number of attempts to map and describe the general minimum field of the sun. One such attempt, by Bachmann (1957), led to a very precise conclusion: that the field could not be either dipole, quadrapole, or octapole, but that a bar magnet of length 0.63 solar diameters, or two buried circular currents could describe

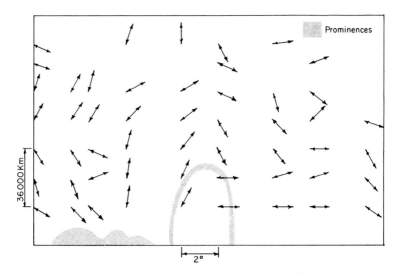

Fig. 10.4. The pattern of magnetic field direction in an active region, as determined from the distribution of λ 5303 emission. It is of interest that an isophotal map of the region in λ 5303 did not give evidence of the loop structure that is so apparent in the magnetic configuration.

the field. Saito (1965) showed that the postulated length of the bar magnet should change with the sunspot cycle. Nesmyanovich (1963), from a study of 38 eclipse photographs, has pointed out changes in the polar pattern as well as ray/inter-ray intensity ratio, and demonstrated that the magnetic field is not symmetric with regard to the solar equator. A major difficulty with a description such as that given by Bachmann is that it cannot be interpreted in terms of any existing theory of the origin and nature of the polar field.

The delineation of the direction of the magnetic field has been carried far into the corona through the study of the scattering of r-f radiation from the Crab Nebula. Since the path of the nebula in the sky intersects the extended solar axis, the information deals largely with the extended polar field. In general, the orientation of the scattering particles indicates that the field at several solar radii is radial—this being the conclusion of Vitkevich and Panovkin (1959) and Hewish (1958). Erickson (1963, 1964) found the orientations to be generally random with some preference for radial. Vitkevich thought it possible that the pattern followed a general magnetic field, and Hewish and Wyndham (1963) concluded that the observations for the 1960–1962 period were consistent with flow lines that bend toward the equator, whereas earlier observations showed purely radial streaming. Thus the pattern of the solar magnetic field at great distances from the sun appears to follow the change in general appearance of the white-light corona with the changes in the solar cycle.

Although the distribution of matter in active centers in the corona provides us one of the most vivid pieces of evidence we have that magnetic fields are present and gives some indication of the shapes of such fields, it is of very limited value for determining the magnitude of the field intensity. The greatest lateral pressure fluctuations that we commonly encounter in the corona can be constrained by a field of 2 or 3 gauss, but we realize that force-free fields of much greater intensity may be present but not inter- acting with the coronal matter. An even greater difficulty is that if we consider the matter to be truly in a state of equilibrium—the gas plus the magnetic pressure being equal at all points on a spherical surface surround- ing the solar center—we conclude that the magnetic field is least at exactly the locations in which we think from other evidence that it is the greatest: in the regions overlying sunspots. On the other hand, it is not unreasonable to apply such magnetohydrostatic considerations to the polar corona, since, for reasons that we have already discussed, the magnetic field there may not be force free. Högbom (1960) did precisely this, at 3 solar radii, and obtained a field of 3.0×10^{-2} gauss. He then demonstrated that this result was reasonable by extrapolating it back to the photosphere to obtain 1.5 gauss, in good agreement with photospheric observations. In the active regions, on the other hand, we conclude that the concentrations of matter exist in a quasistable state, being maintained by the inertia in the photospheric and subphotospheric layers in which the major sunspot current systems are located. In other words, we assume that the time scale for the disruption of the resulting magnetic fields in the corona by the concentrated higher temperature gas trapped in these fields is long.

Although the excess gas pressure in coronal enhancements appears to be inadequate to disrupt the coronal magnetic fields overlying sunspot groups, it does not follow that electric currents in the corona do not greatly modify these fields. Such modification is demonstrated in dramatic manner, for example, whenever a prominence structure becomes eruptive. Thus we must recognize that under certain circumstances, at least, it is not possible to compute or even approximate the magnetic field in the corona as being that which would extend into a vacuum over the observed sunspot fields. It is possible, however, that in many, or perhaps even the majority of cases a field so computed would be adequate. Furthermore, if the entire pattern of both radial and transverse photospheric fields can be observed over an extended portion of the sun, it is possible to compute the coronal fields precisely, as demonstrated by Schmidt. This is a consequence of the fact that any alteration of the fields by current systems above the photosphere must necessarily also modify the fields at the photosphere.

Let us consider the fragmentary information now available on magnetic fields in the active regions, or at sunspot latitudes in the corona. Billings (1959), from very crude evidence of a periodicity with height in emission-line width, suggested hydromagnetic waves with a magnetic field perturbation of about 0.02 gauss. Since the perturbation would probably be considerably less than the field itself, this uselessly low value may be considered to be a lower limit for the field intensity. Warwick (1957), in contrast, from the curvature of the trajectories of blobs of prominence material in a flare spray, deduced field intensities of 116 to 469 gauss. We should note, however, that he equated magnetic pressure to centripetal force as follows:

$$\frac{H^2}{8\pi} \geq m_{\mathrm{H}}Nh\,\frac{v^2}{r},\tag{1}$$

where h is a dimension of the blob, v its speed, and r the radius of curvature of the trajectory. In other words, the blob is pictured as a diamagnetic material that has thrust the magnetic field aside, and each square centimeter of the magnetic field that is in contact with the blob must exert centripetal force on the entire column of prominence material extending from that unit area entirely through the blob. If this picture is accepted, the computed magnetic fields do not necessarily give any information about the fields in the corona before the blob entered, since adjacent to the moving prominence material the coronal fields may be compressed to many times their initial intensity, and particularly strongly compressed along the curved part of the trajectory. Furthermore, if one considers the prominence material to be threaded by the coronal magnetic field, as seems entirely possible, all of Warwick's field intensities are reduced by a factor of $\sqrt{h}$ to less than 4 gauss. Other indirect suggestions of magnetic field intensity come from Stepanov and Petrova (1959), who concluded that plage is bright only in fields of intermediate intensity (50–200 gauss) and is dark for stronger fields—thus giving a suggestion for the magnitude of the fields entering the base of the corona—and Uchida (1963), who found that a theory for heating the corona could be brought closer to observations by the introduction of a 10-gauss field into the corona.

A number of techniques from radio astronomy have given results of a more definitive nature. Kawabata (1960), Korol'kov and Soboleva (1962), and Kakinuma and Swarup (1962) have all studied the intensity and polarization of centimeter-range radiation in centers of intense thermal emission, and have all concluded that the phenomena indicate the presence of low-lying magnetic fields of hundreds of gauss. More specifically, Kawabata assumed an exponentially decreasing field with a scale height of twice the density scale height, and concluded that the field intensity at the base of the system was 1000 gauss. Korol'kov and Soboleva found that the transverse component of the magnetic field in the emitting region, at 0.05 to 0.07 $R_\odot$ above the sunspot, was about 400 gauss, with a gradient at the boundaries of the region greater than 0.3 gauss/km. Finally, Kakinuma and Swarup found it desirable to assume a field dropping from 1700 gauss to 250 gauss in the region of emission of the thermal radiation.

Takakura (1964) applied magnetoionic theory to the problem of the escape of radio noise from Type-I, -II, and -III bursts and derived thereby upper and lower limits for the magnetic fields at the heights from which various frequencies originate. Over the height range from about 2×10^5 to 10^6 km he found magnetic fields from about 50 to 20 gauss from Type-I bursts, 20 to 10 gauss from Type-III, and 10 to 2 gauss from Type-II bursts. These fields would all be appropriate for active regions, but it is possible that the burst types leading to the more intense fields may occur more directly over the sunspots than those leading to less intense fields.

Two different methods of deriving magnetic fields from Type-III burst observations have been suggested by Cohen (1961) and Akabane and Cohen (1961). The former has studied the phenomenon of the reversal of direction of circular polarization in bursts with change in frequency and concluded that a plausible explanation is the passage of the source through a region in which the longitudinal component of the magnetic field in the region changes sign. Under such circumstances frequencies below a certain transitional frequency change sign, those above this frequency do not. The transitional frequency is given by

$$f_t^4 = 10^{17} N_e S H, \tag{2}$$

where S is the scale of the magnetic field, and H the field intensity. From the observation of transition frequencies Cohen concluded that at about 10^5 km the field intensities are between 2 and 6 gauss. Akabane and Cohen interpreted the smaller polarization in Type-III bursts at 200 Mc/s for band widths of 22 Mc/s than for band widths of 10 Mc/s as indicating Faraday rotation in the wave as it passed through the corona. Since the various frequencies would be rotated different amounts, the greater band widths would encompass radiations with plane of polarization rotated through a greater variety of angles, hence in the aggregate would be less strongly polarized. They concluded that the observed Faraday rotation could be achieved in a plasma 1000 km thick, $N_e = 10^8$, $H = 1$ gauss. Although there is considerable uncertainty of the height of the source, or at what height Faraday rotation takes over, the observations indicate that at a height less than 1 $R_\odot$, the coronal magnetic field has dropped to quite a low value.

Uchida, in 1960, provided the background for what should be an elegant method for use of Type-II bursts for determining the magnetic field in the corona. He derived a relation between the velocity of a surge and a shock front preceding the surge as a function of the magnetic field through which the two pass. Now if a density model for a region is available from either eclipse or K-corona observations, and optical observations of a surge may be compared with radio spectrograms so that the surge velocity can be computed from the former, the shock velocity from the latter, the magnetic field remains the only unknown quantity.

Zirin (1962), from the Zeeman splitting of Hβ, determined that the magnetic fields in active prominences is about 200 gauss, and that in quiescent prominences, 25–50 gauss. Hyder (1964) concluded from rotation of the plane of Hα polarization that the field at the top of a prominence loop was 45–60 gauss. Considerable uncertainty is involved in concluding from these data what magnetic fields are indicated for the corona. For example, since active prominence loops in a region generally lie parallel to loops of coronal material, should we expect the field in the two systems of loops to be the same, or does the difference in temperature of the two systems indicate some magnetic difference also? Quiescent prominences almost certainly produce some concentration in the coronal magnetic field in which they are located. If we accept the hypothesis that they are supported by fields threading them normal to their long axis, and that the evacuated space lying above them has been depleted by the sagging of the lines of force under the weight of the prominence material, we conclude that the field intensity, on the average, is about twice what it would be in the absence of the prominence. Also, the field intensity in prominences must decrease with height, since the density gradients are obviously much less than that of an atmosphere of prominence temperature. The resulting concentration of magnetic field in the base of the prominence would not lead to any great field enhancements, however. A prominence of density 10^{10} particles/cm^3 and 40,000 km height could be maintained at constant density by a difference of magnetic pressure between the bottom and top of about 1 dyne/cm^2, which would be supplied by a magnetic field of 5 gauss.

The scanty information that we have outlined so far indicates that in he lower corona near sunspots the intensities are of the order of 1000 gauss, ut that these drop off rapidly, and at heights of about 100,000 km are lown to about 10 gauss or less. The fields spread out from sunspot regions, nd in the neighborhood of quiescent prominences are also about 10 gauss. n polar regions near the photosphere at sunspot minimum they are of the rder of 1 gauss, and drop off in the manner indicated by their extended-dipole configuration to hundredths of gauss at a few solar radii. Beyond his point, one may as well use an inverse-square law for computing the ield, since the Crab Nebula occultation data indicate that the field at great distances is primarily radial.

Emission-line polarization gives promise of more definitive information. From a brief superficial examination of Savart-plate photographs of the .965 eclipse in λ 5303, Hyder (1965b) was able to state:

(1)   Coronal regions diametrically opposite on the sun differed sharply n that one was significantly polarized, the other not.

(2)   Polarization increases with height to at least 1.4 $R_\odot$.

(3)   In those locations where no polarization is present, either the ransverse component of the magnetic field is less than 5% of the total ield and the total field is greater than 10^{-4} gauss or collisional excitations ompletely dominate in an isotropic velocity field. More definitive statements will be possible when the data have been reduced.

The space-probe measurements are even more definitive. Those made rom *IMP-1* during the six-month period following November 27, 1963, gave intensity measurements grouped strongly about 5×10^{-5} gauss. We have already mentioned how the field typically remained quite constant n magnitude and direction over several days, with the same pattern repeating on successive solar rotations. Since these patterns, corresponding o 100° or more of solar longitude, were significantly less irregular than the underlying photospheric magnetic fields with which they correlated highly, one concludes that the coarser photospheric magnetic features extend far out in the corona, whereas the smaller-scale fields close between the sun and the earth. A final interesting observation was that the fields were predominantly directed from above to below the ecliptic plane, indicating flux linking the leader spots in the northern to those in the southern solar hemisphere.

The high quality and internal consistency of the space-probe magnetic data, as well as its close agreement with solar wind-theory and correlation with the gross pattern of photospheric magnetic fields, tempts us to discard all other observations and determine the magnetic field at each point in the corona, at each point in time, by an inverse-square, solar-wind computation from measurements made at 1 A.U. Such a computation will give at the solar surface, for example, the very plausible typical field intensity of 2.2 gauss. It is well to proceed in this direction with caution, however. The space-probe observations made to date can tell us little about the magnetic field outside of the vicinity of the plane of the ecliptic, or about magnetic-field lines that close between the sun and the earth's orbit. The less-quantitative magnetic evidence from monochromatic observations, etc., can still play a useful role in building up a complete picture of the magnetic configuration.

REFERENCES

Akabane, K., and Cohen, M. H. (1961). Polarization of Type III bursts and Faraday rotation in the corona. *Ap. J.* **133**, 258.

Bachmann, H. (1957). On the designation of the polar rays as magnetic field lines. *Z. Ap.* **44**, 56.

Biermann, L., and Lüst, R. (1964). The problem of the plasma flux and the magnetic fields in interplanetary space. *Astrophysica Norvegica* **9**, 61.

Billings, D. E. (1959). Velocity fields in a coronal region with a possible hydromagnetic interpretation. *Ap. J.* **130**, 215.

Billings, D. E., and Roberts, W. O. (1964). The origin of M-region magnetic stroms. *Astrophysica Norvegica* **9**, 147.

Cohen, M. H. (1961). Microwave polarization and the coronal magnetic field. *Ap. J.* **133**, 978.

Cooper, R. H., and Billings, D. E. (1962). A long-lived polar coronal region. *Z. Ap.* **55**, 24.

Correll, M., and Roberts, W. O. (1958). *Ap. J.* **127**, 726.

Erickson, W. C. (1963). Coronal properties inferred from radio wave scattering data. *Ap. J.* **68**, 536.

Erickson, W. C. (1964). Rzdio wave scattering properties of the solar corona. *Ap. J.* **139**, 1290.

Hewish, A. (1958). The scattering of radio waves in the solar corona. *M. N. R. A. S.* **118**, 534.

Hewish, A., and Wyndham, J. D. (1963). The solar corona in interplanetary space. *M. N. R. A. S.* **126**, 469.

Högbom, J. A. (1960). The structure and magnetic field of the solar corona. *M. N. R. A. S.* **120**, 530.

Hyder, C. L. (1965b). Personal communication.

Hyder, C. L. (1964). Magnetic fields in the loop prominence of March 16, 1964. *Ap. J.* **140**, 817,

Hyder, C. L. (1965a). The polarization of emission lines in astronomy. III. The polarization of coronal emission lines. *Ap. J.* **141**, 1382.

Kakinuma, T., and Swarup, G. (1962). A model for the sources of the slowly-varying component of microwave solar radiation. *Ap. J.* **136**, 975.

Kawabata, K. (1960). A model of the coronal condensation. *Publ. Astr. Soc. Japan* **12**, 512-523.

Kellogg, P. J., and Ney E. P. (1959). A new theory of the solar corona. *Nature* **183**, 1297.

Kippenhahn, V. R., and Schluter, A. (1957). A theory of solar filaments. *Z. Ap.* **43**.

Korol'kov, D. V., and Soboleva, N. S. (1962). Results of polarization observations made at centimeter wavelength during the solar eclipse of April 19, 1958. *Sov. Astr.-A. J.* **5**, 491.

Lüst, R., and Zirin, H. (1960). Condensation of prominences from the corona. *Z. Ap.* **49**, 8.

Mustel, E. R. (1962). The spatial structure of the solar corona. *Sov. Astr.-A. J.* **6**, 333.

Nesmyanovich, A. T. (1963). Some peculiarities of the magnetic field in the solar corona. *Sov. Astr.-A. J.* **6**, 774.

Ness, N. F., and Wilcox, J. M. (1965). Extension of the photospheric magnetic field into interplanetary space. Goodard Space Flight Center Bulletin X–612–65–79.

Ness, N. F., Scearce, C. S., Seek, J. B., and Wilcox, J. M. (1965). A summary of results from the IMP-1 magnetic field experiment. Goodard Space Flight center Bulletin X–612–65–180.

Newkirk, G., Jr. (1957). Doppler motions in the corona. *Ann. d'Ap.* **20**, 127.

Ney, E. P., Huch, W. F., Kellogg, P. J. Stein, W., and Gillett, F. (1961). Polarization and intensity studies of the eclipse of October 2, 1959. *Ap. J.* **133**, 616.

Obashev, S. O. (1961). On the structure of the corona over prominences. *Izv. Astrofiz. Inst., Akad. Nauk Kaz. S. S. R.* **12**, 78.

Parker, E. N. (1958). Suprathermal particle generation in the solar corona. *Ap. J.* **128**, 677.

Saito, K. (1965). Polar rays of the solar corona II. *Publ. astr. Soc. Japan* **17**, 1.

Saito, K, and Billings, D. E. (1964). Polarimetric observations of a coronal condensation. *Ap. J.* **140**, 760.

Stepanov, V. E., and Petrova, N. N. (1959). The brightness of flocculi, magnetic fields and mechanisms of heating. *Izv. Krymsk. Astrofiz. Obs.* **21**, 152.

Takakura, T. (1964). Estimates of the distribution of the sun's magnetic field intensity in the corona using radio burst measurements. *Publ. Tokyo Astr. Obs.* **16**, 230.

Uchida, Y. (1960). On the exciters of Type II and Type III radio bursts. *Publ. astr. Soc. Japan* **12**, 376.

Uchida, Y. (1963). An effect of the magnetic field in the shock wave heating theory of the solar corona. *Publ. astr. Soc. Japan* **15**, 376.

van de Hulst, H. C. (1950). Polar rays of the corona. *B. A. N.* **11**, 150.

Vitkevich, V. V., and Panovkin, B. N. (1959). On the structure of the non-uniformities of the solar super-corona. *Astr. Zhurn.* **36**, 544.

Warwick, J. W. (1957). Flare-connected prominences. *Ap. J.* **125**, 811.

Warwick, J. W., and Hyder, C. L. (1965). The polarization of emission lines in astronomy. I. Resonance polarization effects in the field-free case. *Ap. J.* **141**, 1362.

Wilcox, J. M., and Ness, N. F. (1965). A quasi-stationary co-rotating structure in the interplanetary medium, NASA Bulletin. Goddard Space Flight Center Bulletin X–612–65–302.

Zanstra, H. (1950). An attempt to explain the polarization in Hα and D_3 for prominences. *M. N. R. A. S.* **110**, 491.

Zirin, H. (1962). Magnetic fields in solar prominences. *Sov. Astr.-A. J.* **5**, 660.

CHAPTER 11

RELATION TO OTHER ACTIVITY

A. Introduction

The corona is the most variable part of the sun. Whereas the only obvious manifestations of the sunspot cycle in the photosphere are the spots surrounded by more widely scattered magnetic fields and the faculae, and in the chromosphere, plage and flares, the corona undergoes a complete metamorphosis as the cycle progresses. It is possible that a closer scrutiny of the granular structure in the photosphere or of the spicular structure in the chromosphere will reveal fundamental changes in these two layers during the cycles also, but such changes are certainly not nearly as apparent as those in the corona. Perhaps one should expect the most tenuous part of the solar atmosphere to be the most subject to changes during the cycle of solar activity. In any event, an enumeration of the manifestations of solar activity must include changes in coronal structure, intensification of optical emission from lines of more-highly-ionized atoms, and intensification of coronal X-ray emission.

We must keep in mind, in such an enumeration of the photospheric chromospheric and coronal manifestations of solar activity, that the various activity features are not isolated events. On the contrary; to borrow a term from medicine, they are various aspects of the same syndrome. The faculae, most apparent as a slight brightening in white light near the limb, are greatly enhanced through an Hα or Ca—K filter—i.e., in the chromosphere. Also they are larger and coarser, particularly in the calcium K$_3$ emission, which originates from higher in the chromosphere. The same features are repeated in the uppermost layers of the chromosphere, in Lyman-α photographs, again with increasing size and coarseness. The coronal enhancements are simply continuations of the same sequence.

Since optical observations must be made at the limb, then transferred to the disk on the basis of assumptions concerning the location of emitting features along the line of sight, and since XUV photographs are still quite primitive, we cannot say for sure that the progression in size and coarseness continues, but the indications are that this is the case.

Photospheric faculae, chromospheric plages, and coronal enhancements are linked by magnetic flux. It is obvious that any adequate theory of one of these features must be a theory of all three, and in the theory magnetic fields must play a basic role. Also, magnetic fields must certainly be fundamental in any explanation of the linkage of the corona with prominences and also with flares, as we shall point out in the remainder of the chapter.

B. Relation to Prominences

Prominences were once regarded as extensions of the chromosphere outward into the more remote regions of the solar atmosphere. During the past two decades, however, the trend has been to think of them rather as coronal material in a cooled, condensed condition. In discussing prominences we shall distinguish only between quiescent and active prominences. The former (Fig. 11.1), which appear in Hα spectroheliograms and filtergrams of the disk as elongated, dark filaments (Fig. 11.2), are generally some distance from sunspot groups for the greater part of their extent. Although they occasionally undergo rather abrupt changes, including winking in and out of view and sudden disappearances with subsequent reforming, their lifetimes may be weeks or months, during much of which they are remarkably stable. There is a certain amount of internal motion, including a steady, slow downward streaming, but of only a few kilometers a second. More violent motion is often evident at the end of the filament, which frequently extends near and points toward a sunspot group, and at other times motion is apparent in the form of streaming in arched trajectories from the sides of prominences or from the tops of prominences—often from one prominence to another. The spectroscopic characteristics of quiescent prominences are similar to those of the lower chromosphere, indicating temperatures of about 10,000°K, with an upper limit of 20,000°K.

Active prominences, on the other hand, lie directly over sunspot groups. They are sometimes distinguishable in disk spectroheliograms as short, curved filamentary structures, sometimes dark, sometimes bright, against the disk. On the limb they take various configurations, all of which are

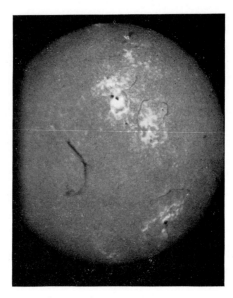

Fig. 11.1. An Hα photograph of the solar disk, showing a rather large variety of filaments. Included are several filaments that appear to lie along the outer perimeter of plage areas, others that have one terminus in or near spot groups, and the very large filament on the left that has no apparent association with any active region.   Courtesy, High Altitude Observatory.

related in one way or another to loops (Fig. 11.3). They may simply be an intricate system of loops or arches that appear to terminate at or near sunspots. They may be a sequence of knots of material that appear to originate in space, then follow curved trajectories that define a system of loops downward to the limb of the sun, or a suspended cloud continually feeding material into such trajectories (Fig. 11.4). Surge material often follows loops as it leaves and returns to the limb. Motions in these active prominences are frequently very violent, corresponding to hundreds of kilometers per second.

The spectroscopic characteristics of active prominences are very different from those of quiescent prominences. Whereas the Doppler displacements in quiescent prominences are very small, unless they happen to be in a state of eruption, the knots of material in the spectral lines of active prominences display constant motion, randomly oriented toward and away from the observer, with a mean velocity of 30–50 km/sec (Fig. 11.5). More highly excited and ionized states of the atoms are prevalent than in the quiescent prominences, indicating temperatures of 50,000°K or more.

Distances along lines of sight occupied by active prominences are generally considerably less than along quiescent prominences. As a consequence of this, and also of the higher degree of ionization of hydrogen, the active prominences frequently appear in monochromatic photographs to be much more fragile and tenuous than the quiescent. This appearance is deceptive. When coronagraph spectrograms of the two types are compared, active prominences generally show a well-defined continuum, whereas such a continuum is only faintly apparent with the most intense quiescent prominences. If we estimate the length of the line of sight through the prominences in each case, we conclude from the continuum intensity that the active prominence density may be 10^{10} electrons/cm^3 or more, whereas in the quiescent prominences it is rarely greater than 10^9. Either figure is highly uncertain. In both cases the extent of the line of sight through the prominence material is difficult to determine. In the case of the active prominence it is also frequently difficult to separate the electron scattering in the prominence from that in the coronal condensation with which it may be intimately associated. Our quiescent-prominence density is about two orders of magnitude less than that computed by Jefferies and Orrall

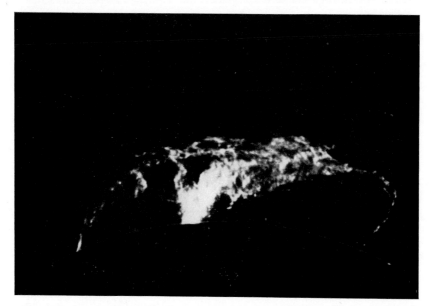

Fig. 11.2. A rather typical quiescent prominence on the limb. Such prominences, although quiescent, frequently have active tails along which material moves in curved trajectories toward sunspots.   Courtesy, High Altitude Observatory.

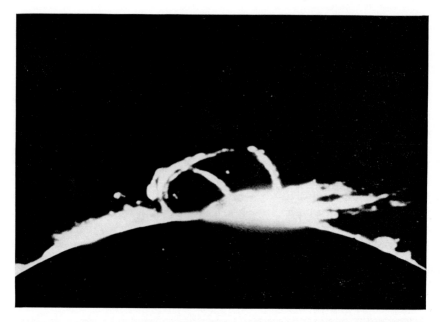

Fig. 11.3. Loop structure in a very active prominence. Courtesy, High Altitude Observatory.

(1961) from the Balmer and Paschen continuum for one quiescent prominence. It is unlikely that we overestimate our line of sight by such a factor. We contemplate an extensive study of many prominences in the near future in the hope of determining which value is more typical.

The interrelation of the two types of prominences to the corona is very different. Quiescent prominences generally lie along the border between photospheric fields of opposite polarity, or at least parallel to isogauss lines near the periphery of one such magnetic field distribution. Such a location is consistent with the concept first suggested by Menzel (1951) and then developed by Kippenhahn and Schluter (1957), namely, that coronal material accumulates along the horizontal portions of magnetic lines of force — there cooling because of the increased rate of radiation resulting from its increased density state—until ultimately it is a filament. The same concept is further developed by Brown (1958).

Because the matter is highly ionized, it cannot fall vertically across the lines of force. Instead, it depresses the lines of force that thread it normal to the long axis of the filament. One might expect that in such a situation it would be in a state of stable equilibrium, held in the trough of the downward-bending lines of force. This is not necessarily true, however. A displacement of the filament along the magnetic field will carry the trough with it, and the magnetic configuration will not exert a force on the filament toward its initial position. An equivalent concept is that the magnetic field in the corona in the absence of a prominence arises primarily from electric currents below the corona. Only small currents can flow in the corona normal to the field. Otherwise, the electromagnetic force $1/c(\,jxB)$ becomes greater than the relatively small gravitational forces or pressure differentials. In the prominence, however, gravitational forces on each unit of volume are one or two orders of magnitude greater than in the corona. For these to be balanced by electromagnetic forces a considerable current must flow in the prominence. It is the magnetic field arising from this current that distorts the lines of force of the total field, bending them downward at the location of the prominence. A displacement of the prominence along the field results in an accompanying displacement of the distorting current, and there is no force toward the original prominence position. Thus the prominence is in stable equilibrium only if the original

Fig. 11.4. Clouds of suspended prominence material from which matter, luminous in Hα, follows curved trajectories to the solar surface. Courtesy, High Altitude Observatory.

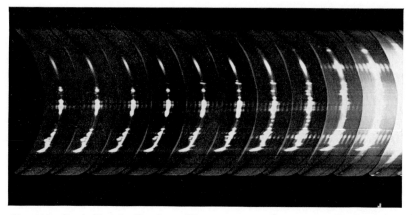

Fig. 11.5. Graded-height Hα, from Climax coronagraph spectrograph. A number of interesting features are evident here. Near the top of the arc in each spectrogram is a quiescent feature that is very bright near the limb, is indicated by the intense grating ghosts. Its brightness decreases rapidly with height. Just above the center of each arc is an active feature made up of several bright knots in considerable motion relative to each other. Adjacent to it is a quiescent feature with an active tail. This feature remains bright to a considerable height above the limb. Another slightly active feature of a few low-lying knots follows. Finally, a very complex object completes the picture. This object appears to consist of active and quiesent material along the same line of sight. The active part contains a small loop moving rapidly toward the observer, and a very rapidly moving terminating feature—probably a surge. Courtesy, High Altitude Observatory.

undistorted magnetic field is concave upward at the location of the prominence. The horizontal field lying between pairs of magnetic poles of opposite polarity in the solar surface does not fit this criterion. However, the field lying between two parallel rows of oppositely oriented pairs of vertical dipoles is concave upward over the height range from the solar surface to a height $1/2\sqrt{3}$ times the distance between the rows of dipoles, and is therefore suitable for supporting a prominence. An exception to the requirement that the magnetic field in the absence of the prominence be concave upward for stable equilibrium arises if the weight of the prominence material pulls lines of force completely down below the corona. This has the effect of setting up current systems in the more dense layers of the solar atmosphere, which will not be displaced as a consequence of displacements of the prominence. In this case, although the magnetic field configuration before the prominence was present might not have been suitable for stability, if the prominence can exist long enough to produce so extreme a deformation of the field, it will induce stability into the field. "Bridge" type prominences may be examples of prominences that have achieved stability through such a sequence of events.

Kippenhahn and Schluter found too difficult the problem of computing the distortion that a given amount of suspended prominence material would produce on a given field, so solved the inverse problem of setting up distorted fields in special ways, then computing the density of sus-pended material held in equilibrium by such fields. In the case of the field from two parallel rows of oppositely-oriented vertical dipoles, for instance, they assumed the distorted field on either side of the prominence to be approximated by that from the row of dipoles on one side of the prominence only. This is equivalent to approximating the field-distorting effect of the current in the prominence by a simple shielding effect. Their computation for this case, for the distribution of mass per square centimeter of the sheet prominence postulated, gave

$$f = \frac{1}{\pi g} \frac{1}{r^8} z(1 - z^2), \tag{1}$$

where the dipoles are taken at unit distance on either side of the base of the prominence. r is the distance from a dipole to the designated point in the prominence, z is the height of the point, and the dipoles have unit magnetic moment.

This solution indicates not only matter in the stable region of the promi-nence, $0 < z < 1/\sqrt{3}$, but also in the unstable region, $1/\sqrt{3} < z < 1$. Further-more, it gives a negative density for $z > 1$. Kippenhahn and Schluter con-sidered both the matter in the unstable region and the negative density as evidence of weakness in the theory, but this is not necessarily true. The tops of quiescent prominences often appear unstable, even though the rest of the prominence shows very little motion. Furthermore, the region of negative density corresponds nicely to the near vacuum in the corona that is seen at eclipse as a dark halo around the upper portion of every quiescent prominence. The density distribution has a maximum positive value at $z = 0.316$, and a maximum negative value at $z = 1.38$. The ratio of the densities at these two points is about $11/1$. In other words, the negative density can be interpreted as an absence of corona over a promi-nence, which is about an order of magnitude more dense than the corona.

In the above case the prominence is confined to a sheet of infinitesimal thickness by a magnetic field whose direction changes discontinuously. In case the magnetic field varies continuously, the horizontal density dis-tribution across the short dimension in the prominence will have a scale comparable to the thermal scale height of the prominence material divided by the slope of the magnetic field outside the prominence. (More precisely, the prominence thickness is about 4× scale height/slope of field lines.) We can see that this is so if we consider that the vertical density distribution along any magnetic tube of force is approximately barometric, and that the ratio of horizontal to vertical extent must be inversely proportional to the slope of the magnetic field. This relation suggests a completely independent method for determination of the temperature of a prominence. From prominences viewed edge-on, streams of material are often apparent, issuing from the vertical sides of the slab. Also, when so viewed, the thickness can be estimated, or at least an upper limit can be given. Now if the shape of the issuing streams is taken as the shape of the magnetic field threading athwart the prominence, the scale height of prominence material can be determined immediately. Such a determination assumes that the prominence is laterally stable—a condition that is obviously not fulfilled, or material would not be issuing from it. However, if the prominence is not changing rapidly as a result of the streaming, we may conclude that stability is approached.

Another form of the same relation, but with gravitational force introduced and vertical magnetic field eliminated, is

$$\text{width} \approx \frac{2}{\pi} \frac{H_x^2}{gf} h. \tag{2}$$

Now assuming that we know the thermal scale height, h, of the prominence material—either from such an observation as described in the preceding paragraph or from optical considerations—the thickness of the prominence, and the number of atoms along the thickness, we can find the intensity of the magnetic field threading the prominence. Some estimate of the number of electrons through the short dimension of a prominence should be possible from the enhancement of scattered photospheric light by prominences so viewed, except that this enhancement is likely to be too small to observe. The contribution to the white-light continuum of intense quiescent prominences viewed end-on is barely distinguishable on coronagraph spectrograms—hence is about 10 millionths of the solar disk brightness—and the end-on line of sight may be 10 or more times as long as the cross-wise line of sight. From such considerations we estimate that $f \approx 3 \times 10^{-6}$ gm, and can use this figure to illustrate the approach that might be used with a careful analysis of available data. Similarly, let us suppose the temperature of the prominence is 10,000°K, and the short-dimension thickness about 10 times a thermal scale height. We immediately find that the magnetic field is about 1 gauss.

Concepts of active prominences have not been incorporated into as satisfactory and comprehensive a theory as the Kippenhahn–Schluter theory of quiescent prominences. Whereas the locus of a quiescent prominence is a surface normal to the magnetic field lines at their horizontal points, that of an active loop is almost certainly along the field. Hence, since the density of the matter in the loop should assume a barometric vertical distribution, we must invoke either highly nonequilibrium conditions or diverging magnetic fields to explain the loops in which visible prominence matter appears to be of about constant density throughout. Whereas the supply of matter in quiescent prominences may be sustained by material entering it along the field lines, and the open space in the corona adjacent to such prominences indicates quite strongly that matter is continually passing into them, the much more profuse falling-out of matter along the active loops requires that they must be replenished, if from the corona, by material moving normal to the rather strong magnetic field overlying the active region—a process that we believe to be impossible. Only two alternatives remain: the formation of loops from the collapse of much more extensive tubes of force, as suggested by Lüst and Zirin (1960), or a continual feeding of high-speed material into the loops from the photosphere or below, as postulated by J. W. Warwick (1962) to explain flares. The former would be difficult to maintain over an extended period of time, and the latter requires processes for which we yet have no clear-cut observational evidence. The configuration of loops seen in Hα and those seen in coronal emission lines in the same region are similar. In other words, some loops in an active region are at prominence temperatures, others at coronal temperatures. This raises the difficult question: Why are some loops at one temperature, some at such a different temperature? Finally, there now is fairly clear-cut evidence that systems of Hα loops appear following flares. All of the above considerations must be incorporated into a satisfactory theory of active prominences.

Although monochromatic photographs of active regions in the corona in both λ 5303 and λ 6374 often show loop structures that parallel the prominence loops, emission in λ 5694 of Ca XV seems to be most intimately related to active prominences. A preferred location for such emission is at the top of a prominence loop, or particularly a nest of such prominence loops. Prominences most closely associated with yellow-line emission are characterized by matter appearing from space, particularly at a highly localized point, and streaming either in scattered knots or continuous thin streams along highly curved trajectories toward locations on the limb that exert a strong focussing effect on it. All three wavelengths—λ 5303, λ 6374, and λ 5694—give evidence of enhanced coronal density in the vicinity of active prominences—in contrast to the strong depletion of coronal material near quiescent prominences. The higher coronal density is indicated by the simultaneous enhancement of both λ 5303 and λ 6374 (Gantvoort and Billings, 1960). Temperature effects could favor one, but not both lines at the same time. Also, for Ca XV emission to appear in the corona at all a high coronal density is necessary. Thus we are confronted with the paradox that the type of prominence that appears to deplete matter from the corona most vigorously is the one in whose vicinity the corona remains most dense. This paradox strongly indicates that the source of descending material in the prominence is not the corona but the same source that enhances the coronal density.

C. Relation to Flares

Flares, for many years, were not considered to be coronal phenomena, but as one of their names designated, "chromospheric eruptions." This concept arose as a result of their having been first studied in disk spectroheliograms—primarily in Hα (Fig. 11.6), but sometimes in Ca H or K. In such spectroheliograms or filtergrams flares appear to be sudden brightening of a portion of the chromosphere—usually of a plage that is already bright against the general background of the chromosphere. We realize now, however, that flares are exceedingly complex phenomena involving events in the corona as well as in the chromosphere. Furthermore, those flare events that take place in the corona are in no way secondary to the chromospheric events viewed in the spectroheliograms.

Early records of limb flares well above the chromosphere are summarized by Dodson and McMath (1952) in their report of a brilliant limb flare completely detached from the chromosphere. Later, Hansen and Gordon (1960) noted a succession of limb flares describing the base of a giant loop. Zirin (1964) and others have studied flares well above the limb, and J. W. Warwick (1955) and C. S. Warwick (1955), from the statistics of the apparent areas of flares on various parts of the disk, concluded that all could be described by a three-dimensional configuration extending, frequently, from 10,000 to 20,000 km in height. Thus it is certain that at least an occasional Hα flare manifestation occurs well above the chromosphere, and that flares generally are at least bulged above the chromosphere. In either case they appear in or protrude into the corona and may therefore be considered coronal phenomena.

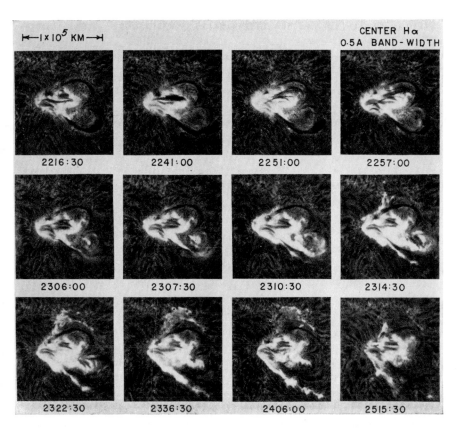

	CENTER Hα
←—1 x 10⁵ KM—→	0·5A BAND-WIDTH

Fig. 11.6. A succession of Hα filtergrams showing the development of a Class-I flare, July 6, 1965. Although the flare depicted here is of relatively low importance, the sequence of photographs shows in remarkable detail the evolution of the loop system (dark filaments in and near the flare) and its intimate relation to the flare. Courtesy, Lockheed Solar Observatory.

Other flare manifestations are even more intimately related to the corona. Type-III bursts generally appear at the time of sudden brightening of flares, and in their rapid change from higher to lower frequencies indicate that successive pulses of low-density electrons are coursing with near-relativistic velocities outward through the corona. These are succeeded by Type-V radiation, described as synchrotron radiation from sources a solar radius or more above the limb. At the moment of the origin of the Type-III bursts, much larger aggregates of matter also originate from the flares and move outward through the corona. These are observed visually in filtergrams as "fast dark" flare surges, although at the moment of their origin they are usually bright instead of dark against the disk, and in some cases the brightness persists for many tens of thousands of kilometers from the flare. The radio concomitant of the flare surge is the Type-II burst, which probably originates from a shock wave moving in front of the surge with a velocity somewhat in excess of the surge itself. Although the velocity of the surge is typically only a few hundred kilometers per second, the particles it contains appear to be of relativistic velocity, trapped in the surge by a tangled magnetic field; or, alternatively, they may be being continually accelerated to relativistic velocities within the magnetic field of the surge itself as it progresses through the corona. Such high-energy particles are manifest by the spurts of Type-III bursts, as well as the long-lived Type-IV bursts, far above the solar surface following the Type-II bursts.

In addition to Type-III, -IV, and -V bursts, solar X-ray enhancement, particularly at wavelengths shorter than 1 Å, indicates the presence of high energy electrons in the solar atmosphere during flares; and finally, high energy protons can be observed directly, from a few minutes to several hours after most major flares, incident upon the earth's magnetosphere.

The mechanism for the production of MeV particles in flares is far from being understood, and the same may be said concerning the more basic problem of the release of the vast amount of flare energy evident in both electromagnetic and particle radiation. The only energy source preexisting in the solar atmosphere adequate to produce flares is magnetic field, but no hypothesis has yet been postulated for the catastrophic release of such energy that will explain the suddenness of the flash phase of the flare. In general, however, the observed time scale can be approached more closely by a collapse in a magnetic field at coronal than at higher densities. Similarly, although high-energy particles could be further accelerated at almost any level in the solar atmosphere by a Fermi mechanism, provided they were initially moving fast enough that their mean free paths were smaller than the dimensions of the magnetic field, only in the corona could such a mechanism accelerate thermal electrons and ions. Thus there is some basis for considering the flare event to be primarily a coronal rather than a chromospheric phenomenon. Within the framework of such a concept the initial event in the flare is the sudden acceleration of both electrons and protons by a rapidly collapsing unstable magnetic field configuration, at a height of one or two tens of thousands of kilometers above the chromosphere. Those electrons that move downward excite the photosphere to X-ray emission; those moving upward and outward give rise to Type-III emission. The nature of the reaction on the chromosphere has not been delineated. Hence the most familiar aspect of a flare—its Hα feature—may be the least understood.

Instead of the hypothesis of the preceding paragraph that the basis event in flares lies in the corona, let us now consider the possibility that the seat of the disturbance is beneath the photosphere. J. W. Warwick (1962) examined this proposition, suggesting that particles of several MeV are generated beneath the solar surface, and pass out into the solar atmosphere along prominence and coronal loop structures. The collision cross section of these particles is so small because of their high velocity that they get well out into the corona before being stopped by collisions. The high-energy particles leaving the sun at the time of a flare are only the fraction of the original high-energy particle beam that escape from solar magnetic fields. Remaining particles dissipate their energy in producing radiation.

The Warwick hypothesis explains the high-energy component of flares and may explain the heating of the corona in active regions by interaction of the coronal plasma with streams of high-energy particles, as in Type-III events (Warwick, 1964). It does not explain the excess material in a coronal enhancement or the observation that a system of prominence loops frequently appear after a limb flare. The High Altitude Observatory prominence films contain at least two events that may be pertinent to these questions. In each case a large, structureless mound appears like a blister on the solar limb, grows rapidly while brightening to near-flare brightness, then separates into a myriad of prominence loops. Following the appearance of the loops a great deal of prominence material appears out of the corona and falls toward the sun—many times the amount usually seen in the "coronal rain" phenomenon. These events strongly suggest the violent birth of a solar active region by the upthrust of a flux tube through the photosphere. The tube carries into the corona far more material than it can support, and much of it falls back; but it is reasonable to postulate that enough material is heated to coronal temperatures by the violence of the event that the coronal enhancement comes into being in the same event.

An observation by Waldmeier (1960) seems to describe the birth of a coronal enhancement. A sunspot group that had its polarity reversed in a unique manner appeared ten days before its west-limb passage. When it was within two days of the limb, the coronal-line emission over it was weak. Then a brightening of the chromosphere, probably a flare, occurred a few hours after a flare had been reported from Pakistan. A system of Hα loops and a coronal condensation bright in both $\lambda 5303$ and $\lambda\, 5694$ rose at about

3 km/sec over several hours to a height of about 100,000 km. On days following this event there was strong emission in λ 5303.

Whether flares actually originate in the corona, or whether they originate beneath the photosphere and affect the corona, there exist close corona–flare relationships. The optical coronal feature most closely associated with flares is the yellow-line–emitting coronal condensation. Dolder *et al.* (1954) studied the statistics of occurrence of yellow-line emission on the same day as a flare, within 5° of the flare, and concluded that the chance probability of the number of associations thus observed was less than 2×10^{-5}. Their study was based on coronal observations made once a day, so it was not possible to conclude whether the few-hour lifetimes of intense condensations are actually coincident with the flares, or whether conditions favorable to both flares and coronal condensations tend to exist in a region on days of high activity. However, Zirin (1959), on the basis of time sequences of spectrograms of very active limb regions, concluded that the λ 4086 emission of Ca XIII, the λ 5694 emission from Ca XV, and the intensification of the coronal continuum were as intimate parts of the flare process as the intensified Hα and He II emission. In the December 18, 1956, flare that Zirin studied in detail the first spectroscopic feature to appear was the strongly intensified continuum, 16 minutes before the appearance of the flare in the familiar flare lines of hydrogen, calcium and helium. Brightening in the coronal and the flare lines occurred as nearly simultaneously (to within a few minutes) as the interval between spectrograms would permit one to judge. There were small differences between the spatial configuration of the corona and the flare lines on the spectrograms, as one would think necessary, since the temperature of the source of the former must be more than 10 times as high as that of the latter. The remarkable aspect of the observation is that the two seem to come from so nearly the same space at the same time.

Detailed spectroscopic observations of limb flares are very rare, but each such observation throws a great deal of light on the subject of flare–corona interrelation. Every effort should be made at coronagraph stations to increase the number of such observations.

REFERENCES

Brown, A. (1958). On the stability of a hydromagnetic prominence model. *Ap. J.* **128**, 646.

Dodson, H. W., and McMath, R. R. (1952). The limb flare of May 8, 1951. *Ap. J.* **115**, 78.

Dolder, F. P., Roberts, W. O., and Billings, D. E. (1954). Solar flares and the yellow coronal line. *Ap. J.* **119,** 120.

Gantvoort, N. C., and Billings, D. E. (1960). Prominence characteristics in regions of bright coronal emission. *Ap. J.* **132,** 213.

Hansen, R., and Gordon, D. (1960). The limb flares of October 13, 1958. *P. A. S. P.* **72,** 194.

Jefferies, J. T., and Orrall, F. Q. (1961). On the interpretation of prominence spectra. IV. The balmer and paschen continua in a quiet prominence. *Ap. J.* **134,** 747.

Kippenhahn, V. R., and Schluter, A. (1957). A theory of solar filaments. *Z. Ap.* **43,** 36.

Lüst, R., and Zirin, H. (1960). Condensation of prominences from the corona. *Z. Ap.* **49,** 8.

Menzel, D. H. (1951). "Report of Conference on the Dynamics of Ionized Media". London.

Waldmeier, M. (1960). The coronal activity of April 5, 1960. *Z. Ap.* **51,** 1.

Warwick, C. S. (1955). Flare heights and association with sid's. *Ap. J.* **121,** 385.

Warwick, J. W. (1955). Heights of solar flares. *Ap. J.* **121,** 376.

Warwick, J. W. (1964). Personal communication.

Warwick, J. W. (1962). The source of solar flares. *P. A. S. P.* **74,** 302.

Zirin, H. (1959). Physical conditions in limb flares and active prominences. *Ap. J.* **129,** 414.

Zirin, H. (1964). The limb flare of November 20, 1960—a coronal phenomenon. *Ap. J.* **140,** 1216.

CHAPTER 12

THE CORONA IN THE UNIVERSE

A. The Extent of the Corona

The inner surface of the corona, according to Zirin and Dietz (1963), lies about 2000 km above the photosphere, being separated from the chromosphere by a transition layer not over 500 km thick. The distinguishing characteristic of the transition layer is that within this very short distance the temperature rises from about 7000° to coronal temperatures, the density having already increased to near-coronal values in the top of the chromosphere. Further knowledge of the nature of this transition layer could be the key to the riddle of the origin and maintenance of the corona. The close proximity of the corona to the photosphere is indicated by a scale height in continuum emission corresponding to 1.1 million degrees or more above 1500 km (Athay and Roberts, 1955); by line emission present to within less than 10,000 km of the photosphere (ibid.); by millimeter-range radio observations, which precluded a deep, high-temperature upper chromosphere (Coates et al., 1958); and by far-ultraviolet observations, in which the Lyman continuum emission corresponds to a temperature of 7000° for the upper chromosphere, and line emission in which lines that would be expected from a transition layer are notably weak (Zirin and Dietz, 1963).

The lower surface of the corona is punctuated by several tens of thousands of spicules, which vary in height from 7000 to 10,000 km. The cross sections of such spicules are 500–1000 km (Dunn, 1960), and their nature is that of upward-moving jets of gas with velocities of about 25 km/sec and temperatures of 20,000°K or greater. The lower portion is also interrupted by prominences of various configurations, states of motion, and temperature. Finally, according to Ivanov-Kholodnyi (1963), the lower surface of the

292

corona, as defined by a specified temperature, would vary in height, being lower over plages than over the undisturbed sun, the polytropic product $(TN_e{}^k)$ being higher in the active regions of the corona, however.

Throughout the book we have made no arbitrary division between an inner and an outer corona, since, as a matter of fact, there is no natural level for such a division. The emission line corona appears to terminate at approximately one-half solar radius above the photosphere, but strong emission that is accessible to coronagraph observation ceases at half this height, and some emission is visible during an eclipse out to one solar radius. The majority of the bright loop structures that dominate monochromatic photographs of the sun terminate at or below 50,000 km above the photosphere, but some extend to 200,000 km or more. Finally the extremity of the white-light corona as it appears on a photograph depends entirely on the exposure time, the observing conditions, the photographic contrast, etc. From its base the density of the corona drops continuously out to the earth's orbit and beyond. We know much less about how the temperature behaves, but have no evidence of a thermal structure that would define an inner and an outer corona.

The limit of the visible corona should be set, perhaps, at 15 solar radii—the extent of the long, thin streamer that was photographed by Maunder in 1898, and called to our attention recently by Chapman (1961). Photometry has been carried out to 20 solar radii by Dolginova (1961), with meaningful results to 5 solar radii; by Allen (1956) to 12 solar radii; by Blackwell (1956) to 20 solar radii; and by Waldmeier (1961) to 30 solar radii.

The study of the corona has been extended far beyond the limit of optical visibility through the observation of its occultation of various radio sources—particularly the Crab Nebula. The extensive literature on these observations is reviewed elsewhere. We note here only the following conclusions: (1) The corona so studied shows solar-cycle effects out to 8 solar radii but not out to 16 solar radii, being more nearly spherical at sunspot maximum, as in the case of optical observations. (2) The corona at great distances from the sun is characterized by slender, elongated streamers or density irregularities, but there is some disagreement both on the magnitude of the density variations and the dimensions of the streamers. Out to 20 solar radii the streamers appear to be oriented in a configuration suggesting an extensive general magnetic field, but beyond this distance they appear to be radial. The evidence for nonradial streamers anywhere in the path of the occulted radio sources is not strong, however. (3) At great distances from the sun occultation by the corona fluctuates strongly—an effect that may be due to either space or time irregularities. Regular scattering of radiation from discrete sources extends out to about 55 solar radii only, but sporadic scattering is observed out to 120 solar radii. Marked variations show up within a 24-hour period, indicating either that the outermost corona is highly variable with time or that the source moves through structures of dimensions of about 3.5 solar radii. Such dimensions are consistent with the extension of visible coronal streamers, but much wider than the structural features that must be postulated to explain the scattering processes that effect the occultation.

At the present moment the corona must be considered as essentially unobserved between the outer limit of the occultation observations and the inner extent to which space-probe detection of the solar wind has been carried out, but this is only from about 120 to 150 solar radii and we may expect that the region will soon be explored. Brandt (1962) has suggested that information concerning this region might be gained from Lyman-α radiation in the night sky, but it would appear from computations by Parker (1962) that coronal particles carried in the solar wind would maintain essentially the same state in the interplanetary space that they have near the sun, and therefore that no significant recombination would take place. Night-sky Lyman-α radiation, as well as the interplanetary Lyman-α absorption manifest by the sharp self-reversal in the Lyman-α line, should then be explained by neutral hydrogen within the earth's magnetosphere.

The streaming corona at the orbits of Earth and Venus has already been discussed in Chapters 3, 7, and 11. Our knowledge of the corona beyond the earth's orbit should soon be greatly extended when the Mars probe observations become available. We have mentioned conclusions concerning it out to 2 or 3 A.U., based on the behavior of comet tails. The modulation of cosmic-ray flux by the solar cycle similarly indicates a variable corona extending well beyond the earth's orbit. We should also mention Saito's hypothesis (1961) of the Gegenschein as extended coronal streamers. Parker (1957) demonstrated that an outward-streaming corona might become dynamically unstable at several A.U. and break up into turbulent motions and a tangle of magnetic fields. He used this concept to explain the long decay time of solar cosmic rays following violent flare events—the concept being that the cosmic rays that reach the earth from a variety of directions many hours after the flares have undergone a sequence of reflections from the tangled magnetic fields that form the inner wall of a cavity enclosing both the sun and the earth. Gold (1960), on the other hand, has postulated that the delayed particles are stored in magnetic loops in the corona that ultimately become distended to include the earth's orbit; and Warwick (1962), that they are interrupted and delayed by magnetic irregularities between the sun and the earth at times of high sunspot activity.

B. Corona–Terrestrial Interrelationships

The concept of an interrelation between such terrestrial events as aurorae and geomagnetic storms and the extended coronal streamers is as old as the awareness of solar effects in causing these events. For many years the association of the corona with these phenomena remained purely speculative, and early theories of both geomagnetic and ionospheric phenomena tended to discount the role of the corona. Geomagnetic storms, with the exception of M-region storms, were attributed to clouds of gas expelled from the sun by violent events such as flares, which were considered to be chromospheric in origin, and both D- and E-layer ionization were attributed to Lyman-α radiation, which was also chromospheric. Developments of the past decade, however, have linked more and more geophysical phenomena of the outer atmosphere to the corona.

The discovery by Friedman and colleagues, since 1949, of a significant X-ray flux from the sun reaching the earth's upper atmosphere has pointed out the importance of such radiation, which except possibly during flares must originate in the high-temperature corona, for explanation of the ionosphere. Havens *et al.* (1954) considered the E layer in its entirety, and the F layer to some extent, to be due to X-ray ionization. Friedman (1960) still considered this point of view to be essentially correct, although he recognized that the base of the E layer may be also influenced by Lyman-β and Lyman-continuum radiation.

Except during flares, the D layer remains best explained by Lyman-α ionization. At the time of a flare, however, short-wavelength X radiation is observed as low as 65 km above the earth's surface, whereas no comparable enhancement has been observed in Lyman-α radiation at any height. Consequently, the ionization of the lower D layer, responsible for sudden ionospheric disturbances and accompanying blackout of short-wave radio transmission, must be attributed to X-ray ionization. Also, the magnetic crochet accompanying a flare is attributable to a short-lived X-ray enhancement acting on the E layer. As we have noted in Chapter 11, however, there is a question as to whether the X rays associated with flares should be attributed to high-temperature and high-density coronal regions, or to bombardment of the more dense layers of the solar atmosphere by high-energy particles. Even in the latter case, though, the particles may have been accelerated to their high energy by processes in the corona—in which case the X radiation is still indirectly of coronal origin.

Chapman, in 1957, suggested a novel connection between the corona and the ionosphere—namely, that the F layer is heated by thermal conduction through the extended corona. We have noted how this suggestion played a key role in the development of the concept of the solar wind, and as such it is of great historic importance. The picture of the magnetosphere that has resulted from space-probe observations since 1957 introduces difficulties in such a mechanism, however, since such a region must be an effective thermal insulator lying between the extended corona and the ionosphere.

The old idea by Chapman (Chapman and Bartels, 1940) of geomagnetic storms resulting from clouds of ionized particles traversing the space between the sun and the earth, impinging on the magnetic field of the earth, and producing the changes in the current systems in the earth's upper atmosphere that are recognizable as geomagnetic storms is readily reinterpreted in terms of a solar wind. As such, the clouds become irregularities in the solar wind, either as localities of enhanced velocity or enhanced density. Thus magnetic storms are the result of irregularities in the expanding corona.

Several significant discoveries by space probes have contributed to an understanding of the processes involved. One of the most striking is the discovery by Ness et al. (1965) that the geomagnetic index fluctuates in a characteristic manner during each passage of a semipermanent interplanetary magnetic field feature. More specifically the index goes through a maximum two days after the edge of a sector (see Chapter 10) passes the earth. The same IMP satellite measurements have also disclosed that the earth's magnetosphere is separated from interplanteary magnetic fields by a well-defined boundary of irregular fields. This boundary has the shape of the surface of a raindrop, being pushed closer to the earth by solar wind on its sunlit side, but trailing far out, perhaps even as far as the moon's orbit, on the side away from the sun. The $Mariner\ II$ space probe operating between Earth and Venus also disclosed several phenomena pertinent to the question of geomagnetic disturbances. One was that magnetic disturbances following flares were detected both by the probe and on the earth, the time lapse between the two observations being consistent with solar-wind velocity (Neugebauer and Snyder, 1963). Another was a strong correlation between solar-wind velocity and geomagnetic activity (Snyder et al., 1963).

The details of the interaction between the solar wind and the earth's magnetic field are outside the scope of this book, as are the various hypotheses for explaining the complex pattern of magnetic and auroral events. The hypotheses tend to be based on a general picture of the earth's magnetosphere acting as an elastic barrier to the incident particles of the solar wind, with the impulses from the varying wind being transmitted through this barrier by hydromagnetic waves or shocks. These impulses produce local heating, which explains certain ionospheric and geomagnetic effects, and an injection of particles from the ionized belts into the ionosphere to cause the aurora. The detailed description of such processes is the work of the geophysicists. From the point of view of the student of the corona the task is to trace the physical processes in the coronal gas from the regions of its origin on the sun to the portion of the earth's outer atmosphere in which geomagnetic disturbances are initiated.

C. Origin and Replenishment of the Corona

Prominence motions carry a great deal more material downward from the corona into the sun than is ever observed to go upward. Rough estimates of this difference imply that descending prominence material alone should deplete the corona in a matter of hours. Similarly, the solar-wind flux should deplete the corona in a comparable time. The fact that the corona is not thus depleted but remains a remarkably stable feature of the solar atmosphere day after day and month after month implies a persistent and profuse source of coronal material. The theory of accretion, discussed in Chapter 6, gives a hypothesis for the origin of both the matter and heat of the corona as coming from outside the solar system. Conversely, any hypothesis of heating of the corona from within the sun must be accompanied by a hypothesis for replenishment from solar material. The most likely mechanism for such replenishment is the spicule. 50,000 such spicules, each of cross section 500 km with densities of 10^{11} particles/cm^3 and moving upward with velocities of 20 km/sec, would provide approximately the requisite amount of matter, provided all of the matter in the ascending spicules entered the corona. The observation of spicules is sufficiently difficult that it is impossible to say whether they all fade into the corona or whether some of them descend again after ascending. Also, it is impossible to assign a precise number to the spicules, or to determine whether all of them are moving upward with the velocity of 20 km/sec that has been measured in some of them.

One difficulty with the spicule hypothesis is that whereas spicular activity has not been observed to be highly dependent on solar activity, the density of the coronal gas is completely determined by the level of activity. Spicule details cannot be observed easily, however, and there may be more variation with activity than that of which we are now aware. It is possible that the massive loop-prominence structures that are sometimes seen to rise out of the solar limb carry a very large amount of matter into the corona, but these events are relatively rare, as are also surges containing large amounts of matter. Also, it is possible that the magnetic fields in coronal structures impede the solar-wind flux, thereby concentrating the material that goes into the corona via spicules. This explanation would not hold in the case of loss of matter by prominence activity, however, for the greatest amount of descending matter is present in the locations of the greatest concentration of coronal material, as we mentioned in the preceding chapter.

D. Coronas of Other Stars

The only possibility of observing the corona of another star is during an eclipse by a dark companion, and the low brightness of coronas make such observations unlikely. Consequently, the topic of coronas of other stars is a highly speculative one. Correspondingly, the number of stars that we would expect to have coronas depends on our concept of how such coronas arise. If we accept the accretion theory of the corona, for example, we would expect almost all stars to have coronas—the amount of matter in the corona being controlled by the density of matter through which the star is passing, the speed of the star, and the extent of its effective cross-section in sweeping up interstellar matter. The temperature of the corona, on the other hand, would depend entirely on the gravitational potential at the surface of the star. If, however, we explain the corona as a consequence of energetic processes within the sun, we limit considerably the stars that we would expect to have coronas. A basic requirement for a corona that is heated by waves or shocks is the presence of a hydrogen convective zone, for no radiation or conduction phenomenon would lead to an outer atmosphere of a higher temperature than that of the photosphere of the star. Possible heating processes involving the direct conversion of magnetic into thermal energy may also be dependent on such a convective zone, since it is likely that the dynamo action in a star that generates magnetic fields depends on nonuniform rotation, which in turn may be driven by convective processes. The requirement that there should be a convective zone puts an upper limit on the photospheric temperature of a star with a corona—at higher temperatures the degree of recombination of hydrogen is inadequate to give the necessary opacity for such a zone. According to Barbier (1958) the convective zones of A5 stars lie very near the stellar surface, whereas B0 stars have no convective zones; hence, in the main sequence the line of demarcation between stars with and without convective zones lies between these two classifications.

Since convection is important in all later type main sequence stars, we expect all cool stars to have coronas unless dissipation processes prevent transfer of convective mechanical energy to the outermost portions of the stellar atmosphere. There is a possibility that this may be the case if the H^- zone lies too deep under the photosphere of a cool star. We recall that the theories of transfer of mechanical energy in the solar atmosphere do not explain the heating of the solar corona in a satisfactory manner, and the observed great decline in both temperature and density of the corona at the 1954 sunspot minimum suggests that were it not for sunspots and accompanying phenomena in the solar atmosphere the corona would not exist. Consequently, it is possible that among stars as cool as the sun or cooler, only those with adequate electromagnetic activity have coronas— but of course this may include all cool stars; we do not know.

In addition to the interval of main-sequence stars that we have considered, certain stellar types with extended atmospheres, such as Be and Ae stars, may be expected to have coronas as well as chromospheres. In these, as in Wolf-Rayet stars, coronas, if they exist, would have quite a different origin from those in G2 stars, and therefore would be expected to be very different in character and appearance. The use of the word *corona* for the extended atmosphere of such a star may be only a matter of terminology.

E. Coronas of Planets

A similar problem of terminology arises in the case of the coronas of planets. In a sense the radiation belts surrounding the earth may be called a corona. They contain charged particles with kinetic energies corresponding to temperatures of millions of degrees or more; and even more than in the case of the solar corona their density distribution is determined by the presence of a magnetic field. At this point the resemblance stops. Whereas in the solar corona the energy distribution is essentially Maxwellian, and the same for all particles, the energy spectra of the different particles in the earth's radiation belts are neither Maxwellian or identical. Furthermore, whereas the solar plasma in the corona is electrically neutral, the inner radiation belt of the earth appears to be predominantly protons, and the second belt, electrons (Frank *et al.*, 1963).

The differences between the solar and terrestrial corona reflect the more basic difference—a great disparity in density. Whereas 10^8 cm^{-3} is a typical electron density for the solar corona, the same number, in cm^{-2} sec^{-1}, is a typical total electron *flux* for the terrestrial corona, for particles of energy $>$ 40 keV. Lower-energy particles have not been studied in the radiation belts, so it is impossible to make a correct comparison between densities, but it would appear that the ratio of solar to coronal densities is about that of the velocity of light. The basic difference between the terrestrial and the solar corona is that the former is an aggregate of independent charged particles, each executing independently of the other particles a motion appropriate to the magnetic field in which it is located. Interactions are insufficient to bring about either charge neutralization of equipartition of energy. The behavior of each particle is individually and completely dominated by the magnetic field. The solar corona, on the other hand, is a plasma. Its characteristics are determined by the collective action of all particles in the environment. The magnetic field interacts with the plasma and is in turn modified by it. Thus we must consider the resemblance between the solar and the terrestrial corona as somewhat superficial.

The possibility exists that other planets have coronas that resemble the solar corona more than the earth's radiation belts do. Radio noise from the planet Jupiter, for example, suggests emission from high-energy particles trapped in a magnetic field—the center of the dipole being considerably displaced from the center of the planet (J. W. Warwick, 1964). By extrapolation of solar-wind flux to Jupiter, one concludes that the planet's magnetosphere may extend out to 50 planetary radii. The particle density appears to be several hundred or several thousand times as great as that in the earth's radiation belts. At such densities the gas may be beginning to exhibit collective phenomena. Our concepts of the outer atmospheres of the planets may be modified radically in the next few years, so it is probably too early to write further on the subject of planetary coronas.

F. Conclusion

In summary, we may say that although stars similar to the sun may and probably do have coronas, and although stars of a different nature and certain planets have extended atmospheres that bear a certain resemblance to the corona of the sun, the solar corona is unique among observed natural phenomena. Nowhere except in the extended atmosphere of novae and in high-energy laboratory devices are comparable temperatures and degrees of ionization available to our observation. Compared to the novae, the corona is near at hand and accessible on every clear day. Compared to laboratory devices, its scale provides freedom from edge effects and measurable radiation with very low emissivity. Compared to both laboratory high temperatures and novae, it is a much less transient phenomenon. The persistence of coronal features day after day and month after month and their gradual evolution through the solar cycle permits investigation of the small-scale transient effects that we must ultimately understand in order to thoroughly describe the plasma.

REFERENCES

Allen, C. W. (1956). Coronal photometry of the eclipse of June 30, 1954. *M. N. R. A. S.* **116**, 69.

Athay, R. G., and Roberts, W. O. (1955). Coronal line intensities at the Khartoum Eclipse. *Ap. J.* **121**, 231.

Barbier, D. (1958). General theory of stellar atmospheres, *in "Handbuch der Physik"* S. Flügge, ed.), Vol. 50 p. 274. Springer, Berlin.

Blackwell, D. E. (1956). A study of the outer solar corona from a high altitude aircraft at the eclipse of June 30, 1954. *M. N. R. A. S.* **116**, 56.

Brandt, J. C. (1962). Interplanetary gas IV. Neutral hydrogen in a model solar corona. *Ap. J.* **133**, 668.

Chapman, S. (1957). Notes on the solar corona and the terrestrial ionosphere. *Smithsonian Contributions to Astrophysics*, **2**, 1.

Chapman, S. (1961). The solar corona and interplanetary gas, *in "Space Astrophysics"* (W. Liller, ed.), p. 133. McGraw-Hill, New York.

Chapman, S., and Bartels, J. (1940). "Geomagnetism," Vol. II. Oxford Univ. Press (Clarendon), London and New York.

Coates, R. J., Gibson, J. E., and Hagen, J. P. (1958). The 1954 eclipse measurements of the 8.6 mm solar brightness distribution. *Ap. J.* **128**, 406.

Dolginova, Y. N. (1961). Determination of the degree of polarization of the solar corona from observations of the solar eclipse of June 1954. *Geomagnetism and Aeronomics* **1**, 572.

Dunn, R. B., (1960). Photometry of the solar chromosphere. Ph.D. thesis, Harvard University.

Frank, L. A., Van Allen, J. A., Whelpley, W. A., and Craven, J. D. (1963). Absolute intensities of geometrically trapped particles with explorer 14. *J. G. R.* **68**, 1573.

Friedman, H. (1960). The sun's imizing radiations. *In "Physics of the Upper Atmosphere"* (J. A. Ratcliffe, ed.), Chapter 4. Academic Press, New York.

Gold, T. (1960). Energetic particle fluxes in the solar system and near the earth. *Ap. J.* Suppl. **4**, 406.

Havens, R. J., Friedman, H., and Hulburt, E. O. (1954). "Physics of the Ionosphere." Phys. Sco., London.

Ivanov-Kholodnyi, G. S., and Nikolskii, G. M. (1963). Extreme UV radiation and the structure of the solar atmosphere in active and undisturbed regions. *Sov. Astr.-A. J.* **6,** 609.

Ness, N. F., Scearce, C. S., Seek, J. B., and Wilcox, J. M. (1965). A summary of results from the IMP-1 magnetic field experiment. Goddard Space Flight Center Bulleitn X-612-65-180.

Neugebauer, M., and Snyder, C. W. (1963). The mission of Mariner II preliminary observations. *Science* **138,** 1095.

Parker, E. N. (1957). The gross dynamics of a hydromagnetic cloud. *Ap. J. Suppl.* **3,** 51 (abst.); *Ap. J.* **126,** 229.

Parker, E. N. (1962). Kinetic properties of interplanetary matter, *Planetary Space Sci.* **9,** 461.

Saito, K. (1961). The Gegenschein and coronal streamers of the sun. *Publ. Astr. Soc. Japan* **13,** 376.

Snyder, C. W., Neugebauer, M., and Rao, U. R. (1963). The solar wind velocity and its correlation with cosmic ray variations and with solar and geomegnatic activity. *J. G. R.* **68,** 6361.

Waldmeier, M. (1961). White light corona 1954 brightness and components. *Z. Ap.* **53,** 81.

Warwick, C. S. (1962). Propagation of solar particles and the interplanetary magnetic field. *J. G. R.* **67,** 1333.

Warwick, J. W. (1964). Radio emission from Jupiter. *In* "Annual Reviews of Astronomy and Astrophysics" (L. Goldberg, ed.), vol. II, p. 1. Annual Reviews, Inc., Palo Alto, Calif.

Zirin, H., and Dietz, R. D. (1963). The structure of the solar chromosphere I. A picture based on extreme UV, Millimeter and λ10830 data. *Ap. J.* **138,** 664.

APPENDIX 1

CORONAL OBSERVATORIES

Station	Location	Nation	Elevation (meters)	Coronal equipment	Year started
Pic du Midi	Pyrenees	France	2860	Spectrograph coronagraph White-light coronameter	1938
Arosa	Alps	Switzerland	2050	Spectrograph coronagraph	1938
Climax	Colorado Rockies	USA	3500	Large and small spectrograph coronagraphs	1941
Wendelstein	Wendelstein	Germany	1838	Spectrograph coronagraph	1941
Kanzelhöhe	near Villach	Austria	1900	Spectroscope coronagraph	1948
Sacramento Peak	New Mexico	USA	2760	Large and small spectrograph coronagraphs with both photographic and photoelectric recording	1949
Norikura	Mt. Norikura	Japan	2900	Spectrograph coronagraph	1950
Gornoya	Kislovodsk	USSR	2130	Spectrograph coronagraph	1952
Alma Ata	Kazakh	USSR	2600	Photoelectric spectrograph, white-light coronameter	1954
Meudon	Paris	France	160	White-light coronameter, photoelectric spectrometer	1959
Haleakala	Hawaii	USA	3120	Spectrograph coronagraph	1963
Lomnický Štít	—	Czechoslovakia	2634	Spectrograph coronagraph	1964
Ulan-Bator	—	Mongolian People's Republic	—	Spectrograph coronagraph	1964
Huancayo	—	Peru	3313	Spectrograph coronagraph	1965
Mauna Loa	Hawaii	USA	3378	White-light coronameter	1965

APPENDIX II

IDENTIFIED OPTICAL CORONAL EMISSION LINES

$\lambda(\text{Å})$	Ion	Transition	I.P.	A.	References
3010	Fe XII	$^2P_{1/2}-^2D_{3/2}$	291	—	2, 3
3170 (3180)	Cr XI	$^1D_2-^3P_1$	246	23	2, 3 (1, 6)
3326.7 (3329)	Ca XII	$^2P_{1/2}-^2P_{3/2}$	592	488	2 (1)
3388.0	Fe XIII	$^1D_2-^3P_2$	330	87	1, 2
3533.5 (3534.0)	V X	$^1D_2-^3P_1$	206	17	2 (1, 6)
3600.9	Ni XVI	$^2P_{3/2}-^2P_{1/2}$	455	193	1, 2
3642.8	Ni XIII	$^1D_2-^3P_2$	350	18	1, 2
3685	Mn XII	$^1D_2-^3P_2$	288	68	1, 2, 3, 6
3800.7 (3801.2)	Co XII	$^1D_2-^3P_1$	306	14	1, 3, 6 (2)
3987.3 (3987.1)	Fe XI	$^1D_2-^3P_1$	262	9	2 (1)
(3997) 3998 (3998.4)	Cr XI	$^1D_2-^3P_2$	246	53	(6) 1, 3 (2)
4086.5 (4086.1)	Ca XIII	$^3P_1-^3P_2$	655	319	1 (2)
4220.2	Mn X	$^1D_2-^3P_1$	248	—	2 (6)
4232.0	Ni XII	$^2P_{1/2}-^2P_{3/2}$	321	237	1, 2
4256.4	K XII	$^2P_{1/2}-^2P_{3/2}$ $(^2P_{3/2}-^2P_{1/2})$	504	250	1, 2 (3, 6)
4312.0	V X	$^1D_2-^3P_2$	206	—	2
4351.0; 4350.6; 4351.4	Co XV	$^2P_{3/2}-^2P_{1/2}$	412	110	1, 2, 3, 6
4412.4; 4412.6; 4412	Ar XIV	$^2P_{3/2}-^2P_{1/2}$	687	108	1, 2, 3
4566.6 (4566.2)	Cr IX	$^1D_2-^3P_1$	185	8	1 (2, 6)
4744	Ni XVII	$^3P_2-^3P_1$	500	—	2 (6)
5116.0 (5114.8)	Ni XIII	$^3P_1-^3P_2$	350	157	1 (2)
5188.5	Co XI	$^2P_{1/2}-^3P_2$	290	—	2
5302.9	Fe XIV	$^2P_{3/2}-^2P_{1/2}$	355	60	1, 2
5446.4	Ca XV	$^3P_2-^3P_1$	820	78	1, 2, 3, 5

5536 (5539.5)	Ar X	$^2P_{1/2}-^2P_{3/2}$	423	126	1 (2)
5620.1	Ca VII	$^1D_2-^3P_2$	109	—	2, 3
5694.5	Ca XV	$^3P_1-^3P_0$	820	95	1, 2, 3, 5
5774	Co XVI	$^3P_2-^3P_1\ (^3P_1-^3P_0)$	444	66	1, 3, 6 (2)
5926 (5974)	Ar XV	$^3P_2-^3P_1$	755	—	2, 4 (3)
6374.5 (6374.2)	Fe X	$^2P_{1/2}-^2P_{3/2}$	235	69	1 (2)
6535	MnXIII	$^2P_{3/2}-^2P_{1/2}$	350	—	6
6701.8	Ni XV	$^3P_1-^3P_0$	430	57	1, 2
6740 (6777)	K XIV	$^3P_2-^3P_1$	717	41	2, 3, 6 (1)
6917	Ar XI	$^3P_1-^3P_2$	479	—	2
7059.6	Fe XV	$^3P_2-^3P_1$	390	—	1, 2
7143.9	Ni IX	$^1G_4-^1D_2$	169	—	2
7891.9	Fe XI	$^3P_1-^3P_2$	262	—	1, 2
8024.2	Ni XV	$^3P_2-^3P_1$	430	—	1, 2
8425.1	Ni XV	$^3P_2-^3P_1$	430	—	—
8475.7	Ar XIII	$^3P_2-^3P_1$	621	—	1, 3
10746.8	Fe XIII	$^3P_1-^3P_0$	330	14	1, 2
10797.9	Fe XIII	$^3P_2-^3P_1$	330	14	1, 2

REFERENCES

1. Allen, C. W. (1963). "Astrophysical Quantities," 2nd ed. Oxford Univ. Press (Athlone), London and New York.

2. Pryce, M. H. L. (1964). The origin of coronal emission lines. *Ap. J.* **140**, 1192

3. Rohrlich, F., and Pecker, C. (1963). Highly ionized atoms. *Ap. J.* **138**, 1246.

4. Collins, P. D. B. (1964). Relativistic calculations of the Z-dependence of atomic energy levels and application to the identification of some coronal lines. *Ap. J.* **140**, 1206.

5. Boardman, W. J., and Billings, D. E. (1965). Wavelength of the yellow coronal lines. *Ap. J.* **141**, 1289.

6. Pecker, C., and Rohrlich, F. (1961). Forbidden lines in the ground configurations with special regard to the coronal emission spectrum. *Mem. Soc. Roy. Sci. Liège* **4**, 190.

APPENDIX III

Line	Ion	References	Line	Ion	References
1058.7	Al VIII	1	292.79	Si XI	3, 5, 6, 11
1048.9	Si VII	1	290.68	Si IX	3, 5, 6
1037.6	O VI	2	288.6	Fe XIV	9
1031.9	O VI	2	284.11	Fe XV	2, 3, 5, 6
952.4	Si X	1	278.44	Mg VII, Si VII	3, 11
780.3	Ne VIII	2	277.10	Si VIII, Si X	3, 5, 6. 11
770.4	Ne VIII	2	275.33	Si VII	3, 6
658.7	Ar XIII	1	274.2	Fe XIV	9, 11
625.3	Mg X	2	271.99	Si X	3, 6, 11
609.8	Mg X	2	270.5	Fe XIV	9
558	Ca X, Ne VI	6, 11	264.5	Fe XIV	9, 11
521.1	Si XII	2	264.29	S X	3, 11
499.4	Si XII	2, 3	261.38	Fe XVI	6
465.3	Ne VII	2, 2	261.02	Si X	6
444	Mg IX	6	259.53	S X	3, 11
436.70	Mg VIII	3, 6, 11	*258.38*	*S X*	*3, 11*
430.47	Mg VIII	3, 6, 11	258.22	Si X, XI	6, 11
368.08	Mg IX	2, 3	*257.29*	*S X*	*3*
361.7	Fe XVI	2, 11	*256.6*	*S X*	*5*
360.81	*Fe XVI*	*3*	253.83	Si X	3, 5
356.04	Mg VIII, Fe XIV	3, 11	251.8	Fe XIV	9
349.93	Si IX	3, 6	249.25	Si VI	6
347.39	Si X	3	248.60	C V	6
347	Fe X	6, 11	246.08	Si VI	6
345.07	Si IX	3, 6, 11	235.41	Si VIII	6
342	Si IX, Fe XIV	6, 11	233.01	Si VIII	6
339.00	Mg VIII	3, 11	231.38	Fe XV	6
336.62	Fe XVI	2	*227.06*	*Si IX*	*3, 6*
335.31	*Fe XVI*	*2, 3*	225.08	Si IX	3, 6, 11
332.81	Al X	3	*224.69*	*Si IX*	*3, 11*
319.79	Si VIII	3, 6, 11	223.70	Si IX, FE XIV	3, 6, 11
317.01	Mg VIII	3	*217.04*	*Si VIII*	*6*
316.19	Si VIII	3	214.71	Si VIII	6
315	Mg VIII	3, 6	*211.74*	*Fe XIV*	*6, 9*
314.29	Si VIII	3	204.0	Fe XIV	6, 9
313.75	Mg VIII	3, 6	196.69	Fe	4
311.96	Mg VIII	3	195.09	Fe	4
308.33	Si VIII	3, 6	193.53	Fe	4
303.37	Si XI	3	*193.09*	*Fe XIII*	*6*
296.17	Si IX	3, 5, 6, 11	192.37	Fe	4

(Continued)

APPENDIX III (continued)

Line	Ion	References	Line	Ion	References
191.20	Fe, S XI	4, 11	90.11	Fe XI	6
190.20	*Fe XIII, S XII*	*4, 6, 11*	89.21	Fe XI	6
188.23	Fe	4	88.12	Fe XI, Ne VIII	6
187.0	*Fe XIII*	*4, 6*	86.79	Fe XI	6
185.18	Fe	4	83	Ne VIII	12
184.7	O VI	12	82.85	Mg VIII	6
184.52	Fe	4	82.57	Mg VIII	6
184.12	Fe	4	81.7	Mg VIII	6
183.94	O VI	3	81.6	Si VII	6
182.25	C VI	4	79.5	Fe XII	6, 11
182.17	Fe	4	79.1	Fe XII	6
179.76	Fe	4	77.74	Mg IX	6
177.13	Fe	4	75.8	Fe XIII	6
175.26	Fe	4	75.28	Fe XIII	6
174.54	Fe	4	*74.8*	*Mg VIII, Fe XIII*	*6, 11*
173.13	*O VI*	*4, 5, 6*	74.32	Si VIII	6
172.94	O VI	3	72.4	Fe XIV, Si VIII	6
171.1	Fe IX	8	72.26	Mg IX, Si VIII	3, 6
170.2	Mg X	6	72.1	Si VIII	6
164.13	Ni XIV	7	71.5	Fe XIV	6
159.97	Ni X	7	69.9	Mg IX, Fe XV	3, 6
158.37	Ni X	7	*69.53*	*Si VIII, Mg VIII*	*6, 11*
157.75	Ni XIII	7	68.48	Mg VIII	6
154.15	Ni XII	7	67.2	Mg IX, Mg VIII,	
152.95	Ni XII	7		Ne VIII	3, 6
152.14	Ni XII	7	66.37	Fe XVI	3
150.00	*O VI*	*3, 6, 12*	65.67	Mg X	3
148.4	Ni XI	7, 8	65.6	Mg IX	6
147.13	Ca XII	6	63.7	Fe XVI, Si VIII	3, 6
144.99	Ni X	7	63.29	Si VIII, S VIII, Mg X	3
144.22	Ni X	7	63.05	Mg X	6
141.06	Ca XII	6	62.80	Si VIII, Mg IX,	
129.85	O VI	6		Fe XVI	3
118.18	Ca X, Si V	6, 11	62.65	Mg IX	6
116.41	O VI	6, 11	61.9	Si VIII, Si IX, Mg IX	3, 6
115.80	O VI	6, 11	61.6	Si IX	3, 6
111.00	Ca X	6	61.05	Si VIII	3, 6
106.08	Ne VII	6	60.7	Ne VIII	6
105.3	Fe IX	6	59.3	Si IX, Si VIII, Fe XIV	3, 6
104.81	O VI	6	58.82	Fe XIV	6
103.69	*Fe IX*	*6, 11*	57.6	Mg X	3, 6
98.12	*Ne VIII*	*6*	58.80	Si X	3
96.64	Fe X	6	56.64	Si X	3
96.14	Fe X	6	56.03	Si IX	3
95.35	Fe X	6	55.34	Si IX	3
94.07	Fe X	6	55.12	Si IX	3

(Continued)

APPENDIX III (continued)

Line	Ion	References	Line	Ion	References
54.75	Fe XVI	3	43.18	O VII	3
54.56	Si X	3	42.54	S X	3
54.16	Fe XVI, S IX	3	40.92	Si XII	3
52.83	Si IX	3	33.75	C VI	3
52.49	Si X	3	24.8	N VII	10
52.33	Si XI	3	23.2	N VI	10
52.09	Si X	3	21.7	O VII	10
50.70	Si X	3	21.55	O VII	10
50.52	Si X, Fe XVI	3	20.8	N VII	10
50.33	Fe XVI	3	18.8	O VIII	10
49.67	Si X	3	18.6	O VII	10
49.23	Si XI	3	17.7	O VII	10
47.60	Si XI, Si X	3	16.27	Fe XVII	10
46.32	Si XI	3	16.0	O VIII	10
45.66	Si XII	3	15.25	Fe XVII	10
44.18	Si IX, Si XII, Mg X	3	15.0	Fe XVII	10
43.75	Si XI	3	13.7	Fe XVII	10

[a] Lines outstanding in intensity are italicized.

REFERENCES

1. Pagel, E. J. (1963). Ultraviolet emission from the sun. *Planetary Space Sci.* **11**, 333.
2. Pottasch, S. R. (1963). The lower solar corona: Interpretation of the ultraviolet spectrum. *Ap. J.* **137**, 945.
3. Tousey, R., Austin, W. E., Purcell, J. D., and Widing, K. G. (1965). The extreme ultraviolet emission from the sun between the Lyman alpha lines of HI and Ca VI. *Ann d'Astrophys.* **28**, 755.
4. Elton, R. C., Kolb, A. C., Austin, W. E., Toursey, R., and Widing, K. G. (1964). Origin of certain solar emission lines between 170 and 220 Å. *Ap. J.* **140**, 390.
5. Hinteregger, H. E., Hall, L. A., and Schweizer, W. (1964). Solar XUV spectrum, from 310 to 55 Å. *Ap. J.* **140**, 319.
6. Zirin, H. (1964). Identification of extreme ultraviolet solar emission lines. *Ap. J.* **140**, 1332.
7. Gabriel, A. H., and Fawcett, B. C. (1965). Identification of the solar spectrum in the region 60–170 Å. *Nature* **206**, 808.
8. Alexander, E., Feldman, V., Fraenkel, B. S., and Hoory, S. (1965). $3p^6 - 3p^53d$ transitions of Fe IX and Ni XI in the solar spectrum. *Nature* **206**, 176.
9. Stockhausen, R. (1965). The ultraviolet lines of Fe XIV in the solar corona. *Ap. J.* **141**, 277.
10. Blake, R. L., Chubb, T. A., Friedman, H., and Unzicker, A. E. (1965). Measurement of solar X-ray spectrum between 13 and 26 Å. *Ann d'Astrophys.* **28**, 583.
11. Ivanov-Kholodnyi, G. S., and Nikolskii, G. M. A prediction of solar line emission in the extreme ultraviolet. *Sov. Astr.-A. J.* **5**, 632.
12. Violett, T., and Rense, W. A. (1959). Solar emission lines in the extreme ultraviolet. *Ap. J.* **130**, 954.

APPENDIX IV[a]

BRIGHTNESS, DENSITY, AND POLARIZATION OF THE CORONA[b]

r (1)	Log $K + F$ (2)	Log F (3)	Log K (4)	k (5)	Log N (6)	p (7)	pk (8)
			Maximum, Equator, and Pole				
1	4.74	3.30	+4.73	0.96	8.61	0.18	0.17
1.03	4.58	3.22	+4.56	0.96	8.50	0.24	0.23
1.06	4.42	3.15	+4.40	0.95	8.37	0.28	0.27
1.1	4.24	3.06	+4.21	0.93	8.20	0.32	0.30
1.2	3.87	2.86	+3.82	0.90	7.85	0.41	0.37
1.4	3.34	2.55	+3.26	0.84	7.36	0.51	0.43
1.6	2.96	2.32	+2.84	0.77	7.00	0.57	0.44
1.8	2.65	2.14	+2.49	0.69	6.70	0.60	0.42
2.0	2.40	2.00	+2.18	0.60	6.45	0.62	0.37
2.5	1.95	1.73	+1.56	0.41	5.92	0.65	0.27
3.0	1.66	1.51	+1.10	0.28	5.50	0.65	0.18
3.5	1.45	1.34	+0.77	0.21	5.21	0.63	0.13
4.0	1.28	1.20	+0.52	0.17	4.95	0.61	0.10
5	1.02	0.95	+0.17	0.14	4.65	0.58	0.08
6	0.81	0.75	−0.06	0.13	4.46	0.56	0.07
8	0.50	0.48	−0.40	0.13	—	—	—
10	0.26	0.23	−0.64	0.12	—	—	—
			Minimum, Equator				
1	4.50	3.30	+4.48	0.94	8.36	0.18	0.17
1.03	4.34	3.22	+4.31	0.92	8.25	0.24	0.22
1.06	4.19	3.15	+4.15	0.91	8.12	0.28	0.25
1.1	4.01	3.06	+3.96	0.89	7.95	0.32	0.28
1.2	3.65	2.86	+3.57	0.84	7.60	0.41	0.34
1.4	3.14	2.55	+3.01	0.74	7.11	0.51	0.38
1.6	2.77	2.32	+2.59	0.65	6.75	0.57	0.38
1.8	2.50	2.14	+2.24	0.56	6.45	0.60	0.34
2.0	2.27	2.00	+1.93	0.46	6.20	0.62	0.29
2.5	1.86	1.73	+1.31	0.28	5.67	0.65	0.18
3.0	1.60	1.51	+0.85	0.18	5.25	0.65	0.12
3.5	1.40	1.34	+0.52	0.13	4.96	0.63	0.08
4.0	1.25	1.20	+0.27	0.10	4.70	0.61	0.06

(Continued)

APPENDIX IV (continued)

r (1)	Log $K + F$ (2)	Log F (3)	Log K (4)	k (5)	Log N (6)	p (7)	pk (8)
			Minimum, Pole				
1	4.35	3.30	+4.31	0.91	8.24	0.17	0.16
1.03	4.15	3.22	+4.10	0.88	8.10	0.24	0.21
1.06	3.97	3.15	+3.90	0.85	7.94	0.28	0.24
1.1	3.75	3.06	+3.65	0.79	7.73	0.33	0.26
1.2	3.29	2.86	+3.08	0.62	7.21	0.42	0.26
1.4	2.73	2.55	+2.26	0.34	6.44	0.52	0.18
1.6	2.42	2.32	+1.72	0.20	5.93	0.58	0.12
1.8	2.21	2.14	+1.33	0.13	5.57	0.62	0.09
2.0	2.04	2.00	+1.00	0.09	5.30	0.64	0.06
2.5	1.74	1.73	+0.32	0.04	4.70	0.69	0.03
3.0	1.52	1.51	−0.24	0.02	4.23	0.71	0.02
3.5	1.35	1.34	−0.70	0.01	3.87	0.73	0.01
4.0	1.20	1.20	−1.10	0.00^5	3.60	0.75	0.00

[a] From van de Hulst, H. C. (1953). The chromosphere and the corona. *In* "The Sun" (G. P. Kuiper, ed.), p. 207. Univ. of Chicago Press, Chicago, Illinois.

[b] Sun's brightness, average of disk: log I = 10.0; skylight with blue-sensitive plate: log I = 1.0–1.5; earth shine: log I = +0.4; K = light scattered by free electrons; F = inner zodiacal light; $k = K/(K + F)$; p = degree of polarization of K; pk = degree of polarization of $K + F$.

APPENDIX V[a]

POLARIZATION PARAMETERS

Ω	A	B	C	D
90°	0	0.250	1.333	0.750
80°	0.168	0.275	1.158	0.704
75°	0.241	0.292	1.069	0.670
70°	0.302	0.304	0.978	0.624
60°	0.375	0.311	0.792	0.515
50°	0.377	0.283	0.602	0.398
40°	0.316	0.225	0.416	0.276
30°	0.216	0.148	0.251	0.169
20°	0.110	0.074	0.117	0.078
10°	0.030	0.018	0.030	0.019
0°	0	0	0	0

[b] From Minnaert, M. (1930), On the continuous spectrum of the corona and its interpretation, *Z. Ap.* **1,** 209.

CONTEMPORARY BIBLIOGRAPHY

(References dated 1965 and later that are not included in the chapter bibliographies.)

Alexander, E., Feldman, V., Fraenkel, B. S., and Hoory, S. (1965). $3p^6-3p^53d$ transitions of Fe IX and Ni XI in the solar spectrum. *Nature* **206**, 176.

Allen, C. W. (1965). The interpretation of the XUV solar spectrum. *Space Sci. Rev.* **4**, 91.

Allen, C. W. (1965). The interpretation of the sun's XUV radiation. *Ann. d'Ap.* **28**, 146.

Babii, V. I., Vitkevich, V. V., Vlasov, V. I., Gorelova, M. V., and Sokhovei, A. G. (1965). The solar supercorona from observations made during 1959-1963. *Sov. Astr.-A. J.* **9**, 81.

Bird, G. A. (1965). The equilibrium state of a shock-heated atmosphere. *Ap. J.* **141**, 1455.

Blake, R. L., Chubb, T. A., Friedman, H., and Unzicker, A. E. (1965). Measurement of solar X-ray spectrum between 13 and 26 Å. *Ann. d'Ap.* **28**, 583.

Boyd, R. L. F. (1965). Techniques for the measurement of extra-terrestrial soft X-radiation. *Space Sci. Rev.* **4**, 35.

Bryant, D. A., Cline, T. L., Desai, U. D., and McDonald, F. B. (1965). Continual acceleration of solar protons in the Mev Range. *Phys. Rev. Letters* **14**, 481.

Bumba, V., Howard, R., and Kleczek, S. (1965). Association of green-line coronal features with photospheric magnetic fields. *Publ. Astr. Soc. Pacific.* **77**, 55.

Burgess, A. (1965). Dielectronic recombination in the corona. *Ann. d'Ap.* **28**, 774.

Burton, W. M., and Wilson, R. (1965). Observations of the sun in the extreme Ultraviolet made from a stabilized skylark rocket. *Nature* **207**, 61.

Carovillano, R. L., and King, J. H. (1965). On the solution of Parker's hydrodynamic theory of solar and stellar winds. *Ap. J.* **141**, 567.

Castelli, J. P. (1965). Occultation of the Crab Nebula by the solar corona at centimeter wave-lengths in June 1964. *Nature* **205**, 1301.

Castelli, J. P., and Aarons, J. (1965). A survey of radio observations of solar eclipses. Air Force Cambridge Research Laboratories, AFCRL-65-533.

Chamberlain, J. W. (1965). On the existence of slow solutions in coronal hydrodynamics. *Ap. J.* **141**, 320.

de Jager, C. (1965). Solar X-radiation. *Ann. d'Ap.* **28**, 126.

Dolan, J. F., and Fazio, G. C. (1965). The Gamma-Ray spectrum of the sun. *Rev. Geophysics* **3**, 319.

Fokker, A. D. (1965). Coronal scattering from solar radio sources. *Bull. Astr. Inst. Netherlands* **18**, 111.

Gabriel, A. H., and Fawcett, B. C. (1965). Identification of the solar spectrum in the region 60–170 Å. *Nature* **206**, 808.

Giacconi, R., Reidy, W. P., Zehnpfennig, T., Lindsay, J. C., and Muney, W. S. (1965). Solar X-ray images obtained using grazing incidence optics. *Ap. J.* **142**, 1274.

Goldberg, L., Dupree, A. K., and Allen, J. A. (1965). Collisional excitation of autoionization levels. *Ann. d'Ap.* **28**, 589.

Hall, L. A., Schweizer, W., and Hinteregger, H. E. (1965). Long-term Variation of solar EUV flexes. *J. G. R.* **70**, 2241.

Hinteregger, H. E. (1965). Absolute intensity measurements in the extreme ultra violet spectrum of solar radiation. *Space Sci. Rev.* **4**, 461.

Hinteregger, H. E. (1965). Experimental determination of absolute intensities in the solar XUV spectrum. *Ann. d'Ap.* **28**, 123.

Jefferies, J. T., and Orrall, F. Q. (1965). Loop prominences and coronal condensation. *Ap. J.* **141**, 505 and 519.

Kernoa, A., Michard, R., and Servajean, R. (1965). Contribution to the study of the corona at the eclipse of 15 February 1961. IV. Photometry of the emission lines. *Ann. d'Ap.* **28**, 716.

Krüger, A. and St. Michel, H. (1965). A new feature of the spectrum of the *S*-component of solar radio emission. *Nature* **206**, 601.

Kundu, M. R. (1965). Occultation of Taurus-*A* by the solar corona at 430 Mc/s in June 1964, *Nature* **205**, 683.

Kuperus, M. (1965). The transfer of mechanical energy in the sun and the heating of the Corona. *Astr. Res. Utrecht Obs.* **17**, 1.

Laborde, G., Michard, R., Oliveri, G., Rayrole, J., and Servajean, R., (1965) Contribution to the study of the corona at the eclipse of 15 February 1961. *Ann. Astrophys.* Suppl. **28**, 1.

Letfus, V. (1965). A coronal condensation model and the abundance of iron in the corona. *Bull. Astr. Inst. Czech.* **16**, 231.

Löchel, K., and Högner, W. (1965). Isophote positions for the solar corona from 15 February 1961 with the help of photographic equal densities. *Z. Ap.* **62**, 121.

Mandelshtam, S. L. (1965). On the X-ray radiation of the quiet sun. *Ann. d'Ap.* **28**, 614.

Michard, R., and Sotirorski, P. (1965). Contributions to the study of the corona at the eclipse of 15 February 1961. *II. Ann. Astrophys.* Suppl. **28**, 96.

Newkirk, G. A., and Bohlin, D. (1965). Coronascope. II. Observation of the white light corona from a stratospheric balloon. *Ann. d'Ap.* **28**, 234.

Nikolskii, G. M. (1965). Observations of the spicule spectrum and the fine structure of the solar chromosphere. *Astr. Zb.* **42**, 86.

Obayashi, T. (1965). The magnetosphere and its boundary. *NASA, Tech. Note* **TN D-2789.**

Obayashi, T. Corpuscular streams related to solar M-regions. *NASA, Tech Notes* **TN D-2790.**

Parker, E. N. (1965). On the existence of slow solutions in coronal hydrodynamics. *Ap. J.* **141**, 322.

Pounds, K. A. (1965). Recent solar X-ray studies in the United Kingdom. *Ann. d'Ap.* **28**, 132.

Russell, P. C. (1965). Soft X-ray image of the sun. *Nature* **205**, 684.

Russell, P. C. (1965). Further soft X-ray images of the sun. *Nature* **206**, 281.

Saito, K. (1965). Polar rays of the solar corona II. *Publ. astr. Soc. Japan* **17**, 1.

Scarf, F. L., and Noble, L. M. (1965). Conductive heating of the solar wind. II. The inner corona. *Ap. J.* **141**, 1479.

Stockhausen, R. (1965). The UV lines of Fe XIV in the solar corona. *Ap. J.* **141**, 277.

Thekaekara, M. P. (1965). Survey of the literature in the solar constant and spectral distribution of solar radiant flux. *NASA*, Special Publication No. 74, Washington, D. C.

Tousey, R. (1965). Observations of the white-light corona by rocket. *Ann. d'Ap.* **28**, 600.

Tousey, R., Austin, W. E., Purcell, J. D., and Widing, K. G. (1965). The extreme ultraviolet emission from the sun between the *L*Ω lines of HI and C VI. *Ann. d'Ap.* **28**, 755.

Tuominen, J. (1965). On Babcock's theory of the sun's magnetic field. *Observatory* **85,** 82.

Waldmeier, M. (1965). Form of the coronal magnetic field at the solar eclipse of 5 February 1962. *Z. Ap.* **61,** 186.

Waldmeier, M. (1965). The radial intensity decrease of one λ5303 *Z. Ap.* **61,** 144.

Warwick, J. W., and Hyder, C. L. (1965). The polarization of emission lines in astronomy. I. Resonance polarization effects in the field-free case. *Ap. J.* **141,** 1382.

Weiss, A. A. (1965). The nature and velocity of the sources of Type II solar radio bursts. *Aust. J. Phys.* **18,** 167.

Weiss, A. A., and Stewart, R. T. (1965). Solar radio bursts of spectral Type V. *Aust. J. Phys.* **18,** 143.

Wild, J. P., and Tlamicha, A. (1965). Spectral evidence of the origin of Type I solar radio storms and the coronal magnetic field. *Bull. Astr. Inst. Czech.* **16,** 73.

AUTHOR INDEX

Numbers in parentheses are reference numbers, and are inserted to enable the reader to locate a reference when the authors' names are not cited in the text. Numbers in italic indicate the page on which the full reference is cited.

A

Aarons, J., *311*

Abel, W. G., 52, *53*, 255, *257*

Acton, L. W., 76, *87*, 162, *172*

Akabane, K., 51, *53*, 271, *274*

Alfvén, H., 11, *13*, 182, 198, *211*

Allen, C. W., 10, *14*, 19, 24, *53*, 59, 67, 80, *87*, *88*, 123, 126, 130, 131, 137, 141, *142*, *143*, 152, 161, *172*, 206, 209, *211*, 221, *235*, 238, *259*, 293, *301*, 304(1), 305(1), *305*, *311*

Allen, J. A., *311*

Aller, L. H., 126, *142*, 161, *172*

Alexander, E., 307(8), *308*, *311*

Altschuler, M., 170, *172*, *173*

Aly, M. K., 24, *53*, 67, *88*, 127, 134, *142*

Anderson, C., 193, 209, *212*

Athay, R. G., 24, *53*, 68, *88*, 130, 134, *142*, 192, 199, *212*, 219, 220, 224, *235*, *236*, 239, 241, *257*, 292, *301*

Austin, W. E., 76, 78, *88*, *89*, 306(3, 4), 307(3, 4), 308(3), *308*, *312*

Avignon, Y., 85, *88*

Axtell, J., 28, *55*

B

Babcock, H. W., 203, *212*

Babii, V. I., *311*

Bachmann, H., 267, *274*

Barbier, D., 299, *301*

Bartels, J., 296, *301*

Barthle, R. C., 52, *54*, 255, *258*

Basu, S., 86, *88*

Baturova, G. S., 221, *236*, 252, *257*

Baumbach, S., 217, *236*

Bazer, J., 199, *212*

Behr, A., 69, *88*, 103, 107, *115*

Bell, B., 74, *88*, 103, 107, *115*, 209, *212*

Bezrukikh, V. V., 86, *89*, 253, *258*

Biermann, L., 10, 11, *13*, 131, *142*, 196, 197, 200, *212*, *213*, 238, 251, *257*, *258*, 267, *274*

Billings, D. E., 11, *13*, 67, 69, 70, 72, 73, 74, 81, *88*, *89*, *90*, 111, 112, *115*, 123, 126, 128, 140, *142*, *143*, 153, *173*, 187, 193, 201, 202, 203, 209, 210, 212, 224, 229, 230, 231, *235*, *236*, 241, 243, 244, 246, 247, 253, 255, *257*, *258*, 260, 261, 262, 270, *274*, 286, 290, *291*, 267, *275*, 304(5), 305(5), *305*

Bird, G. A., *311*

Blackwell, D. E., 21, *53*, 59, *88*, 94, *115*, 195, *212*, 220, *236*, 293, *301*

Blaha, M., 137, *142*

Blake, R. L., 43, *53*, 76, 77, 78, *88*, 308(10), *308*, *311*

Bloch, M., 19, *54*

Boardman, W. J., 67, *88*, 126, 140, *142*, 244, 247, *257*, 304(5), 305(5), *305*

Bodenheimer, P., 141, *142*, 165, *172*

Bohlin, D., 39, *54*

Boischet, A., 49, *53*, 82, 83, *88*, *312*

Bowen, P. J., 42, *55*, 77, *88*

Bowen, I. S., 8, *13*

Boyd, R. L. F., 42, *53*, *311*

Bracewell, R. N., 46, *54*

Brandt, J. C., 86, *88*, 141, *142*, 165, *172*, 209, *212*, 294, *301*

Giovanelli, R. G., 81, *89*
Gillett, F., 21, *54*, 169, *173*, 223, *236*, 253, *258*, *275*
Glazer, H., 103, 107, *115*, 209, *212*
Gold, T., 294, *301*
Goldberg, L., 127, *143*, *311*
Goldstein, J. J., Jr., 82, *89*
Gordon, D., 286, *291*
Gorelova, M. V., *311*
Greene, J., 159, 162, *172*
Griem, H. R., 168, *172*
Gringuaz, K. I., 86, *89*, 253, *258*
Grotrian, W., 7, *13*, 99, *115*

H

Hagen, J. P., 292, *301*
Hall, L. A., 76, 77, *90*, 306(5), 307(5), *308*, *311*
Hansen, R., 103, 107, *115*, 210, *212*, 286, *291*
Harvey, G. A., 79, *91*, 250, *259*
Havens, R. J., 295, *302*
Hebb, M. H., 131, 136, *143*
Hepburn, N., 220, 232, 233, *236*, 252, *258*
Heppner, J. P., 87, *89*
Heroux, L., 42, *54*
Hewish, A., 51, *54*, 85, *89*, 234, *236*, 268, *274*
Hill, E. R., 10, *13*, *258*
Hinteregger, H. E., 42, *54*, 76, 77, *90*, 306(5), 307(5), *308*, *311*, *312*
Hirayama, T., 127, *143*
Högbom, J. A., 51, *54*, 85, *90*, 269, *274*
Högner, W., *312*
Hoory, S., 307(8), *308*, *311*
House, L. L., 128, *143*, 245, *258*
Howard, R., 198, *214*, *311*
Howard, W. E., III, 48, *54*
Hoyle, F., 194, *213*
Huang, Kun, 9, *13*
Huch, W. F., 21, *54*, 169, *173*, 223, *236*, 253, *258*, 261, *275*
Hulburt, E. O., 295, *302*
Hyder, C. L., 24, *54*, 130, 134, 139, *142*, *143*, 165, *172*, 239, *257*, 264, 265, 272, 273, *274*, *275*, *313*

I

Ingham, M. F., 94, *115*, 220, 221, 233, *236*
Ivanchuk, K. I., 65, *91*
Ivanchuk, V. I., 228, *237*
Ivanov-Kholodnyi, G. S., 162, 165, *172*, 292, *302*, 306(11), 307(11), *308*

J

James, J. C., 52, *53*, 86, *88*, 200, *212*, 246, 255, *257*, *258*
Jarrett, A. H., 22, *54*
Jefferies, J. T., 279, 280, *291*, *312*
Jensen, E., 184, *213*

K

Kakinuma, T., 79, *90*, *91*, 168, *172*, 250, *259*, 261, 271, *274*
Karimov, M. G., 28, *54*
Karzas, W. J., 162, *172*
Kawabata, K., 270, *275*
Kazachevskaya, T. V., 162, *172*
Kellogg, P. J., 21, *54*, 169, *173*, 223, *236*, 253, *258*, 261, *275*
Kernoa, A., *312*
King, J. H., *311*
Kippenhahn, V. R., 261, *275*, 280, *291*
Kislyakov, A. G., 79, *90*
Kleczek, J., 76, *90*
Kleczek, S., 311
Kolb, A. C., 78, *89*, 306(4), 307(4), *308*
Kopp, R. A., 127, *143*
Korol'kov, D. V., 270, *275*
Kramers, H. A., 132, *143*, 156, *172*
Kreplin, R. W., 43, *53*, 76, *87*, *88*
Krüger, A., *312*
Kundu, M. R., *312*
Kuperus, M., 184, 198, *212*, *213*, *312*

L

Laborde, G., *312*
Laffineur, M., 19, *54*, 67, 75, *90*, *236*
Landseer-Jones, B. C., 199, *213*

Subject Index

A

Accretion, 194, 297
Acoustic heating, 196, 197
Active region heating, 202ff, 289
Active region magnetic fields, 269
Alfvén velocity, 182

B

Balloon coronagraphy, 37ff
Baumbach distribution, 217
Birefringent filters, 7, 35ff
Bremsstrahlung, 144, 155ff
Brightness, 217, 309
Bursts, radio noise, 47, 81ff, 271, 272, 287

C

Chemical composition, 122
Collision time, 120
Color, white light corona, 151
Condensations, 64, 154, 229, 256, 289
Coronagraph, 6, 7, 24ff, 31, 303
Coronium, 2, 3, 5
Crab nebula, 11, 51, 57, 85, 234, 268, 293

D

Debye potential, 117
Dielectronic recombination, 10, 134, 240

E

Eclipse photography, 2, 4, 15ff, 56, 93ff
Eclipses, historic, 1, 2, 16, 17, 18, 61, 62, 63

E-layer ionization, 295
Electrical conductivity, 175
Electron density, 59, 139, 153, 215ff, 309
Electron scattering, 144ff
Ellipticity of isophotes, 4, 227
Emission lines, optical, 2, 3, 5, 8, 67ff, 93, 102ff, 304
Enhancement, 64, 231, 256, 269, 289
Excitation, 135ff

F

Faculae, 276
Fast mode waves, 182
F-corona, 5
Filters, birefringent, 7, 35ff
Flares, 286ff, 295
F-layer, 295, 296
Forbidden transitions, 8
Free-bound emission, 159ff
Free–free emission, 155ff
Frozen-in magnetic fields, 174

G

Gaunt factor, 158
Geomagnetic storms, 295
Green coronal line, 2, 5, 23, 25, 33, 37, 38, 57, 58, 67, 69ff, 102, 104, 106, 110, 123, 127, 203, 204, 210, 215, 240, 243, 246, 247, 256, 265, 268, 273, 285, 286, 304

H

Heating, 11, 191ff, 289
Helmets, 65, 232